For Reference

Not to be taken from this room

Progress in
PSYCHOTHERAPY
————Volume II. ANXIETY AND THERAPY

Edited by JULES H. MASSERMAN, M.D.

Professor of Neurology and Psychiatry, Northwestern University, Chicago; President, Academy of Psychoanalysis, American Society of Biological Psychiatry, etc.

and J. L. MORENO, M.D.

New York University, New York City; Co-president, International Congress of Group Psychotherapy; Physician in Charge, Moreno Sanitarium, Beacon, New York.

GRUNE & STRATTON   **1957**

NEW YORK   **LONDON**

Library of Congress Catalog Card No. 56-8873

PROGRESS IN PSYCHOTHERAPY:

Coordinating Editor of the Series, J. L. Moreno, M.D.

Printed and Bound in U.S.A.

CONTENTS

Part V: DEVELOPMENTS ABROAD

Part VI: SUMMATION

IT GIVES US GREAT PLEASURE to announce that PROGRESS IN PSYCHO-
THERAPY is now established as a series of volumes, currently planned for
annual publication, with one of us (J.L.M.) as the coordinating editor.
This second volume was prepared as follows:

Selection. To the scientific proceedings of the 1956 Section on Psychotherapy of the American Psychiatric Association were added chapters on
specific aspects of psychiatric treatment written on request by qualified
experts throughout the world. Some of these contributions were condensed
to fit available space, but no other liberties were taken with mode or style
since it was desired that each author's presentation reflect his personality
as well as his views.

Organization. Part I consists of an Introduction to global psychotherapy
by one of us (J.L.M.); Part II presents a symposium on anxiety as the
substrate of all need for psychotherapy; Part III then describes special
techniques required at different ages or crises of life; Part IV continues
the survey of schools and trends begun in Volume I; and Part V examines
various geographic and cultural factors in psychotherapy, as was done in
a corresponding section in Volume I. Finally, Part VI presents an his-
torical-biodynamic integration by the other co-editor (J.H.M.).

Objectives. Our aims have been to present a volume at once theoretically
diverse yet authoritative, eclectic but integrated, inquiring and yet clinically
practicable. However, any success this book deserves is attributable far less
to its planning than to the excellence of its contributors, to whom, it is
hoped, many besides the editors will be grateful.

The editors express their appreciation to Dr. Clarence B. Farrar, Editor
of the *American Journal of Psychiatry,* and to the Council of the American
Psychiatric Association, who approved the publication in book form of the
papers presented at the Section on Psychotherapy.

JULES H. MASSERMAN
January, 1957   J. L. MORENO

KENNETH E. APPEL, M.D., Professor of Psychiatry, University of Pennsylvania.

HAROLD BASOWITZ, Ph.D., Institute for Psychosomatic and Psychiatric Research and Training, Michael Reese Hospital, Chicago, Illinois.

FRANCIS A. BOARD, M.D., Institute for Psychosomatic and Psychiatric Research and Training, Michael Reese Hospital, Chicago, Illinois.

MEDARD BOSS, M.D., Professor of Psychotherapy, University of Zurich, Switzerland.

JOSE ANGEL BUSTAMANTE, M.D., Havana University, Havana, Cuba.

E. A. D. E. CARP, M.D., Professor of Psychiatry, University of Leiden, Holland.

JACQUES A. CHEVALIER, Ph.D., Institute for Psychosomatic and Psychiatric Research and Training, Michael Reese Hospital, Chicago, Illinois.

L. Z. COSIN, M.D., Clinical Director, Geriatric Unit, United Oxford Hospital, England.

W. HORSLEY GANTT, M.D., Associate Professor of Psychiatry and Director, Pavlovian Laboratory, Johns Hopkins University, Baltimore, Maryland.

JOHN GILLIN, Ph.D., Consultant in Anthropology, Veterans Hospital, Downey, Illinois.

ALBERT J. GLASS, M.D., Col. M.C., Chief, Department of Neuropsychiatry, Walter Reed Army Hospital, Washington, D.C.

KURT GOLDSTEIN, M.D., Private practice, New York City.

ROY R. GRINKER, M.D., Director, Institute for Psychosomatic and Psychiatric Research and Training, Michael Reese Hospital, Chicago, Illinois.

DAVID A. HAMBURG, M.D., Institute for Psychosomatic and Psychiatric Research and Training, Michael Reese Hospital, Chicago, Illinois.

ROBERT W. HYDE, M.D., Superintendent, Butler Hospital, Providence, Rhode Island.

FAY B. KARPF, Ph.D., Private practice, Beverly Hills, California.

HENRIETTE R. KLEIN, M.D., Columbia University, New York City.

SHELDON J. KORCHIN, Ph.D., Institute for Psychosomatic and Psychiatric Research and Training, Michael Reese Hospital, Chicago, Illinois.

JULES H. MASSERMAN, M.D., Professor of Neurology and Psychiatry, Northwestern University, Chicago, Illinois.

DAVID MCK. RIOCH, M.D., Director, Division of Neuropsychiatry, Walter Reed Army Institute of Research, Washington, D.C.

ROLLO MAY, Ph.D., Private practice, New York City.

JAMES G. MILLER, M.D., Chief, Mental Health Research Institute, University of Michigan, Ann Arbor, Michigan.

J. L. MORENO, M.D., Physician in Charge, Moreno Sanitarium, Beacon, New York; Graduate School of Arts & Sciences, Department of Sociology, New York University, New York City.

HAROLD PERSKY, Ph.D., Institute for Psychosomatic and Psychiatric Research, Michael Reese Hospital, Chicago, Illinois.

K. V. RAJAN, M.A., Nur Manzil Psychiatric Center, Lucknow, U.P., India.

ARNALDO RASCOVSKY, M.D., Private practice, Buenos Aires, Argentina.

MELVIN SABSHIN, M.D., Institute for Psychosomatic and Psychiatric Research and Training, Michael Reese Hospital, Chicago, Illinois.

I. H. SCHULTZ, M.D., Professor of Psychiatry, University of Berlin, Germany.

EMANUEL K. SCHWARTZ, Ph.D., Postgraduate Center for Psychotherapy, New York City.

HANS SYZ, M.D., Research Associate, Lifwynn Foundation, Westport, Connecticut.

NIC WAAL, M.D., Physician in Charge, Nic Waal's Institute, Oslo, Norway.

JACK WEINBERG, M.D., Private practice, Chicago, Illinois.

LEWIS R. WOLBERG, M.D., Director, Postgraduate Center for Psychotherapy, New York City.

Part I: INTRODUCTION

Global Psychotherapy and Prospects of a Therapeutic* World Order

_____J. L. MORENO

THE PERIOD of global transformation through which mankind is traveling has brought about a growing rapprochement between the various disciplines, the physical sciences, psychiatry and religion. Psychiatry, and especially psychotherapy, is broadening its horizons and incorporating new knowledge from physics, chemistry, anthropology, sociometry and sociatry. Religions, on the other hand, in order to halt their declining influence, are making desperate efforts to borrow the skills which social science and psychiatry have developed. A large number of ministers are now openly combining theological counseling with modern psychotherapeutic methods in order to sustain the moral power of their particular church. Psychotherapists are in the middle between the scientists who follow the prescription of scientific method and the religionists who lean upon spiritual authority and faith.

Facing the patient, singly or in groups, we are frequently in the dilemma of having to give him answers to questions for which there is no strict scientific evidence. But we have to give him answers or share with him our ignorance of ultimate truth. The custom of passing the patient to the minister of his religion as soon as vital questions of the purpose of life, or the hereafter, arise, refraining from crossing the border between science and metaphysics, is unsatisfactory and unrealistic. If the therapist has any set of values to which he is privately committed, be he an agnostic, a nihilist, an atheist, a communist, a Buddhist, a Catholic, a Quaker, or an adherent of any other philosophy of life, they will emerge in the particularly sensitive patient-therapist situation. The mental patient reacts to the total personality of the therapist. He has an exaggerated idea of his wisdom and resourcefulness; he expects total responsibility. A psychotherapist who

---

*Therapeutic is here applied within the context of "sociatry." Sociatry derives from two roots: _socius_—"companion" and _iatreia_—"healing." Sociatry is remedial sociometry, the science of social healing. It is concerned with sick societies. In contrast to this, social psychiatry deals with the social influences bearing upon sick individuals. A sociatrist is a therapist skilled in sociatry. (Cf. my "Foundations of Sociatry," _Sociatry_, Vol. I, 1947.)

1

unites in *one* person the scientist, psychiatrist and "cosmic philosopher" may well be the outcome of this dynamic conflict of aspirations.

We are at the crossroads of either developing an all-embracing therapeutic philosophy or remaining a limited and controversial specialty of medicine. This is a crucial problem, not of one school or another, but of all schools of psychotherapy, and involves its past, present and future position in the world.

MEANING OF THE UNIVERSE

The profound anxiety of our time is the fear that the "end of the world" has again become a possible outcome of man's ephemeral situation, and that all mankind and, perhaps, all animated life may cease to exist within a reasonable future. In the religions of the past centuries, the end of the world has been often feared, but associated with mystic advents, the "second coming" of Christ, or with cosmic events outside of man's decision and power; man expected fatalistically the nearness of the end. But in our time the coming of the "end" has a different emphasis, since it is man himself who may provoke the end. He himself may be the destroyer. He himself has cosmic forces at his command. He himself is the cosmic force which science put into his hands to destroy the cosmos. The conditions of life in the twentieth century are those of people who know that the end of their entire world may come at any time, because of the circumstances they themselves have created. The expectancy of Christ's second coming was a metaphysical projection but in our time the end of the world is a calculated reality, expected to come because of our doings or undoings. The therapist can ill afford to ignore the collective fear that all mankind may perish, that the universe itself may cease to exist. What compensation could psychotherapy offer if there would be no ultimate meaning to life? The philosophical acceptance of collective nonexistence may be the only answer.

It is told of the biologist Haeckel* that someone once asked him, "If in some way you could address a question to the universe and be assured of a truthful answer, what question would you ask?" Haeckel remained absorbed in thought for some moments, and then replied, "The question I would most like to see answered is this, 'Is the universe friendly?'"

The question remained unanswered but it was, as we would say now, a sociometric question. As in sociometric testing, he wanted to be assured that he would get a truthful answer and that there is someone who could

---

*Ernst H. Haeckel, "Die Welträtsel," 1870. From Haeckel, following Darwin, stems one of the first scientific studies of the biological processes which underlie human society.

answer. But a sociometrist would have asked two alternative questions: "Is the universe hostile?" and "Is the universe neutral?"

Every individual man, dog, butterfly, amoeba, stone or physical atom may give a different answer. Haeckel wanted to know whether the universe is so inclined that, by its very structure, it is bound to initiate, to support and extend our existence. In times of distress and agony, would it lend us a helping hand? Or, is the universe hostile and, by its very structure, bound to destroy us? It may well be that our existence does not matter even that much. Is the universe neutral? It may well be that the universe is cold and indifferent, that it does not care whether we live or perish. If it happens that we will be destroyed, it may happen by pure chance.

But the sociometrist would not have started to investigate the universe; instead, he would have turned the question around and asked Haeckel, "Are *you* friendly or hostile towards the universe? It is with you, Haeckel, that the question begins, not with the universe. You act as if you are outside of the universe, but you are a part of it. You may indeed be its very center." We cannot answer Haeckel's question as he put it. In order to make it answerable, we must reverse it. The question is then: "Are *we* friendly toward the universe?"

Haeckel's question and the answer we give to it have obvious connotations for all forms of psychotherapy. Can the psychotherapist neglect to deal with the structure of the universe and continue to depend on his intuition? If the universe is friendly, is it not important for the psychotherapist to know the structure of the universe so that he can adapt his methods to it? If the universe is unfriendly and hostile in its very essence, what can psychotherapy accomplish unless it could repair the universe itself or replace it by another? And, finally, what should be the attitude of the psychotherapist in a universe which is entirely *un*human, cold and indifferent towards the very existence of man?

Since the time when Haeckel formulated his question, the world situation has changed and some scientific advances have been made. Now the question can be answered to an extent, but the answer is not simple. It is comparatively recently that three things have happened: (a) the atomic age has been ushered in, dramatizing the robot and the nuclear structure of the atom; (b) empirical studies of social structure have given us a new insight into its dynamics, an amazing picture of the friendly-hostile-neutral substructure of mankind; and (c) psychotherapy has spread on a global basis. They are interrelated and used as points of departure for reviewing the science and the universe of man (cf. my "Sociometry and the Science of Man") in its three dimensions: I. The cosmic; II. The biosocial and sociometric; III. The therapeutic.

I. Cosmic Dynamics

1. THE ROBOT

Robot derives from the Slavic root robota, "work." The invention of robots is a skill of homo sapiens. Man became the first implement-making animal, at least several hundred thousand years ago, perhaps even a million years ago. The robot in its various forms—the work tool, the weapon, the cultural conserve, the zoomaton, the atomic bomb, and the calculating machine—is at the core of the process of alienation,* of man from nature, from himself and from society. The "cultural conserves"— alphabet, language, number and book—have played a leading role in sharpening the conflict between self and alien elements. The author has tried to analyze the process of robotization and to show that it exerts an altering and often disturbing effect upon the mainsprings of human resources, spontaneity and creativity (cf. my "Who Shall Survive?," 1934, and "Creativity and the Cultural Conserves," 1939).

The reason for the origination and systematic development of robots is mysterious. All animals prosper without robots, they just multiply themselves and, if necessary, use each other as co-workers and fight each other with their own bodily weapons. Man, too, like other animals, multiplies himself. But he craved for other resources and extra-individual extensions. Perhaps when he found himself in the days of the jungle, failing in his struggle to live on creativity alone, he divided from his will to create his will to power, and invented robots. The fate of man may well become that of the dinosaur in reverse. The dinosaur perished because he extended the power of his own organism in excess of its usefulness. Man may perish because of reducing and splitting the power of his organism by fabricating robots in excess of his control.

The reasons for inventing robots are manifold. The human infants, the biological robots of animal reproduction, do not satisfy man "entirely;" therefore, he created the technological kind. The robots have the passivity and obedience of the mechanical creature; they are more precise and reliable than animals and human beings; they work promptly, they are the perfect slaves. A robot is lifeless, it does not grow. It does not have and cannot produce an ounce of spontaneity. A human infant results from the conjugation of a man and a woman. A robot results from the conjugation of man with nature. In both cases the offspring takes over some feature from both parents. In the atomic robot, for instance, there is some feature of the man-producer and some feature of the physical cosmos.

The control of the robot is complicated for two reasons. One is that

---

*Alien—"foreign;" alienation—"foreign to the self."

the robot is man's own creation. He does not meet it face to face, as he did the beasts of the jungle, or his fellowmen, measuring his strength, intelligence and spontaneity with theirs. The robot comes from within his mind; he gave birth to it. He is confounded in the manner of every parent toward his own child. Rational and irrational factors are mixed, therefore, in his relationship to robots. In the excitement of creating them he is unaware of the poison which they carry, threatening to kill, alienate and substitute their own parent; he sees only the blessing and protection they may bring. The second reason is that in using certain robots, man unleashes forms of energy and perhaps touches on properties which far surpass his own little world and which belong to the larger, unexplored and, perhaps, uncontrollable universe. His task of becoming a master on such a scale becomes a dubious one, since he may well find himself more and more in the position of Goethe's Sorcerer's Apprentice who could unleash the robots but who could not stop them. The apprentice had forgotten the master's formula; we never had it.*

But robotization and automation have become intrinsic parts of man's existence. A return to a prerobot world is unimaginable; its opposite is bound to happen: further development of automation beyond any of our present dreams. The problem is to counter the effects of alienation by making robots as real and as nearly a part of our bodies and selves as our arms and legs are, and by bringing them into the service of autonomous creative strivings. The ideal antidote for pathology and loss of spontaneity

---

*The author has frequently pointed out this dilemma: "It is the greatest, longest, most difficult, most unique of all wars man has ever waged during his career. It has no precedent, no parallel, in the history of the universe. It is not a war against nature, it is not a war against any other animals, it is not a war of one human race, nation or state against any other. It is not a war of one social class against another social class. It is a war of man against ghosts, ghosts that have been called, and not without reason, the greatest makers of comfort and civilization. They are the machine, the cultural conserve, the robot. The critically weakest point in our present-day universe is the incapacity of man to compete with machine-like devices otherwise than through external forces—submission, actual destruction, social revolution. The problem of remaking man himself and not only his environment, will become more and more the outstanding problem the more successfully technical forces prosper in the realization of the machine, the cultural conserve and the robot, and although the development of these is far from having reached its peak, the final situation of man and his survival can be clearly visualized, at least theoretically." ("Impromptu Journal," 1931, pp. 4-5; "Who Shall Survive?", 1934, p. 363). Erich Fromm reaffirms this: "Man today is confronted with the most fundamental choice; not that between Capitalism or Communism, but that between *robotism* (of both the capitalist and the communist variety), or Humanistic Communitarian Socialism. Most facts seem to indicate that he is choosing robotism, and that means, in the long run, insanity and destruction." ("The Sane Society," 1956, p. 363).

is spontaneity training (cf. my "Who Shall Survive?", 1934). The psychotherapist is vitally concerned with the effect of a replacement of the direct
human contact by robots, e.g., a bottle for the mother's breast, a book for
the real encounter, a playback-from-a-tape-recorder for a therapeutic
session, a worker of parts for the craftsman of an entire job.

2. ANXIETY AND THE END OF THE WORLD

Man is the cosmic animal. "The origin of anxiety is the separation of the
individual from the rest of the universe—the result of being cut off."
Anxiety is cosmic.* Rioch concludes from his experiments on animals that
the phenomena constituting anxiety are not "limited the human beings."†
Grinker says that anxiety is a "monistic" affect.† Glass confirms that it
"occurs when an individual is unable to cope with or reasonably control
his environment."† Appel says, "It is the background of many unidentified
cultural tensions."† Frieda Fromm-Reichmann points out that "mild degrees
of anxiety are in our culture the common fate of all."‡ May defines it as
"the apprehension cued off by a threat to some value which the individual
holds essential to his existence as a self."† Goldstein calls it a "catastrophic
condition . . . anxiety is related to a situation which endangers self-realization".† But the self is inseparably linked to the cosmos. Anxiety, then, is
a universal phenomenon, the result of cosmic apprehension. It needs cosmic
therapy, methods and arts rooted in spontaneity and creativity.

In the course of birth the infant is separated from the mother, but he
is compensated for the loss; he enters the great adventure of living. In
death, however, he is separated from life and the universe itself, without
compensation. The birth trauma is an adult projection. Although operationally experienced, it is less anxiety-producing than the "death trauma,"
which is only anticipated. Death in all its forms—the passing of time,
aging and dying,§ alienation of values—is the greater source of anxiety
throughout life, far surpassing the event of being born. The psychotherapist
cannot afford to ignore the fact of permanent nonexistence after death
which is at the core of the patient's anxiety. Even the hope that life will

---

*J. L. Moreno, "The Third Psychiatric Revolution." *In:* Fromm-Reichmann, F. and
Moreno, J. L.: Progress in Psychotherapy, Vol. I. New York, Grune & Stratton,
1956. P. 29.

†David McK. Rioch, this book, page 32; Roy Grinker et al., page 47; Albert
J. Glass, page 71; Kenneth Appel, page 91; Rollo May, page 82; Kurt Goldstein,
pages 62 and 63.

‡Frieda Fromm-Reichmann, *op. cit.,* p. 17.

§For effects of aging and death, see: J. Weinberg, this book, page 105; L. Z. Cosin,
page 111; J. L. Moreno, page 119; Jules H. Masserman, pages 128-130.

go on forever in "some" form may be only a sweet dream. Spontaneity centers around birth, anxiety centers around death.

Soon after astronomical and geological research had pronounced him a speck of dust, a most negligible and least accountable part of the universe, man learned that he could annihilate the whole of mankind and some day even manipulate the functions of the universe at large. Perhaps not since the Peking man, who is credited with having kindled the first fire and used the first hatchet, has a similar sensation of megalomania filled his mind. How can he be stopped from using this power except by filling the cosmos with an army of spies?

At the same time this new power has aroused the opposite effect, a keen awareness of the extreme "unimportance" of his existence, not only of the single individual, but of the entire species—a fear of the worthlessness of life. Man had hardly become adjusted to the idea that there is no "hereafter" when he found himself threatened with loss of his own world, of the "here and now." Aggression among organized groups of men, nations and religions began to take unprecedented forms of violence. The secular world of human values—his sciences and arts, of which he is so proud— seemed ready to evaporate forever. Suddenly he found himself without a final purpose and without a future.

3. "COSMODYNAMIC" PRINCIPLES AND MODELS OF THE UNIVERSE

Magic, theological and metaphysical models of the universe have dominated the field as far back as there are tangible human records of cultural evolution. Metaphysical models are, at least from the point of view of the individual, superior to scientific models. Metaphysical models, like the Zen-Buddhistic system, for instance, provide man with a complete picture of the universe, with a place for him in it. Whether we accept its speculations or not, it has the virtue that the entire man, his origins, his birth, his death, his morals, and the farthest stages of his past and future evolution, is involved in the cosmos. In contrast, the scientific models of the modern cosmos are incomplete; they have not tried to integrate man into a universal system except as a physical existence.

For several thousand years the most popular article of religious faith has been the idea that there is a Supreme Being who is the creator of the Universe and who has, among other things, created Man as a kind of special creation. He was visualized as a fatherly figure, the great helper in need, countering any of the demonology of the universe. It was because of him that the universe was considered friendly. After the great promise of the theological and metaphysical systems—and Haeckel did his part to destroy the faith in their validity by replacing them with a biological theory of world evolution—a big vacuum was left. This vacuum was never properly filled. The age of science was ushered in and began to encourage agnosticism and atheism. When Haeckel was a small boy, he knew that the universe was friendly because there was a "father in heaven," but now there was no one there. He felt guilty because of what he had done to it; therefore, he asked in desperation, "Is the universe friendly?"

There is a deep, unconscious resistance against dealing with the problem of God and the universe openly. "Hast du nicht gehört dass Gott gestorben ist?" spake Nietzsche's Zarathustra. Religion is an "illusion," said Freud. This is as far as the most radical pronouncements went. Efforts to replace the old cosmogonies by a new one have failed to date. This paradoxical situation cannot endure forever; man does not live only within himself, within a society, or within biological evolution. The universe at large has its own cosmic evolution and man is a part of it. His relationship to the universe must be spelled out and structured. In order to feel comfortable he requires an understanding not only of the meaning of his individual existence and of the society in which he lives, but also of the universe which envelops him. The consequence of facing and accepting the non-existence of God would mean his "loss of status" in the cosmos. How could man go on living meaningfully, whither should he turn to find a similarly powerful anchorage?

The religious crisis and the development of nuclear science has provoked fantastic speculations about man's role in the universe. It is probable that scientific discoveries will find the universe full of mysteries man has not been able to penetrate, and his survival may increasingly be threatened by the "fruits" of his knowledge (Tree of Knowledge, Garden of Eden). The ignorance of prescientific man was a protective device. If there are no deities, if the universe is a huge enterprise of cosmic forces, man may envision himself as gradually assuming a new role in the affairs of the universe. He who has been relegated to being a negligible creature, perishable like dust, may, if he survives long enough—parallel to the role of the destroyer—assume the role of the commander, of a "proto-creator." In order to elevate himself, he may eventually become the Supreme Being of the future (if the megalomaniac dreams of atomic man have any prediction value), assuming for himself the role which he had assigned to God in the fables and mythologies of the past. The stories of creation in the Genesis may become validated in a distant future, only in reverse. If the very distant future is reversed and made the very distant past, man's idea that God created the universe will be verified ex-post-facto. Man will either turn out to be the destroyer of the world, and so of himself, or he will be victorious and become the God of the world. Is man on the way to becoming the Lord of the universe? It is the Faustian dream of man in a godless world.

4. THE SPONTANEOUS-CREATIVE MODEL

An alternative solution to overcome the mirage of nihilism is to envision the faint outlines of a modern science of the universe. "In the face of a mood that had led science to seek progress largely in the direction of elementalism, the sense for units or totalities through integration has not made equal progress," remarked Adolf Meyer ("Spontaneity," *Sociometry*, Vol. IV, 1941, p. 150). "The sense for totalities has been exaggerated before in philosophic, religious and animistic thinking. It had to undergo and face a deflation. Today it is at an unnecessarily low ebb in scientific concern, and has not as yet absorbed as much of the concept of integration as it well might." Psychotherapy has evolved through many stages: from the magic and religious to the biologic and psychological to the sociologic and cultural, and now to the offering of cosmic models which, of course, should include in its construction all previous stages.

A new theoretical frame of reference involving man and the universe must encompass the physical *and* the behavioral sciences. One set of laws after another has been discarded, with full regard for their heuristic value— the laws of conservation of energy, of causality, of gravity, of parity, etc.— in order to interpret adequately the processes taking place in the physical atom. The physical sciences are moving toward the point where they can learn a lesson from the psychological and social sciences, applying the "subject's frame of reference" to their own data. There are no absolute uniformities. Even on the physical level, one atom is *not* like another.

A central model of the universe hovers continuously in our minds, if not consciously, then unconsciously. It influences the form which the central model of man takes. We propose that five "cosmodynamic" principles are active in the universe: *creativity, spontaneity, chance, conserve,* and *tele* or *universal interaction*. The further development of a cosmodynamic system will require the collaboration of a multitude of workers. It will have to be reformulated from time to time, taking into account the advances in every branch of science.

The first principle is *creativity*. The universe is infinite creativity. (Cf. my "Sociometry and the Science of Man.") It is featured in all the great religions. The Genesis opens with the "Creator" of the world; it implies that "creativity" and "to create" are the essence of being. It is worshipped by eminent scientists and artists in their official and private philosophies (Goethe, Nietzsche, Beethoven, Bergson, Einstein, Planck, Whitehead, etc.).

Creativity is the true cosmic reality, the essence of cosmic evolution. It is impossible to imagine that it can ever cease to operate. It is the farthest which a human mind can grasp as the *all-inclusive* principle.* It is obvious that the phenomena of creativity have not only psychological and social but also physical, biologic and cosmic aspects. Creativity is the problem of the universe; it is, therefore, the problem of all existence, of every religion, of science, psychology, human relations and psychotherapy.

Creativity is self-sufficient; it has no other meaning except to be what it is, the operational principle par excellence. It has innumerable forms and levels but these are all ultimately of the same origin. The creativity in the world of sub-atomic physics irregularly scattered in space and time differs in character but not in principle from the creativity experienced on the human level, e.g., in Dostoevski's "Brothers Karamazov" or Marconi's idea of the antenna. We dare say if there is a supreme creative nuclear structure of the universe, no matter whether we call it "x," "God," or any other symbol, it is nothing else but pure creativity—the mysterium aeternum et illuminosum.

At the opening session of the hundred and twenty-third annual meeting of the American Association for the Advancement of Science, December 26, 1956, Dr. George Wald, Professor of Biology at Harvard University, said, "We are beginning to understand that we live in a universe which is some five to ten billion years old. We realize that the universe has its own cosmic evolution. Stars and galaxies are born, they grow, become old and die. Our life has a place as part of the order of nature. Life is a part of the physics of our universe. If you started with a universe containing protons, neutrons and electricity, life will eventually appear. It will pursue evolution. And this gives man his place in the universe." It is generally accepted, then, that man is a natural and orderly development of the physical universe, like a river or a mountain range. But how did the physical universe itself develop? The answer is simple: The hypothesis of creativity applies to physical systems. The physical universe is a development of creativity; thus, it is creativity which links the physical universe with all the dimensions of the nonphysical universe and so merges the two universes into one.

On the human level it has been possible to differentiate several varieties of creativity: *unconscious, active, floating, traumatic* and *conserving*. Creativity may be "unconscious" for long periods but suddenly break out and take the form of wilful design. There are rare individuals who are endowed with what one may call "floating creativity" and spontaneity, whose

---

*Collective unconscious, for instance, is a derivative of "collective creativity." Creativity is prior to unconsciousness and consciousness, and envelops them both.

readiness to create never stands still. They are out to be creative every moment in the here-and-now, sensitive to respond to emerging situations. Men like Jesus, Socrates, and Buddha are particularly prone to submerge the world around them creatively. They never wrote a book or permitted any of their experience to freeze into a conserve. Their entire life was an ongoing creative act. It is significant to differentiate the bearers of this over-all universal floating kind of creativity from individuals who from time to time become "traumatized" by a profound experience and are then absorbed for a given period in a process of creative thinking, writing, composing or inventing, after which they return to their drab existence. This may be called a "traumatic creativity," which is characteristic of the majority of producers of cultural products. The trend towards conserving creativity terminates in the formation of "cultural conserves."

The second principle is *spontaneity,* the variable degree of adequate response to a situation of a variable degree of novelty. As the constant companion of creativity it has universal distribution. An illustration of "physical" spontaneity is the behavior of a small aggregation of atoms or of elementary particles. An illustration of "biological" spontaneity is spontaneous generation, the manner in which inert matter may have first started to show signs of life, or the creation of new organisms, at the time when animal life was confined to the sea. An illustration of "psychocreative" spontaneity is Beethoven starting out to create his monumental Ninth Symphony.

"By placing the subject into new situations in which he has to produce various states of behavior, the spontaneity test gives us an estimate of personality as a whole." (Moreno, "The First Book of Group Psychotherapy," 1932, p. 19.) Adolf Meyer (*op. cit.,* pp. 151 and 153) confirms this idea: "It is spontaneity that I want to study and inquire into and cultivate and respect as the *all-important* characteristic quality of a person. It is the range of spontaneity, with its ranges of occasions and demands and opportunities of life . . . By the *person's spontaneity,* I mean that which the person may be expected to rise to and to rise with on his own, 'sua sponte,' with his 'spons' and 'responses' and finally 'responsibility.' " Spontaneity (or call it intuition, inspiration, or by any other name) is the existential factor "intervening" for creative processes to be released. It counters the "law" of conservation of energy, which has become an axiom in the physical sciences and a model for some of the best known psychochological and social systems. Take, for instance, the concept of the libido in psychoanalytic theory. In accordance with this theory Freud, like most scientists of his generation, biased by the physical idea of the conservation of energy, thought that if the sexual impulse does not find satisfaction in its direct aim, it must find a way out in sublimation. But by following a more inclusive principle, the principle of spontaneity-creativity, which assumes that a certain amount of irregularity and lawlessness is essential to all existence, a person can be trained to produce the amount of emotion, thought and action demanded from him in any novel situation, instead of depending upon a "bank account." Spontaneity is the principle of "unconservability" and "unpredictability." As Charles S. Peirce remarked, "We enormously exaggerate the part that law plays in the universe. An element of pure spontaneity or lawless originality mingles or at least must be supposed to mingle with law everywhere." ("Principles of Philosophy," Vol. I. Cambridge, Harvard Univ. Press, 1931. Pp. 222 and 223.) Heisenberg's principle of indeterminacy is the other side of the coin, a secondary effect of spontaneity.

The third principle is *chance,* a mathematical and statistical concept; it provokes arbitrariness and creativity but it has no existence of its own. The fourth principle is *conserve,* the transitory products of creativity. It may be a biological conserve, e.g., an animal organism; a cultural conserve, e.g., a book, a musical symphony, a motion picture; or a mechanical conserve, e.g., a calculating machine (robot). The cultural conserve is one of the major roads of man's hunger for immortality. There are three forms of cultural conserves: (1) the "burned"-out conserve—a battery which cannot be charged because it is dead; (2) the "inflammable" conserve—still warm, coming from its creator's mind, representing current, collective experiences whose essential content is active in everyone's experience: light music or book-of-the-month novels; (3) "eternalized" or idolized conserves which remain alive and vital for dozens of generations, arousing every generation anew (the Old and New Testaments). Spontaneity and creativity never entirely cease to affect cultural conserves; some "amount" of them enters into every one of its renderings, in a greater or lesser degree. By "amount" of spontaneity we do not mean amounts which are stored up or conserved. Even the greatest possible amount of stored-up spontaneity and creativity could not make a butterfly anything but a butterfly. Yet even the smallest amount of "free" spontaneity, summoned and created by a being on the spur of the moment—a product, in other words, of the moment —is of greater value than all the treasures of the past, of past "moments." Spontaneous creativity—however supreme it may be in itself—once conserved is, by definition, no longer spontaneity; it has lost its actuality in the universe. What "conserved" creativity truly represents, at best, is power, a means of expressing superiority when actual superiority has ceased to be available. A universe which is pure creativity, one in which creative acts are perpetually emerging without ending in conserves is a paradox. A universe in which conserves are "verboten" is in utter contradiction with the kind of world in which we live at present. But we can imagine the emergence of a musical genius like Beethoven, determined not to deliver his spontaneous creativity to the world of conserves, a Beethoven who would prefer to let his creative embryos die in their conceptual state, who would make an effort, at the same time, not to give up the incessant production of musical energy, but who would stubbornly try to remain permanently in that initial creative state—the spontaneous-creative matrix. Such a Beethoven may refuse to give birth to musical conserves, but express his musical creativity as it comes to him, hic et nunc, in status nascendi. Such creative behavior by itself is by no means a barrier to communication. In a world which lives on spontaneity and creativity alone, the creator would have remained creator and never would have chosen to fill the universe with organisms, conserves and people, the universe as we know it. The universe might have remained in that state of creativity in which it was on the first day of creation. The process of the universe may have moved into an entirely different direction; it would have been creativity without a world. A Beethoven who would turn against himself and return, so to speak, to the first day of creation to stay there permanently, would be like a modern Prometheus who starts a "creative revolution" on the cosmic level.

The fifth principle is *tele* or *universal interaction*. The operational aspect of tele is limited, of course, to empirical verifiable evidence on the human level. There is no evidence for "operational correspondences" between dimensions as far apart as astronomic magnitudes and interpersonal relations. Every individual interaction represents a moment in the cosmos. Creativity is integral with every moment. There are innumerable moments which accumulate or cohere into that which is a "present" of the entire cosmos at any point of its existence. The "unpresentness" of the universe is an expression of its hidden omnipresence.

Creativity, spontaneity and tele or mutuality are the ultimate source of all existence and of all values. As a hypothesis, they are the key to the idea of physical gravitation as well as to the idea of biological evolution, to the genesis of human society as well as to the phenomenon of creativity in man.

II. Biosocial and Sociometric Foundations of a Therapeutic Society

1. SOCIOMETRIC HYPOTHESES

The hypothesis of creativity applies to social systems. A therapeutic world order must be based upon a social system which cultivates spontaneity and creativity. The lives of individuals are most creative when their associates in a particular activity are of their own choice. Sociometry made possible the "creation" of groups according to the precepts of this fundamental hypothesis. It has tried to test the degree of creativeness in groups organized upon the foundation of friendliness and to compare the creativity in such groups with the creativity of groups organized by chance, or those organized upon the basis of unfriendliness. The greatest release of creativity is possible only in a therapeutic world order.

Man will hardly survive the internal struggle against robotization, the risks and gambles of nuclear war, experimental journeys into an expanding universe, if he does not have as his ultimate protector a well organized global society to carry him over into safety. A therapeutically integrated society is the only imaginable safeguard. The tendencies in the last century to develop a world order are expressions of this need. They represent a craving for a balanced global society in which man will find protection. One of the systems which was recently held up as the solution to man's social ills was Marxist socialism. Its failure was one of the factors that provoked the development of new sciences of the group—sociometry, and, subsequently, sociatry, a discipline for the treatment of sick societies. By a systematic analysis of the structure of groups and social interaction, they developed precise methods of investigation and, in the course of studying them, made a number of discoveries (cf. my "Who Shall Survive?," 1934, and symposium on "Sociometry of Human and Subhuman Groups", *Sociometry,* Vol. 8, No. 1, 1945).

Human society has three dimensions: the external society, the sociometric matrix, and the social reality, which is the interaction of the two, the *surface* and *depth* dimensions. The depth dimension is composed of affective relationships, distributed along the continuum of attraction-through-neutrality-to-repulsion. It functions underneath the formal social fabric, influencing it and being influenced thereby.* The sociometric, psychotherapeutic and sociatric implications of a two-dimensional societal structure, of an official versus an unofficial society, can be directly and experimentally explored. The relationships of a sociometric matrix can be charted with almost the same precision as the anatomy of the human body. But the conflict between these two societal dimensions cannot be resolved by individual or group psychotherapy. Because of the global implications of

---

*The dynamic reason for this split is the underground existence of innumerable social constellations which impinge continuously upon external society, whose structure may vary from one cultural order to another, partly in an effort toward its disintegration, partly in an effort toward their realization and, last but not least, because of the resistance which external society puts up against its substitution or change. As the profound and chronic conflict between these two tendencies is never fully resolved, the result is a compromise in the form of the "social reality." The sociometric matrix is like a huge "social unconscious" with sociogenetic and sociogeographical dimensions.

all human relations the final arbiter is a psychotherapy of the entire human society.

Sociometry has further demonstrated a *"law"* or *hypothesis of socio-dynamics.* The income of choices, affective retrojection relations of an individual, is unevenly distributed among members of a collectivity regardless of the size of the group or its kind. Groups are stratified with respect to relevant sociometric criteria. Hence, we speak today of "sociometric status," "choice-rejection status" and the "sociometric inequality" of individuals. We frequently speak of a "socio-dynamic effect"; it postulates that *isolated and neglected individuals will tend to remain isolated and neglected,* that *over-chosen individuals will remain over-chosen,* and that *they will even accumulate a surplus of choices if the number of permitted choices is increased.* This "effect" has the same meaning when employed with reference to groups. It cuts across all economic classes and ethnic groups; it produces new varieties and degrees of poor and rich, emotional "haves" and "have-nots."

The sociometric inequality of patients is of the greatest importance for psychotherapeutic study. The psychological misery resulting from sociometric inequality can be aided by the psychotherapist's making the patient first of all accept his position in the group and then perhaps by trying to change it. It is the supreme task of the sociatrist to explore methods of social organization which are able to reduce to a minimum the tensions produced by the sociodynamic effect.

Sociometry uncovered further a *"law"* or *hypothesis of social gravitation:* with constant facilities of communication and constant physical distance between communities, people from one community will move toward people of another community in direct proportion to the amount of collective attraction given and received and in inverse proportion to the collective rejections.

It further demonstrated the existence of *interpersonal, socioemotional and sociometric networks.* Beneath the everflowing and everchanging social currents, there are more or less persistent structures, the live tracks of communication. It is through these channels that people affect or disintegrate one another. The cause of their existence is the economic principle of producing the greatest effect with the least effort. The interpersonal networks are the basis of all dynamic communication. Many puzzling phenomena such as political revolutions and purges, social contagion as prejudices or fashions in art and science can be explained through them and perhaps can be prevented.

The *sociogenetic law or hypothesis* asserts that higher forms of group organization have evolved from simpler ones. As I pointed out in "Two

Sociometries, Human and Subhuman" (*Sociometry,* Vol. 8, No. 1, 1945, p. 75), "Human and nonhuman social structures formed by actual individuals have a characteristic type of organization which differs significantly from structures which are formed by 'chance' or by imaginary individuals. This has been proved for the human group by experiments, statistical and mathematical analysis. There must be a factor, *'tele',* operating between individuals (for instance, in the exploration of appropriate mates) which draws them to form more positive or negative relations, pair relations, triangles, chains, quadrangles, polygons, etc., than on chance. A parallel process should be demonstrable for nonhuman groups as well. *It is the inter-action of the individuals which gives the group its social reality, whatever the hereditary forces are which direct individual maturation, and the environmental forces which surround them.* Their influence is, of course, not denied, but they cannot operate but via the inter-individual channels. By this measure it is possible to determine the degree of social reality of the organization of groups. Certain social configurations have a structure which places them nearer the optimum of cohesion. In accordance with this hypothesis, a group of primates or a group of human infants should rank lower on the scale than, for example, a group of human adults." Observations of infants have led to the differentiation between various developmental stages through which societal structures pass from that of organic isolation to that of horizontal differentiation and, finally, to vertical differentiation. Studies of the frequency of various sociometric configurations serve as convincing evidence of this point.

Cumulative studies on social biology, from Empedocles through Aristotle, Shaftesbury, Adam Smith, Comte, Feuerbach, Spencer, Darwin, Espinas and Kropotkin, parallel and support the sociometric findings on the nonhuman level. They assert that forces of both mutual attraction and repulsion co-exist in animal societies. W. C. Allee states, "It is my mature conclusion that the cooperative forces are biologically more important and vital. If cooperation had not been the stronger force, the more complicated animals, whether anthropoids or vertebrates, could not have evolved from the simple ones." (*Sociometry,* Vol. 8, No. 1, 1945, p. 29.)

And, finally, it is Leslie D. Zeleny's conclusion that *"more creativity-productivity is released in groups organized upon the basis of mutuality (tele) than in groups organized upon a non-mutuality basis or by chance."* ("Validity of a sociometric hypothesis, the function of creativity in interpersonal and intergroup relations," *Sociometry and the Science of Man,* 1956). There is friendliness, then, in the social universe.* It can be traced,

---

*"Mankind is provided with a sound biological foundation for altruistic interpersonal attitudes, which is of the highest importance for individual human satisfaction

harnessed and further developed by means of various methods, as, for instance, psychotherapy and sociatry.

2. THE SOCIOMETRIC OR "THERAPEUTIC" PROLETARIAT

The new knowledge of the microscopic structure of mankind has brought about a total disillusionment in the promises of the dialectic materialism of Marx and Engels—the idea that abolition of capitalism and gradual abolition of private property will not only resolve economic conflict, but will reduce the emotional tensions and hostilities between men and abolish insanity, prostitution and crime. In other words, Marxism unconsciously acted "as if" it would be a therapeutic world order and claimed to be better fitted to meet the needs of the masses than any other social system. Although not a part of the "system," these proposed therapeutic and ethical benefits weighed more heavily for the prestige of Soviet Communism than its economic program. But Marxism, since it was constructed at a time when a firm knowledge of the actual, dynamic structure of human society did not exist, was not aware that the resistance to change and revolution came from the latent social structure itself.

Human society has a structure of its own which is not identical with the social orders or the forms of government currently in power; sociometry showed us that this structure can be charted on sociograms and studied like a geographic atlas. The structure is influenced but never entirely determined by the instrument in charge of its affairs, e.g., the state. The state may "vanish" but the underlying sociodynamic structure of society persists in one form or another. It is into the structure of the sociometric matrix, therefore, that a remedial effort has to put its teeth if a lasting and true resolution of social ills is to be effected.

The oldest and most numerous proletariat of human society are the victims of an untherapeutic world order, the "sociometric proletariat." It consists of all people who suffer from one form or another of misery: physical misery, psychological misery, social misery, economic misery, political misery, racial misery, religious misery. There are numerous individuals and groups whose volume of attractions or role expansion, spontaneity, and productivity is far beneath or above their needs and their ability to consummate them. The world is full of isolated, rejected, rejecting, unreciprocated and neglected individuals and groups. The therapeutic proletariat cannot be "saved" by economic revolutions; it existed in primitive and precapitalistic society, it exists in capitalistic societies, and it exists in socialist Russia. Marxism is an idea of the last century. The war of communism

and for human society." (Whitehorn, John C.: Psychotherapy: Modern trends in Psychological Medicine. New York, Paul C. Hoeber.)

against capitalism is a displacement from the nineteenth to the twentieth century. It is the battle for an idea which has ceased to portray the conditions and problems of our time. The new idea is a therapeutic world order which reflects the cosmic evolution of creativity and the sociodynamic structure of society.

III. THERAPEUTIC WORLD ORDER

The hypothesis of creativity applies to therapeutic systems. A minimum amount of spontaneity-creativity operates in every psychotherapeutic technique, such as free association, suggestion, hypnosis, psychodrama and art therapy.

The forces of cosmic and social evolution pull mankind towards growing unification and integration. The vehicle for attaining this goal is a therapeutic society. Such a society as an "exclusive" aim has probably never existed, but the unconscious intent of all societal productivity has been, since time immemorial, toward its realization, and can be detected, for example, in the Pyramid Texts, the Code of Hammurabi, the Vedas, the Declaration of Independence and the Communist Manifesto. This new society will go beyond sociometric devices; it will try to create a "sociatric atmosphere" which will imperceptibly permeate all dimensions of living, from the supreme ethics of conduct, jurisprudence and economics to the customs and daily acts of the people. By atmosphere we mean a condition which exists but does not have to be preached or expounded, an unconscious which has become external.

A therapeutic world order will not come via a blueprint but will evolve gradually from the synthesis of old and new methods of psychotherapy in the various parts of the world with the aid of one or more therapeutic leaders. There are several promising dimensions of development: (a) adaptation and integration of psychotherapy in the cultural and ethnic settings of each country;* (b) therapeutic trends in the structure of existing political, social and religious organizations; (c) modern existential rituals; (d) therapeutic communities; and (e) theories of the therapeutic world order.

(a) Psychotherapy has become a global influence in our time. The shortening communication lines in a shrinking world accelerate combina-

---

*Professional psychotherapy should try to adapt itself to the "living" psychotherapy of a culture which is the *de-facto* therapy grounded in the mores and norms of the people. Psychotherapeutic methods take deviant forms in different cultural settings, e.g., in India (K. V. Rajan, this book, page 197), South America (J. Gillin, page 224), Spain (R. Sarro, *in* Progress in Psychotherapy, Vol. I, p. 316), Austria (R. Schindler, *op. cit.,* p. 270), or Germany (W. Winkler, *op. cit.,* p. 298).

tions and integrations of all methods—historically, a rapprochement between the modern techniques of psychotherapy with the Judeo-Christian and Greek philosophies; geographically, a confrontation of scientific views of the West with Hindu, Islamic, Chinese and other metaphysical trends. All religions are in a crisis; under the impact of science and technology they have to reconsider critically their old value systems. But, in turn, the West is confronted with the challenge of how to integrate the living wisdom of the oldest cultural traditions of the world with its own logical and methodological panaceas.

The spread of psychotherapy in the last hundred years is a phenomenon which should be faced in its full meaning. It can be traced partly to a productivity in therapeutic ideas, partly to the decline of the religions. The consequences of the credo of the nonexistence of God have been enormous in the western world and are beginning to exert their influence among the people of Asia. God, in His various representations and rituals, as Jahveh, Allah, Brahma, Vishnu and Wotan, has been, and still is, the desired and most universal form of psychotherapy for the masses and, as in the form of Christian Science, more popular than all the modern psychotherapies put together. The growing elimination of God as a "global" psychotherapist has become an expensive item in the budget of many a modern family. In metropolitan centers like New York City,* innumerable families deal with one type of therapist or another, who tries to counsel them or cure their ills. God, the great therapist, is gradually being replaced by millions of little therapists everywhere, to meet the growing need. The therapeutic epidemic is particularly visible in the free Western countries and the flood may have only started. It responds to the enormous need for love and moral support. Should the "Iron Curtain" fall, a flood of psychotherapists will invade Soviet Russia and the rest of the Soviet-dominated world, just as it is gradually being flooded by radios, automobiles, motion pictures, refrigerators and airplanes. It turned out that God and religion are not an "opiate for the masses" (Marx) but a profound necessity enabling them to carry on with living in a stressful universe.†

(b) Trends pointing toward a therapeutic world order can be detected interwoven with the theological principles held by any particular religion ("Love your neighbor as you love yourself"). Love, aside from having meaning in a theological context, is a therapeutic principle. A sovereign

---

*New York City's 8,000,000 inhabitants are 54.9% unaffiliated with any faith. Of the remainder, 27% are Roman Catholic, 10.6% are Jewish, and 7.5% are Protestants. (*Time,* Feb. 11, 1957, p. 56.)

†Jules H. Masserman, *in:* Progress in Psychotherapy, Vol. I, pp. 196-98. See Masserman's exposition of man's system of "Ur-Defenses."

state may have ideas with a therapeutic connotation in its political charter, as, for example, when the French Revolution proclaimed as its motto "Liberté, Fraternité, Egalité." These aspirations may not be scientificially valid or carried out in practice, but "Freedom" and "Equality of status" are indispensable in therapeutic relationships. Similarly, one finds global organizations like the UNO whose charter is full of therapeutic inuendos: the nations represented in its body have unequal power in decision-making but as an "aggressor" nation each is equally condemned. The very survival of the UNO may depend upon its ability to deal effectively with this problem. The "aggressor" is notoriously a therapeutic problem in group psychotherapy, and the treatment of aggression is often decisive.

(c) In the development of a therapeutic society a great role will be played by rituals. Rituals—from the Latin ritus, "a rite"—is any course or method of conduct considered as ceremonial. A magic ritual is one which has for animistic people a talismanic force compelling the higher powers to grant favors to them even against their will. A religious ritual is the one, for instance, of the Anglican church. A secular ritual is the one of war or the May Day of the socialists. Perhaps the greatest secular ritual of the modern world, however, is *science*. A "therapeutic ritual" is one in which a technique of psychotherapy has become a part of the mores: psychodrama, ethnodrama, axiodrama and group psychotherapy methods which have the potential of becoming modern therapeutic rituals.*

Rituals may be existential as well as formal. "Existential rituals" are characterized by total involvement of all participants in a commonly shared collective experience, in contrast to "formal" rituals which are purely ceremonial. From the point of view of the psychotherapist, existential rituals operate like *collective therapeutic binders,* confirming and integrating societal woes and hopes as if by a huge psychodramatic acting out. They have no meaning for onlookers and outsiders. They have meaning only for the actors involved in the act of the ritual; for them they have "existential" validation.† The experience of two lovers or two friends, for example, does not require any validation beyond the consent and enjoyment of the participants. Validation in individual and group psychotherapeutic practice is not imperative so long as no pretense is made that generalizations can be drawn from whatever the events recorded, or that the future behavior of the participants can be predicted from the events. They may have no "scientific" validation and the participants may not

---

*Therapeutic rituals use the method of "therapeutic acting-out" in order to prevent or correct irrational or "uncontrolled acting-out" in life itself. A therapeutic ritual becomes therapeutic life.

†J. L. Moreno, *op. cit.,* pp. 48, 328.

care a bit whether their activities have it or not. Indeed, they may try to make it as difficult as possible for a scientific observer to participate and evaluate. But *scientific and existential validation do not exclude or contradict one another;** the two ways of viewing the same event can be combined effectively, as in sociometric and psychodramatic research (cf. my *Psychodrama,* Vol. I).† The rituals may have also no "esthetic" validation, appearing to the onlooker as ugly, exaggerated, disproportionate and disharmonious. But the participants in a ritual do not care about looking attractive or looking like artists. An existential prayer, individual or group, may take place without overt expression. The bizarre behavior patterns of some psychotic patients can be classified within this context as "private" existential rituals.

The formal ritual, on the other hand, may tend to look esthetic, carefully patterned and pleasing to the eye. It may even lend itself to scientific observation because everything which it is, is projected onto the surface. It is the existential rituals which have disappeared from our modern churches, although they are full of formal ritual practices, whether in the flesh or on television. It is characteristic in this context that Kierkegaard, one of the great Christians of the nineteenth century, had no place in the church because he could not see himself in a church that was void of existential rituals. The greatest sermon he ever gave was "in fantasy," a fantasy which he recorded in his diaries a few months before his death. He visualized himself giving a Sunday sermon in a large church of Copenhagen. He sees himself on the pulpit. The church is packed with people. They are all in their best clothing, clean and smooth, good looking, regular people, smiling benevolently and expecting from the pastor a pat on the back and nice, sweet oratory. Instead, he breaks out in anger and says, "As I look into your eyes, one by one by one, I see nothing but murder and deceit. I hear all the lies you think and speak. This is not the place for liars and thieves and murderers, although you may get away with it. You do not belong here! Get out of church! You are not Christians! This is a House of Christ, not a bank or a marketplace!" And, as he speaks, people get up and protest in anger. The church is seething with revolt. At this moment the pastor speaks gently to the crowd: "This is exactly how I wanted you to be—to become real, to warm up against me in anger and rage, because the Lord, when He was on earth, was not received with sweet words and pleasant sermons. There was anger and hate shown by the priests of His day and by the people in the villages. They spat on Him; they threatened Him with prison, and finally, they crucified Him.

---

*Medard Boss, this book, page 156.
†Ludwig Binswanger, *in* Progress in Psychotherapy, Vol. I, p. 144.

Now that you are properly aroused I can begin my sermon." But what Kierkegaard actually did was to break up the congregation, turning it upside down, transforming it into a psychodramatic session. Kierkegaard's intention was to force the congregation to go back with him to the original meaning of the ritual, its status nascendi, by acting out the sufferings of Christ in situ, turning loose the viciousness of the churchgoers and transforming them into an elementary mob. He was thus preparing himself and them for being truly present and existential for the sermon (the "warming up" in group psychotherapy).

A step beyond Kierkegaard's "psychodrama" is, however, the conduct of the "total psychotherapist,"* the way the real Christ would probably have acted. He would never have preached the sermon because he could not have reached the church. With his "friendliness" toward the universe he would have been stopped on his way to church by innumerable incidents— responding to the immediate needs of the people in the house in which he lived, the beggar on the corner, the little boy pleading to play with him, a lame and tired horse pulling a carriage and an old friend suddenly showing up and stretching out his arm to touch him. Following the therapeutic principle of the Here-and-Now, he would have practiced the ritual of love "on the spot."

The current group therapeutic and psychodramatic methods are of a "congregational" type and produce intensive subjective involvement, as well as the coexperience of super-individual issues. Operating like collective therapeutic binders, they are particularly useful for individuals living in the middle of the twentieth century who have become alienated from the old religions even when maintaining a formal tie. But they may also fertilize and rejuvenate the old religious rituals. The group sessions provide a modern vehicle for individual and collective expression in a framework of concepts and language in which even the uninitiated can get emotionally involved. Their private and collective anxieties relating to birth and death, matrimonial and family life, can find here a groping for solutions.

(d) The therapeutic community† settles disputes between individuals and groups under the rule of *therapy* instead of the rule of *law;* it attacks the problem of community government through the use of "one man as a therapeutic agent of the other, of one group as the therapeutic agent of the other; this checks adverse group formations and insures that the groups are controllable." (Cf. my "The First Book on Group Psychotherapy," 1932 and 1957, p. 103.) In the spontaneous-creative universe of therapeutic

---

*J. L. Moreno, *Die Gottheit als Redner,* 1919; tranl. *The Philosophy of the Here and Now,* 1957.

†John Kelnar and John D. Sutherland, *in:* Progress in Psychotherapy, vol. I, p. 338.

communities, the spontaneity of one individual stimulates the spontaneity of the other, and the quantitative result is the opposite of what we have at present, a robot-dominated world order in which spontaneity is an arbitrary and incidental element. The initiative of the therapeutic group, in contrast to Le Bon's crowd, increases with its size and with the number of interactions of its members.

The modern impulse toward the therapeutic community came from the United States (my "Application of the Group Method to Classification," 1932, and "Who Shall Survive?", 1934). Therapeutic communities have a long history within a religious context but as institutions founded on an exclusively sociotherapeutic basis they represent a new challenge. In the last twenty-five years they have been a testing ground for a therapeutic society on a world scale. The pioneer experiments in the United States have been in hospitals, reformatories and schools—P.S. 191 in Brooklyn, N.Y., 1931; The New York State Training School for Girls at Hudson, 1932; Beacon Hill, Beacon, N.Y., 1936;* Centerville, N.J., 1937;† and Boston Psychopathic Hospital (R. Hyde; cf. this book, page 000). Experiments in Great Britain were inaugurated in Warlingham Park Hospital (T. P. Rees),‡ Marlborough Day Hospital (J. Bierer),§ the Dingleton Hospital, the Social Rehabilitation Unit at Belmont Hospital (Maxwell Jones),|| the Bristol Psychiatric Day Hospital (K. W. Aron and S. Smith),¶ the Cassel Hospital (T. F. Main),** Maudsley Hospital (A. Harris),†† Oxford Hospital (L. Cosin, this book, page 000).

"Open" therapeutic villages, and colonies populated by *normal* groups involving all dimensions of living, from labor to family life, are the promising next step, anticipated by the experiment in colonization by the kwutzoth in Israel.††

---

*Gerhard Schauer, "Patients as Therapeutic Agents in a Mental Hospital," *Group Psychotherapy*, 1945.

†Shepard Wolman, "Sociometric Planning of a New Community," *Sociometry*, Vol. I, 1937.

‡T. P. Rees, *Third Report*, World Health Organization's Expert Committee on Mental Health, 1953.

§J. Bierer, *The Day Hospital*, 1951.

||Maxwell Jones, "The Treatment of Character Disorders in a Therapeutic Community," *Bull. of Ment. Health*, 1954; A. A. Baker, "The Misfit Family: a Psychodramatic Technique used in a Therapeutic Community," *Brit. J. Med. Psychol.*, 1952.

¶K. W. Aron and S. Smith, "The Bristol Psychiatric Day Hospital," *J. Ment. Science*, 1953.

**T. F. Main, "The Hospital as a Therapeutic Institution," *Bull. Menn. Clinic*, 1946.

††A. Harris, "The Group Approach to Leadership-Testing," 1949.

‡‡H. Infield: Utopia and Experiment, New York, Fredrick Prager, 1956. The kvutza Dagania Aleph came into being in what was then Palestine and is now the State of Israel, in 1911.

(e) Mankind as an operational reality is of recent origin, and must be differentiated from the conglomeration of national societies which it contains. It was a metaphor for millennia, known vaguely and indirectly through scattered communications. Since the historical geographers and explorers of the Middle Ages began to circle the globe, the "parts" of mankind began to acculturate and merge. In our time it has become a unified context through telegraph, radio, television and airplane, setting the pace for a single world order.

For millenia nations have been separated by physical and cultural barriers. Within the same nation classes and social groups of all kinds have been at war with one another, in towns and villages, one family against the other. The comparative lack of unity among ethnic groups everywhere did not matter so much as long as the distances between them were great and as long as there was not a threat common to all. The conditions of the world today require the development of the closest possible ties between all men, similar to its existence within a family, only on a global basis. The family is a sort of therapeutic world order on a small scale. The strongest ties which we know to be effective and lasting are among members of a family. Members of a family generally come to each other's rescue in times of stress and emergency. The family, whatever form it takes and with all its shortcomings, is the only grouping we know that has survived the breakdown of all civilizations. It may serve as a model. The family is built not only on economic agreements but on love and mutuality of affection, responsibility and faith.

Efforts towards a single world order have been made on the religious level (Christianity) and on the political level (United Federalist Movement for One World). It has never been made on the therapeutic level since the idea of "therapy" was interwoven with religious and political concepts. Its emancipation from the religious and the political could not be clearly visualized in the past; modern psychotherapy as well as modern social science are hardly more than a century old and the relationship between psychotherapy and social structure was unknown.

The main problem of a therapeutic society is how to reconcile freedom with helping, autonomy with dependence. The concept of "therapy"* often has the connotation of dependence and weakness of the individuals involved and so is frequently placed in contrast to the concept of freedom: free, independent and autonomous individuals. But a therapeutic world order encourages autonomous therapy; it encourages man to be his own therapist. It reduces the need for professional psychotherapists to a minimum.

---

*Therapy, from the Greek therapeutes, "servant." Therapeutes has been redefined (in psychodrama) as auxiliary ego, i.e., extension of the ego, replacing an absentee, a co-helper.

A self therapist cannot live in a vacuum, but in community with other self therapists. Their communal autonomy takes the form of "autonomy of inter-dependence." He is dependent only because he does not live in a world by himself, but in a "with others world." The logic is that a free individual becomes unfree and loses his autonomy in a chaotic, confused society. In order to be free and to attain a stable position within the community setting, he needs to help others and to be helped by them in return. A therapeutic world order must at the same time be autonomous and interdependent. It is not a society of weaklings, of individuals who need care and continuous support from outside sources, but a world which is so constructed that all individuals, the creative and strong as well as the weak, can live effectively. Even the free and the strong can go down in an untherapeutic world; in fact, they may go down first. A therapeutic world order is not for sick people; an untherapeutic world order such as the present one makes healthy people sick.

In the face of the mounting crisis of our entire civilization, we professional psychotherapists cannot evade the responsibility of checking the balance sheet of our own guilt for the global disintegration of faith, character and mental health. We cannot afford to keep our eyes closed to the sufferings inflicted upon mankind by collective atrocities in the course of bloody wars and revolutions. The "case history of mankind of 1956," the massacres of defenseless people, is not only the responsibility of the statesmen and politicians, but also ours. The mental casualties of wars and revolutions eventually become our patients. How can we look into their eyes without blinking, guilty of their sufferings by inaction, silent participants of the most horrid outbursts of acting-out disorders, without raising a finger?

The cardinal concern of professional psychotherapy has been, up to now, the mentally disturbed group. But is not the chief concern of a sick society its *normal* group? Is not its normal group responsible for the general, social and moral decay, for the wars and revolutions which bring untold misery upon mankind? The mentally disturbed and socially harmful individuals are comparatively small minorities, put away in the safety of prisons and asylums. Is not our job bigger than the treatment of individuals? Who is to take over the care of the sick groups and sick nations? Who is to treat our sick social institutions and codes, our laws and morals? It is beyond any particular department of therapy and science to deal with this enormous task. There is no department of human relations which can claim exclusive authority. But the ultimate objective is clear.

"A truly therapeutic procedure cannot have less an objective than the whole of mankind" (cf.my "Who Shall Survive?", 1934, p. 3). The final aim is the creation of a therapeutic society in a world where, in the beginning, none existed. In such a society life itself will be therapeutic. It is easier to create a therapeutic world order than it is to change ourselves in a world order which is untherapeutic. Even if a particular ideological or political system should gain world rule, e.g., capitalism or communism, it cannot last. It is the author's humble opinion that history is "on the side" of a therapeutic society and a therapeutic religion.

BIBLIOGRAPHY

ACKERMAN, N. W.: The family group and family therapy. Internat. J. Sociometry *1*:52, 1956.

ALEXANDER, F. AND ROSS, H.: Dynamic Psychiatry. Chicago, University of Chicago Press, 1952.

ALLPORT, G. W.: The Individual and His Religion. New York, Macmillan, 1950.

ARON, K. W. AND SMITH, S.: The Bristol Psychiatric Day Hospital. J. Ment. Sc. *99*:564, 1953.

BAILEY, P.: The great psychiatric revolution. Am. J. Psychiat. *113*: 387, 1956.

BAKER, A. A.: The misfit family: a psychodramatic technique used in a therapeutic community. Brit. J. M. Psychol. *25*:235-243, 1952.

BALINT, E. AND BALINT, M.: Dynamics of training in groups for psychotherapy. Brit. J. M. Psychol. *28*:135-143, 1955.

BATESON, G. AND MEAD, M.: Balinese Character. New York, New York Academy of Sciences, 1942.

BERGSON, H.: L'Evolution Créatrice. (26th ed.) Paris, 1923.

BEVERSTOCK, A. G.: Group methods applied to youth leader selection. Brit. J. Educ. Psych. *19*:112-120, 1949.

BIERER, J.: The Day Hospital. An Experiment in Social Psychiatry and Syntho-Analytic Psychotherapy. London, H. K. Lewis, 1951.

BINSWANGER, L.: Existential analysis and psychotherapy. *In:* Progress in Psychotherapy (Frieda Fromm-Reichmann & Moreno, Eds.). New York, Grune & Stratton, 1956.

BION, W. R.: Group dynamics, a review. Internat. J. Psychoanalysis *33*:235, 1953.

BJERSTEDT, A: The Methodology of Preferential Sociometry. Sociometry Monograph No. 37. New York, Beacon House, 1956.

BLAIR, D.: Group Psychotherapy for War Neuroses. Lancet *1*:204-205, 1943.

BOWLBY, J.: The study and reduction of group tensions in the family. Human Relations *2*:123-128, 1949.

BRANDEN, C. AND ZANKER, A.: Development of a geriatric club attached to a mental hospital. Ment. Health *14*:91-96, 1955.

BREASTED, J. H.: The Dawn of Conscience. New York, Scribner's, 1939.

BRONFENBRENNER, U.: The Measurement of Sociometric Status, Structure and Development. Sociometry Monograph No. 6. New York, Beacon House, 1945.

CAMERON, D. E.: General Psychotherapy. New York, Grune & Stratton, 1950.

CARTWRIGHT, D. AND ZANDER, A.: Group Dynamics. Evanston. Dow, Peterson, 1953.

CHOLDEN, L.: Observations on psychotherapy of schizophrenia. *In*: Progress in Psychotherapy (Fromm-Reichmann & Moreno, Eds.). New York, Grune & Stratton, 1956.

DARWIN, C.: Origin of Species, 1859.

——: Animals and Plants under Domestication, 1868.

DE VRIES, H.: Die Mutationstheorie. Leipzig, 1901.

DIETHELM, O.: Treatment in Psychiatry. (3rd. ed.) Springfield, Thomas, 1955.

DUBOIS, C.: The People of Alor. Minneapolis, University of Minnesota Press, 1944.

EDDINGTON, SIR ARTHUR: Nature of the Physical World. Cambridge, 1928.

EYSENCK, H, J.: The effects of psychotherapy: an evaluation. J. Consult. Psychol. 16:319-324, 1952.

FAVEZ-BOUTONIER, J.: Psychotherapy in France. In: Progress in Psychotherapy (Fromm-Reichmann & Moreno, Eds.). New York, Grune & Stratton, 1956.

FIEDLER, F.: Quantitative Studies of the Role of Therapists' Feelings Toward Their Patients. In: Psychotherapy—Theory and Research (O. H. Mowrer, Ed.). New York, Ronald Press, 1953.

FISHER, R. A.: Genetical Theory of Natural Selection. Oxford, 1930.

FREUD, S.: Civilization and its Discontents. London, Hogarth Press, 1930.

FROMM, E.: The Sane Society. New York, Rinehart, 1955.

FROMM-REICHMANN, F.: Notes on the history and philosophy of psychotherapy. In: Progress in Psychotherapy (Fromm-Reichmann & Moreno, Eds.). New York, Grune & Stratton, 1956.

———: Principles of Intensive Psychotherapy. Chicago, Univ. of Chicago Press, 1950.

GALTON, SIR FRANCIS: Hereditary Genius. (2nd Ed.). London, 1892.

GUYER, M. F.: Being Well-Born. (2nd Ed.). London, 1928.

HAECKEL, ERNST H.: Die Welträtsel, 1870.

HARRIS, H.: The Group Approach to Leadership-Testing. London, Routledge & Kegan Paul, 1949.

HELLER, A. D.: Group therapy with mental defectives. Ment. Health. 14:97-99, 1955.

HIGHAM, M. H.: Some Recent Work with Group Selection Techniques. Occup. Psych. 26:169-175, 1952.

HILGARD, E. R.: Theories of Learning. New York, Appleton-Century-Crofts, 1956.

HOCH, P. H.: Progress in psychiatric therapies. Amer. J. Psychiat. 112:241, 1955.

HOHN, ELFRIEDE, AND SCHICK, C.: Das Soziogramm. Tübingen.

JAQUES, E.: Interpretive group discussion as a method of facilitating social change. A progress report on the use of group methods in the investigation and resolution of social problems. Human Relations 1:533-549, 1947.

———: The Changing Culture of a Factory. London, Tavistock Publications, 1951.

JEANS, SIR JAMES: The Mysterious Universe. Cambridge, 1931.

JENNINGS, H. S.: The Beginnings of Social Behavior in Unicellular Organisms. University of Pennsylvania Press, 1941.

JONES, M.: Social Psychiatry. Tavistock Publications, London, 1952.

KARDINER, A.: The Individual and His Society. New York, Columbia University Press, 1939.

KEITH, SIR ARTHUR: Man's Origin. London, 1927.

KIERKEGAARD, S.: The Concept of Dread (Transl. Walter Lowrie). Princeton, Princeton University Press, 1946. (Originally published in Danish, 1844).

KLEIN, H. S.: The Therapeutic Group in a Hospital. Brit. J. M. Psychol. 23:101-104, 1950.

KONIG, R.: Jakob L. Moreno, Die Grundlagen der Soziometrie. Psyche, March, 1956, 905-912, Publ. by Klett Verlag.

LAMARCK, J. B.: Philosophie Zoologique, 1809.

LANDERS, J. J., MACPHAIL, D. S., AND SIMPSON, R. C.: Group therapy in H. M. prison, Wormwood Scrubs. The application of analytical psychology. J. Ment. Sc. 100:953-960, 1954.

LIGON, E. M.: Dimensions of Character. New York, Macmillan, 1956.

LINDZEY, G.: Handbook of Social Psychology. Addison-Wesley, Cambridge, 1954.

LOWY, S. AND GUTHEIL, E. A.: Active Analytic Theory. *In*: Progress in Psychotherapy (Fromm-Reichmann & Moreno, Eds.). New York, Grune & Stratton, 1956.

MAIN, T. F.: The hospital as a therapeutic institution. Bull. Menninger Clin. *10*: 66-70, 1946.

MASSERMAN, J. H.: Behavior and Neurosis. Chicago, University of Chicago Press, 1943.

——: Principles of Dynamic Psychiatry. Philadelphia, Saunders, 1946.

——: Psychological medicine and world affairs. *In:* Harris, G.: Modern Trends in Psychological Medicine. New York, Hoeber, 1948.

——: Moreno's "Transference, Counter-transference and Tele." Group Psychotherapy *7*:309, 1954.

——: Moreno's "Interpersonal Therapy." Group Psychotherapy *8*:62, 1955.

——: Practcie of Dynamic Psychiatry. Philadelphia, Saunders, 1955.

MAY, R.: Man's Search for Himself. New York, Norton, 1953.

McCARY, JAMES L.: Six Approaches to Psychotherapy. Dryden Press, 1955.

MONTAGUE, A.: Sociometric Methods in Anthropology. Sociometry *8*:62-63, 1955.

MORENO, J. L.: Die Gottheit als Kommodiant. Vienna, Anzengruber Verlag, 1911.

——: Einladung zu einer begegnung. Vienna, Anzengruber Verlag, 1914.

——: Die Gottheit als Redner. Daimon *2*:1-19, 1919.

——: Das Testament des Vaters. Kiepenheuer, 1920, 1922.

——: Das Stegreiftheater. Potsdam, Kiepenheuer, 1923.

——: Impromptu vs. Standardization. New York, Moreno Laboratories, 1929.

——: Case of Miss X. Impromptu Magazine *1*:27-29, 1931.

——: The Impromptu State. Impromptu Magazine *1*:9, 1931.

——: Group Method and Group Psychotherapy. Sociometry Monograph No. 5. New York, Beacon House.

——: The Creative Revolution. Impromptu Magazine, 1931.

—— AND WHITIN, E. S.: Application of the group method to classification. (2nd ed.) New York, National Committee on Prisons and Prison Labor, 1932.

—— AND ——: Plan and technique of developing a prison into a socialized community. New York, National Committee on Prisons and Prison Labor, 1932.

——: Psychological Organizations of Groups in the Community. Fifty-seventh Yearbook on Mental Deficiency, 1933.

——: Who Shall Survive? Washington, Nervous and Mental Disease Publishing Co., 1934. 2nd Edition, Beacon House, 1953.

——: Organization of the social atom. Sociometric Rev., p. 11, 1936.

—— AND JENNINGS, H. H.: Spontaneity training, a method of personality development. Sociometric Rev., p. 17, 1936.

—— AND ——: Advances in sociometric techniques. Sociometric Rev., p. 26, 1936.

——: A plan for re-grouping of communities. Sociometric Rev., p. 58, 1936.

——: Interpersonal therapy and psychopathology of interpersonal relations. Sociometry *1*:9-76, 1937.

——: Psychodramatic shock therapy—a sociometric approach to the problem of mental disorders. Sociometry *2*:1-30, 1939.

——: Creativity and the cultural conserves. Sociometry *2*:1-36, 1939.

——: Mental catharsis and psychodrama. Sociometry *3*:209-244, 1940.

——: Psychodramatic treatment of marriage problems. Sociometry *3*:1-23, 1940.

——: Psychodramatic treatment of psychoses. Sociometry *3*:115-132, 1940.

——: The philosophy of the moment and the spontaneity theatre. Sociometry *4*: 205-226, 1941.

——: The Words of the Father. New York, Beacon House, 1941.

—— AND DUNKIN, W. S.: The function of the social investigator in experimental psychodrama. Sociometry *4*:392-417, 1941.

—— AND TOEMAN, Z.: The group approach in psychodrama. Sociometry *5*:191-196, 1942.

——: The concept of the sociodrama. Sociometry *6*:434-449, 1943.

——: A case of paranoia treated through psychodrama. Sociometry *7*:312-327, 1944.

——: Psychodrama and therapeutic motion pictures. Sociometry *7*:230-244, 1944.

——: Psychodramatic Treatment of a Performance Neurosis: Case History of a Musician. Psychodrama Monograph No. 2. New York, Beacon House, 1944.

—— AND MORENO, F. B.: Role tests and role diagrams of children. Sociometry *8*:426-441, 1945.

——: The future of man's world. Sociometry *8*:535-542, 1945.

——: (ed.): Group Psychotherapy: A Symposium. New York, Beacon House, 1945.

——: Scientific foundations of group psychotherapy. Sociometry *8*:315-322, 1945.

——: Psychodrama, Vol. I. New York, Beacon House, 1946.

——: Psychodrama and Group Psychotherapy. Sociometry *9*:249-253, 1946.

——: Foundations of Sociatry: An Introduction. Sociatry *1*:10-15, 1947.

——: Open letter to group therapists. Sociatry *1*:16-30, 1947.

——: The Theatre of Spontaneity. New York. Beacon House, 1947.

—— AND SCHWARTZ, M.: Psychodrama combined with iunsulin in the treatment of psychoses. Psychiatric Quart. *22*:621-633, 1948.

——: Psychodrama of an adolescent. Sociatry *2*:7-26, 1948.

——: Psychodrama of a marriage. Sociatry *2*:121-169, 1948.

——: Psychodrama of a pre-marital couple. Sociatry *2*:103-120, 1948.

——: The sociodrama of Mahandas Ghandi. Sociatry *1*:357-358, 1948.

——: Sociology and sociodrama. Sociatry *2*:67-68, 1948.

——: The ascendance of group psychotherapy and the declining influence of psychoanalysis. Group Psychotherapy *3*:121-125, 1950.

——: Cradle of group psychotherapy. Group Psychotherapy *3*:121-125, 1950.

——: Group psychotherapy: theory and practice. Group Psychotherapy *3*:142-188, 1950.

——: Hypnodrama and psychodrama. Group Psychotherapy *3*:1-10, 1950.

——: Sociometry, Experimental Method and the Science of Society. New York, Beacon House, 1951.

——: Die Grundlagen der Soziometrie, Opladen, Westdeutscher Verlag, 1954.

——: Sociometry and the Science of Man. New York, Beacon House, 1956.

——: Fondements de la Sociometrie. Presses Universitaires de France, 1954.

—— AND YABLONSKY, L.: Progress in Psychodrama. *In*: Progress in Clinical Psychology: 2. New York, Grune & Stratton, 1956.

——: First Book on Group Psychotherapy. New York, Beacon House, 1932, 1957.

MORGAN, C. L.: Emergent Evolution. London, 1927.

MORGAN, T. H.: Evolution and Genetics. Princeton, 1925.

MOWRER, O. HOBART: New Perspectives in Psychotherapy, mimeographed, University of Illinois, Urbana.

MUNCIE, W.: Treatment in Psychobiologic Psychiatry: Its Present Status. *In:* Progress in Psychotherapy (Fromm-Reichmann & Moreno, eds.). New York, Grune & Stratton, 1956.

MURPHY, G.: Personality. New York, Harper, 1947.

NEHNEVAJSA, JIRI: Sociometry: Decades of Growth, Sociometry and the Science of Man. New York, Beacon House, 1956.

——: Soziometrische Analyse von Gruppen; Bibliographie der Soziometrie. *In*: Koln. Zeitschr. f. Soziol. u. Soz. Psycho. VII, 1 & 2, S. 119-157, 280-302.

PLANCK, MAX: The Philosophy of Physics, Trans. W. H. Johnston, 1936. George Allen & Unwin.

——: Scientific Autobiography. New York, Philosophical Library, 1949.

POMRYN, B. A.: Techniques in Group Formation. *In*: Social Psychiatry (M. Jones, ed.). London, Tavistock Publications Ltd., 1952.

ROGERS, C. R.: Client-centered therapy: a current view. *In*: Progress in Psychotherapy (Fromm-Reichmann & Moreno, Eds.). New York, Grune & Stratton, 1956.

RUDOLPH, G. DE M.: An experiment in group therapy with mental defectives. Internat. J. Soc. Psychiat. *1*:49-53, 1955.

RUESCH, J.: Psychotherapy and communication. *In*: Progress in Psychotherapy (Fromm-Reichmann & Moreno, Eds.). New York, Grune & Stratton, 1956.

SARRO, R.: Progress in psychotherapy in Spain. *In*: Progress in Psychotherapy (Fromm-Reichmann & Moreno, Eds.). New York, Grune & Stratton, 1956.

SCHINDLER, R.: The development of psychotherapy in Austria since 1945. *In*: Progress in Psychotherapy (Fromm-Reichmann & Moreno, Eds.). New York, Grune & Stratton, 1956.

SCHINDLER, W.: Family pattern in group formation and therapy. Internat. J. Group Psychotherapy *2*:100-105, 1951.

——: Family-pattern group therapy of sex disorders. Internat. J. Sexol. *4*:142-149, 1951.

——: The 'group personality' concept of group psychotherapy. Internat. J. Group Psychotherapy *2*:311-315, 1952.

——: Countertransference in 'family pattern group psychotherapy.' Internat. J. Group Psychotherapy *3*:424-430, 1953.

SECHEHAYE, MARGUERITE: A New Psychotherapy in Schizophrenia. New York, Grune & Stratton, 1956.

SEGUIN, C. A.: Psychotherapy in South America. *In*: Progress in Psychotherapy (Fromm-Reichmann & Moreno, Eds.). New York, Grune & Stratton, 1956.

SENFT, P.: Social clubs; their tensions and stratifications. *In*: Therapeutic Social Clubs (J. Bierer, ed.). London, H. K. Lewis, 1949.

SHUGART, G.: Preventive and treatment method for psychotic children. *In:* Progress in Psychotherapy (Fromm-Reichmann & Moreno, Eds.). New York, Grune & Stratton, 1956.

SMUTS, J. C.: Holism and Evolution. London, 1926.

SOHN, L.: Group therapy for young delinquents. Brit. J. Delinquency *3*:20-33, 1952.

SONNEMAN, U.: Existence and Therapy. An Introduction to Phenomenological Psychology and Existential Analysis. New York, Grune & Stratton, 1954.

SOROKIN, P.: Remarks on J. L. Moreno's "Theory of spontaneity and creativity." Sociometry and the Science of Man. New York, Beacon House, 1956.

SUTHERLAND, J. D.: Notes on psychoanalytic group therapy. I. Therapy and training. Psychiatry *15*:111-117, 1952.

—— AND FITZPATRICK, G. A.: Some approaches to group problems in the British Army. *In*: Group Psychotherapy: a Symposium (J. L. Moreno, Ed.). New York, Beacon House, 1946.

TAYLOR, F. KRAUPL: The pattern of friendliness and dominance in a therapeutic group. J. Ment. Sc. *96*:407-425, 1950.

THOMPSON, CLARA: Sullivan and Fromm. *In*: Progress in Psychotherapy (Fromm-Reichmann & Moreno, Eds.). New York, Grune & Stratton, 1956.

VERNON, P. E.: The validation of civil service selection board procedures. Occ. Psych. *24*:75-95, 1950.

VON WIESE, LEOPOLD: Sociometry. Sociometry *12*:202-214, 1947.

WARNER, W. J.: Common denominators in theory for psychotherapy. Group Psychotherapy *8*:82, 1955.

WELLS, H. G., HUXLEY, J. AND WELLS, G. P.: Science of Life. London, 1931.

WHITEHORN, J. C.: Understanding psychotherapy. *In*: Progress in Psychotherapy (Fromm-Reichmann & Moreno, Eds.). New York, Grune & Stratton, 1956.

WILSON, A. T. M.: Group techniques in a transitional community. Lancet *1*:735-738, 1947.

WINKLER, T: The present status of psychotherapy in Germany. *In*: Progress in Psychotherapy (Fromm-Reichmann & Moreno, Eds.). New York, Grune & Stratton, 1956.

WOLBERG, L. R.: The Technique of Psychotherapy. New York, Grune & Stratton, 1954.

——: Current practices in hypnotherapy. *In*: Progress in Psychotherapy (Fromm-Reichmann & Moreno, Eds.). New York, Grune & Stratton, 1956.

WOOD-JONES, R.: Trends of Life. London, Arnold, 1953.

YABLONSKY, L. & ENNEIS, J. M.: Psychodrama theory and practice. *In*: Progress in Psychotherapy (Fromm-Reichmann & Moreno, Eds.). New York, Grune & Stratton, 1956.

YONGE, K. A. & O'CONNOR, N.: Measurable effects of group psychotherapy with defective delinquents. J. Ment. Sc. *100*:944-952, 1954.

ZILBOORG, G.: A History of Medical Psychology. New York, Norton, 1941.

——: Rediscovery of the patient. *In*: Progress in Psychotherapy (Fromm-Reichmann & Moreno, Eds.). New York, Grune & Stratton, 1956.

ZIFERSTEIN, I. & GROTJAHN, M.: Psychoanalysis & group psychotherapy. *In*: Progress in Psychotherapy. (Fromm-Reichmann & Moreno, Eds.). New York, Grune & Stratton, 1956.

Part II: ANXIETY: the BACKGROUND of PSYCHOTHERAPY

Experimental Aspects of Anxiety

DAVID McK. RIOCH

IN THIS PAPER it is proposed to review briefly certain aspects of a variety of experimental studies which have some bearing on the phenomenon generally referred to as anxiety. In part, the experiments to be considered were designed to investigate the problem of anxiety, but the majority are concerned with determining the behavior, under a variety of conditions, of phenomena which are more or less precisely operationally defined. Most of the experiments to be considered were on animals, in spite of the fact that the late Dr. Harry Stack Sullivan, as well as more recent authors, have maintained that the phenomena constituting "anxiety" are limited to human beings, i.e., to acculturated *homo sapiens*. There is no question that the degree of complexity, modifiability and variability of human behavior in contrast to that of lower forms is of a different order of magnitude and that consequently normal anticipatory behavior—commonly experienced as "the mind"—is dependent on relatively frequent association with other humans. However, some of the grosser patterns of change in mode of interactive behavior in the course of transactions are sufficiently similar by available criteria to justify the use of simplified techniques for their further elucidation.

ADRENAL HORMONES AND "ANXIETY"

Since the work of Walter B. Cannon and Hans Selye, considerable attention has centered on the hypothalamic-sympathetic-adrenal medullary system and the hypothalamic-hypophyseal-adrenal cortical system, both in terms of their response in physical stress and in anticipatory activity following a signal associated with probable future stress. The more recent separation of two hormones from the adrenal medulla, epinephrine and norepinephrine, has further clarified the field in calling attention to different patterns of cardiovascular responses associated with different verbal and gestural patterns of behavior. The well-known experiments of Dr. Daniel Funkenstein and his associates at Harvard demonstrated the different

32

responses of different subjects to a frustrating experience. The subjects who expressed anger at the situation ("anger out" subjects) showed cardiovascular responses similar to those evoked by norepinephrine, whereas the subjects who blamed themselves for poor performance ("anger in" subjects) and those who showed "anxiety" responded in patterns similar to those evoked by epinephrine. Dr. Morton Reiser similarly found differences in the cardiovascular responses of enlisted men to experimental interviews. When the interviewer was an enlisted technician, the subjects expressed resentment freely and showed the norepinephrine type of cardiovascular pattern. With an officer interviewer the verbal and gestural behavior was restrained and the epinephrine cardiovascular pattern appeared.

These observations raise the question of the economy of two systems, both associated with anticipatory behavior implying physical activity and therefore improved metabolic support for muscles and brain. If we assume that functional systems have developed (phylogenetically) in response to interactions of organisms with the environment—which includes each other —we may consider the different requirements of such interaction. It appears that two separate problems need to be solved in emergency situations. The first is the assessment of the situation and shift from the previous, on-going activity to *one or another* pattern of interaction appropriate to the new information. The problem of shift of attitude or set is difficult, since the properties of the central nervous system are such as to maintain on-going behavior (cf. Sherrington's "competition for the final-common-path"), probably necessary to provide some measure of temporal stability. A quick acting system, not only improving cardiovascular support for the brain but also facilitating central scanning mechanisms and temporarily inhibiting innate patterns of interaction until one or another is reinforced, would be called for. The second problem in an emergency system is the longer continued metabolic support once one or another of the interaction patterns is established. It is tempting to speculate that the central and peripheral mechanisms associated with epinephrine and norepinephrine secretion are related to these two problems which arise in emergency situations.

It should be emphasized here that the subjective phenomena of "anxiety" are not simply due to the peripheral response to sympathetic-epinephrine stimulation. Early observations on the effects of intravenous adrenaline showed quite typical responses of "anxiety," with tremor, nervousness, agitation, and so forth. Recent studies by Basowitz et al. have demonstrated quite different effects, depending on personality factors and former experiences the subjects described with "anxiety" manifestations. Dr. Margaret Thaler and Capt. Maurice Goldstein have had occasion to study the responses of subjects to the intravenous infusion of epinephrine in the course of other experiments with similar results. Subjects may merely describe current sensations, such as feeling the heart beat, cold feet, etc., or they may verbally express and act out a full-fledged "anxiety" pattern. The different responses are apparently correlated with previous transactional patterns. It is of interest to note the change in emphasis in the more recent studies as compared with the earlier. This may be due to more attention to detail with repetition of the technique. However, it also calls to mind a change which has occurred more generally in social communication. In World War I neurocirculatory asthenia was an important medical problem, treated largely by internists and cardiologists; in World War II it was rarely seen, the cases of anxiety reaction being handled by the division psychiatrists and, for the most part, returned to duty. That the "anxiety" type of action communication is no longer a socially preferred mode is also evidenced by its decreased frequency in psychiatric practice. Currently, the so-called anxiety neurotic shows a more restrained pattern.

The finding of the increased output of adrenal cortical steroids under conditions of physical stress has led to investigations on the relation of these steroids to anticipatory behavior in response to threat and danger. Dr. John Howard, while studying surgical shock in a field physiological laboratory in Korea, collected urine samples from men under a variety of threatening conditions. He found no changes in the 17-ketosteroid fraction in response to increased danger, but in a number of men, though not in all, there were marked rises in the formaldehydogenic fraction. Very high levels, for example, were found in three men following an episode in which they were blown out of a bunker by a mortar shell, although they suffered no physical injury. Elmadjian found increased 17-ketosteroids in the urine of men engaged for 16 hours in an attack against Chinese positions in which the attacking company suffered relatively high casualties.

Dr. Roy Grinker has conducted probably the most extensive experiments on the correlation of "anxiety states" and adrenal steroid output. As he is presenting the material in this symposium, it will not be reviewed here. Dr. Margaret Thaler, Major Douglas Price, MC, and Dr. John W. Mason, in our laboratories, have made some observations which are pertinent. A battery of psychological tests and psychiatric interviews was used, and the results were correlated with the 17-hydroxycorticosteriod level in the blood of patients in the surgical wards on the day before elective thoracic surgery. The majority of these patients had been in the hospital for one to three weeks, which permitted control observations. Quite routinely, high steroid values were found on the day of admission, subsiding to normal levels in two or three days. (This rise in blood and urine 17-hydroxycorticosteroids has been observed in normal subjects on the day before the start of a three-day, sleep deprivation experiment, and also in monkeys on the first day or two they are brought to the laboratory from the animal farm.) On the day before operation, a quite good correlation was found between indices of "free anxiety" in the psychological and psychiatric examinations and rise of the 17-hydroxycorticosteroids in the blood, although it was only in those patients showing the highest degrees of "anxiety," including a tendency to react with overt physical activity, that the blood steroids were invariably elevated.

In contrast with the rise in adrenal steroids found in subjects responding with signs of increased alertness and activity to unusual, unexpected or otherwise threatening situations, study of the blood and urine 17-hydroxy-corticosteroids in subjects remaining awake for 72 to 90 hours—and thereby suffering a certain amount of discomfort—showed little change or a tendency to fall in the steroid level. During the sleep deprivation period appropriate psychological tests uniformly showed decreased capacity for maintenance of alert attention.

It may also be noted here that in studies on the cardiovascular responses of selected patients from the medical wards of the WRAH, Dr. Margaret Thaler, Dr. Morton Reiser and Dr. Herbert Weiner found that certain patients with duodenal ulcer in a depressed, withdrawn state of mind showed the least physiologic reactivity. In contrast, most ulcer patients showed prompt and fairly strong responses to interaction with the investigator.

In human experiments on anxiety states, the tendency has been to select those situations in which the subjects are faced with threatening, unstructured situations. It needs to be emphasized, therefore, that very pronounced symptoms of anxiety may be quite consistently evoked by situations of isolation, particularly in those cases where the duration of isolation is not defined. In this respect experimental observations confirm the field observations of men like S. L. A. Marshall, who found that the terror of the battlefield was its "lonesomeness."

ANIMAL EXPERIMENTS: EXPERIMENTAL NEUROSIS

It is not proposed to review the extensive literature upon so-called experimental neurosis, but rather to refer to a few studies which illustrate certain principles.

One of the problems of reliably evoking disturbed ("emotional," "anxiety") behavior has been to determine the nature of the situation in which the painful, threatening, or dangerous signal will be effective. It would appear that the most favorable situation is one in which the animal is strongly involved* in arriving at a relatively quickly anticipated goal. Thus, Wikler produced very strong aversive and "fear" reactions to female dogs in heat in a young male dog by giving him a moderately painful electric shock in the hind legs at the moment he achieved intromission for the first time. Hudson routinely obtained single experience aversive conditioning in rats by giving them a painful shock through a metal feeding tube from which they had become accustomed to eat. Indeed, Hudson found that visual objects introduced within one or two seconds *after* the painful shock also became signals for aversive behavior. Some of the most important experiments on aversive conditioning have been described by Dr. Jules Masserman and Dr. Curtis Pechtel. The importance of their work lies in the fact that the threatening stimulus, when applied on other occasions, evokes little or no response in the animal. Thus, a puff of air in the face of a cat under ordinary circumstances results only in shaking the head and licking the nose. If the same stimulus, however, is delivered when the cat is about to take a morsel of food in a situation in which it has learned to open the food box on the presentation of a visual stimulus, very dramatic results ensue. The cat springs away from the box with signs of marked disturbance, and if the experience is repeated once or twice the cat develops strong aversive reactions to the food box and adopts rather bizarre patterns of behavior. Equivalent but more complex manifestations are evoked in monkeys on the presentation of a threatening visual stimulus (a small green rubber snake). The importance of the timing of the aversive stimulus in the course of the interaction between the animal and the apparatus seems to be crucial. The same principle of accurate timing applies in the free operant conditioning technique utilizing what has come to be known popularly as the "Skinner Box." The effectiveness of the automatic methods used apparently depends to a large extent on the possibility of delivering the painful stimulus synchronously with, or at a fixed short interval after, the conditioning signal.

From a somewhat different point of view certain experiments of Dr. Howard Liddell demonstrate the importance of temporal factors. A young ram trained to make discriminative responses to metronome clicks at

---

*I have adopted the term "involved" from Dr. Margaret Thaler, who found it descriptively effective in portraying the interaction of patients with the examiner during studies on cardiovascular responses to a structured interview. She found that withdrawn (schizoid or depressed) patients showed little or no cardiovascular reaction but that patients who became "involved" with the examiner showed pronounced changes. In the animal experiments the term "involved" is used to indicate the degree to which all other activity than that directed toward a shortly anticipated goal is reduced, as well as the degree to which anticipatory preparations for extraneous interruption is reduced.

different frequencies performed accurately on the routine schedule of tests at five minute intervals. When, however, the interval was reduced unexpectedly to one minute the ram showed marked disturbance and discriminative behavior was completely occluded.

In addition to the factors noted, reference should be made here to the classical experiments in which markedly disturbed behavior followed presentation signals increasingly similar, but of different anticipatory significance, such as reward vs. no reward. The breakdown in discriminative behavior is frequently accompanied by vigorous activity as well as by quite bizarre stereotyped patterns appearing in situations other than the testing situation. Dr. W. Horsley Gantt has conducted a detailed study of these phenomena, extending over several years, and his data on his famous dog Nick will survive volumes of theoretical speculations on "anxiety."

In most animal experiments resulting in disturbed behavior the initial response to the change in the environment which precedes the disturbance is usually one of strong striped muscle or autonomic (chiefly sympathetic in overt manifestations) activity. Thus, the animal usually withdraws rapidly, jumps, runs around the apparatus, struggles if restrained, and so on. This is accompanied by increased pulse rate, moderate piloerection, dilated pupils, etc., although defecation and micturition may also occur in some species or situations. The later behavior of these experimental preparations varies widely, both between species and between experimental situations. In general it may be noted that the variety of interaction patterns in which the animal's behavior may be reorganized after the initial common "alarm" or "emergency-action" response is greater in animals higher in the phyletic scale in any standardized situation. Thus, the great majority of individual rats respond in the same stereotyped pattern when subjected to the same experimental procedure. Cats, dogs, monkeys and chimpanzees have an increasingly varied repertoire. The human has a still larger variety of "defenses" or "anxiety binding" patterns, but is somewhat limited in utilizing these capacities due to group pressures to conform to accepted modes of communication. This has been noted particularly in combat psychiatry. Men joining a unit who shortly thereafter become psychiatric casualties show the syndromes typical of the unit, together with the appropriate autonomic manifestations, although these syndromes were not known in the units from which they came.

One other aspect of the change in mode of behavior—which is part of the "anxiety" phenomenon—needs to be mentioned. This is that the new patterns of interaction are only fortuitously effective, depending on the environmental response. In laboratory experiments both the acute responses and the chronic, stereotyped patterns of behavior have been found frequently to be ineffective and occasionally lethal. Thus, Dr. Curt Richter found that wild Norway rats can be literally "scared to death"—the heart precipitously slowing and stopping—in a threatening, but not physically traumatic situation. Dr. Richter, Dr. Masserman, and others have also shown that chronic states of refusal to eat, accompanied or not by other bizarre behavior such as maintained postures, etc., can be evoked when previous threatening experience is associated with food or the feeding situation.

ANIMAL EXPERIMENTS: EXPERIMENTAL MODIFICATION OF CONDITIONED RESPONSES OF THE "ANXIETY" OR "EMOTIONAL" TYPE

It is proposed in this section to review, albeit much too briefly, a series of experiments initiated by Capt. J. V. Brady and Dr. Howard Hunt several years ago and still continuing under Capt. Brady in our laboratories. The free-operant conditioning method developed by Dr. B. F. Skinner has been used and found most elegant for this type of investigation. Most of the work has been conducted on rats but similar effects have been obtained in cats and monkeys.

In the first experiments, two conditioned responses were developed in the rats. One response was pressing a lever to obtain the reinforcement— either a drop of water or a pellet of food. The other response was an aversive reaction. In Group A, the rats were exposed to a signal (usually a clicker noise) for a period of three or five minutes, at the end of which time, coincidentally with the last click, the rat received a moderately painful shock through the grid-floor of the cage. Within six to eight trials of the stimulus and painful shock, the A rats would sit crouched, trembling, fur ruffled and frequently defecating. It should be emphasized that no such response to the clicker was observed before it was paired with the nociceptive stimulus. The B group of rats were also exposed to a clicker, but these animals received the painful shock to their feet only if they pressed the lever for the reward. Again, within six to eight trials, the B rats stopped pressing the lever, but instead of crouching, frozen and trembling, they ran about the cage, fur slick, no defecation, and occasionally approached the lever, touched it, but withdrew without pressing it. Following the establishment of these two types of aversive response, the A and the B groups were subjected to a series of electroconvulsive shocks and then retested. When exposed to the clicker, the A rats had completely lost their aversive reaction and continued to press the lever in a normal fashion. The aversive behavior of the B rats, however, was unmodified by the electroconvulsive experience. Attention may also be called to the fact that in neither group was the conditioned manipulation of the lever for a reward affected. In more recent experiments Capt. Brady has found that reserpine also clearly differentiates these two types of conditioned responses in rats and monkeys, the conditioned emotional response disappearing under reserpine, the other being maintained. In some recent experiments on monkeys in collaboration with Dr. John Mason, it has been found that during a period of several days in which the CER is repeatedly evoked, the blood steroids rise, but under reserpine, coincidentally with the diminution and loss of the CER, the blood steroids fall.

A number of other phenomena have been found with regard to the behavior of this CER in rats over the course of time—the abolition of the CER by electroconvulsive shock has been found to be temporary, the response returning in about a month following the last convulsion. However, of possible importance to therapeutic strategy, it has been found that the CER can be extinguished during that period when it does not appear. That is, if, during the month following the electroconvulsive shocks, the rat is exposed to the clicker but the clicker is not followed by a painful stimulus, the CER does not reappear as it does in the rats which have not been extinguished. Another important observation is that the CER can be repeatedly developed and extinguished by appropriate pairing of the clicker with the painful shock or giving the clicker alone. When the production and the extinction of the CER are repeated sequentially, the rate of "learning" and "unlearning" is markedly increased, so that only one or two reinforcement or extinction experiences are necessary in the sequence. In striking contrast to this result is the effect of rare but random reinforcement. Under such conditions the CER becomes remarkably stable and difficult to extinguish, although the animal has received many fewer reinforcements than he did in the series of regular sequential reinforcement-extinction experiments. These observations strongly emphasize the importance of the temporal structure of the experimental situation. Another important effect of time has recently been discovered. In the early experiments the CER was evoked once or twice a day in the experimental animals and was found to be remarkably stable for periods of months. Recently, the effect of evoking the CER repeatedly during two- to three-hour sessions every day has shown that in a relatively short period of time the animal's behavior changes. Instead of remaining frozen throughout the period of the clicker, he moves about and continues to press the lever for the reward during the first half of the three- or five-minute period during which the clicker sounds. He then returns to the frozen "anxiety" posture during the second half of the clicker until the painful shock is delivered.

Several series of experiments in our laboratories have been designed to investigate further the phenomenon, originally described by Olds, that when electrodes are sterilely implanted in certain parts of the limbic system of the rat's brain and are connected to a stimulator which the rat may activate by pressing a lever, the stimulus behaves as a reward and the rat will stimulate itself for long periods. The most effective points for stimulation appear to be in regions close to the medial forebrain bundle, apparently more medially in the rat and more laterally in the cat and monkey. It has been found that animals will work on experimental schedules in every way similar to the schedules for water, food, or avoidance of painful stimuli. In a number of experiments the self-stimulation reward has been combined with other conditioned responses. The results, in combination with the CER, have been most dramatic. Rats with appropriately implanted electrodes have "learned" to press a lever, either for a water reward or for self-stimulation. They have also "learned" the emotional response to a clicker. When such preparations are working for water and the clicker is presented, they immediately freeze in the typical manner. However, in a number of cases in which the animal is working for the self-stimulating reward, the presentation of the clicker in no way interrupts the on-going behavior. When, at the end of the clicker, the painful stimulus comes, the rat gives a typical jump and then continues with his self-stimulation. It might be argued that the self-stimulation "makes the rats unaware of the situation." However, it has been found that when a rat previously deprived of water is presented with two levers, one of which gives self-stimulation, the other of which provides water, he initially works on the self-stimulation lever but after a time comes to operate both, indicating a quite adequate "awareness" of the situation.

Technical improvements in the construction and use of deep implanted electrodes have recently provided students of animal behavior with a very powerful tool for obtaining continuous records of activity in various loci in the brains of animals during particular patterns of behavior. These methods have been applied by Galambos and Sheatz to the study of the behavior of cats before and after aversive conditioning to auditory signals —namely, a series of clicks. Electrodes were implanted in a number of discrete anatomical structures in the brain, including the auditory cortex, the medial geniculate, the hippocampus and the cochlear nucleus. The animals were exposed to clicks at a rate of one a second for long periods in their home cages. When brought to the experimental cage and continuous recording started, it was found that electrical activity was evoked in the cortex, the geniculate, and the cochlear nucleus quite irregularly, being fairly strong at times and again disappearing in response to the regular clicks of a series. The animal was awake, lay relaxed, or stood, but gave no overt response to the auditory signal. Following these control observations the animal was given a mild electric shock across the chest coincidentally with every sixth to tenth click. After a few such experiences strong activity was evoked not only in the structures of the auditory system, but also in the hippocampus and certain other areas investigated. The overt behavior also changed to one of standing or crouching, the muscles tense and the posture rigid. Discontinuing the unpleasant stimulus resulted in the anticipatory aversive response being extinguished and the electrical activity pattern returning to its previous form. These observations demonstrate the widespread reorganization of central nervous activity during anticipatory aversive behavior. In particular they emphasize central control of activity at the level of the first synapse of the input system. Indeed, the demonstration of the inhibitory functions of the olivo-cochlear tract on transmission of messages from the organ of Corti to the acoustic nerve (Galambos, 1955) shows that the central control of input starts at the peripheral receptor organ.

That the activity at the level of the first central synapse can be selectively modified to particular tones and also depressed by other patterns of alertness or attention has been demonstrated recently by Hernández-Peón, Scherrer, and Jouvert in Dr. H. W. Magoun's department at the University of California at Los Angeles. The importance of these data is the implication that the input is controlled in brainstem nerve-nets (usually classified as reflex or innate mechanisms) as well as to the forebrain (often referred to as "consciousness" mechanisms) by particular patterns of reciprocal activity between these systems.

CONCLUSIONS

Consideration of experimental studies on animals and humans indicates that a number of different phenomena are ordinarily included in the general concept of "anxiety." The varieties of precipitating events and the varieties of responses are sufficiently great that these phenomena are not useful as criteria of a single, general class of events. There is one phenomenon, however, which does differentiate a class of events that would be useful to identify whether or not it is called "anxiety," namely, change in the *form* of behavior (i.e., the *mode* of the interaction pattern) which occurs in the course of a transaction. Such a change is always present in situations with humans in which "anxiety" is diagnosed, but may also occur in situations in which the verbal, gestural and autonomic manifestations are not characteristic of clinical anxiety.

Study of this phenomenon obviously requires more or less continuous observations over the temporal course of a transaction, permitting examination of the precipitating events and later developments. For this purpose animal experiments are preferable since they are simpler and are not contaminated by *post hoc* verbal rationalizations.

In general, the precipitating events have one or another of three characteristics: (a) the more or less sudden arrival of information of environmental response inconsistent with the information the anticipatory behavior is, as it were, prepared for; (b) arrival of information previously associated with situations inevitably (i.e., regardless of any performance the animal is capable of) including "pain" or "doom"; and (c) change in rate or in variability of information such that the interacting system becomes overloaded and functionally disorganized.

The initial responses to the precipitating events would appear to include increased activity in one or another of the mesencephalic and diencephalic mechanisms which either facilitate alertness and capacity for rapid change in anticipatory "set," or which provide somatic, particularly visceral, support for patterns of interaction requiring high energy output, such as attack, flight, etc. It is now quite clear that there is a reciprocal interaction between these "alarm" and "emergency" systems and the anticipatory, informationprocessing mechanisms of the forebrain. The anatomical substrata are in part included in the reticulo-thalamo-cortical ascending system of tracts and in the descending cortical connections to the tectum, the reticular formation, and the subthalamic centers, as well as the descending tracts from the limbic lobe. Activity in certain of the last named is apparently capable of inhibiting parts of the alerting and emergency-action functions. It may be noted here that the variety of innate patterns of behavior mediated by the brainstem is such that the general concept of a diffuse mesencephalicposterior hypothalamic "emergency," "alerting," or "activating" mechanism must be recognized as only a first approximation. Indeed, these aspects of the activity of the systems involved may be secondary functions supportive to relatively precisely integrated behavior patterns.

The later behavior following the more or less acute change in mode of transaction shows wide range and considerable modifiability. The only common characteristic of the numerous patterns seen would appear to be decrease in the area of interaction between the organism and the environment. This appears to be accomplished either by reduction of the motility of the organism or by limitation of the scanning activity of the information processing systems.

It is important to note that the careful, quantitative studies of animal behavior in experimentally limited situations and with attention to the time axis permit differentiation of classes of behavior not readily apparent in field or clinical observations. In particular, the sharp differentiation of two types of "learning," one abolished and the other virtually unaffected by electroconvulsive stimulation or by reserpine, represents an important contribution not only to learning theory but also to knowledge of the anxiety-type of phenomena. Concurrent studies of physiologic, endocrinologic and psychological phenomena promise further differentiation both of patterns of disturbances of anticipatory behavior and also of the control mechanisms which may be sequentially brought into play.

A Theoretical and Experimental Approach to Problems of Anxiety*

_____ROY R. GRINKER, et al.†

GENERAL LAWS OF PSYCHOPHYSIOLOGY have not yet been satisfactorily formulated despite decades of research by psychologists, psychiatrists and biologists. In recent years a shift of emphasis toward a psychosomatic approach to problems of human illness has occurred which has resulted in greater concern with research directly applied to specific illnesses in attempts to pin-point the role of disturbed emotions in their etiology.

An essential problem in psychosomatic research is the inherent difficulty in determining what factors in the personality and which of its past experiences should properly be correlated with the symptoms of an organ dysfunction. In clinical studies variables are chosen in the psychological and the somatic systems, and, without their dynamic and temporal relations being clearly understood, they become the basis for the presumed etiologic understanding of the psychosomatic disease. Such formulations, attempting to relate two discrete processes, necessarily neglect the mechanisms through which disturbances in one system produce change in the other.

Paralleling such work in psychosomatic research, other investigators have explored the effects of psychological stresses on functions of various parts of the organism. These studies include both experimentally induced stresses and naturally occurring life situations capable of arousing emotional disturbances. A partial survey of the major investigations of this type has been made in previous works. [3, 19, 11] Sometimes the experimental conditions used were so contrived or trivial as to raise serious questions concerning the contributions they could make to our understanding of the more profound, pervasive and enduring stresses of life. More often, single variables for brief periods of time have been the only objects of concern, with little effort to study directly multiple interrelated processes.

In previous work we have utilized soldiers with war neuroses,[10] civilians who were in severe panic or anxiety states,[13] and, most recently, paratroopers

*From the Institute for Psychosomatic and Psychiatric Research and Training of the Michael Reese Hospital, Chicago. Supported by the U. S. Army through the Medical Research and Developmental Board under Contract Number DA-49-007-MD-469 and the State of Illinois Mental Health Fund.

†Sheldon J. Korchin, Harold Basowitz, David A. Hamburg, Melvin Sabshin, Harold Persky, Jacques A. Chevalier and Francis A. Board.

in training.[3] In these latter studies we hoped that the close observation of man through a period of time in a well defined situation of danger would allow greater understanding of the mechanisms through which psychological disturbance affects functioning at different biologic levels. Although certain advantages of the natural experimental situation are clear, such a study is also limited in the number and kinds of measurements possible, the inability to assure simultaneity of measurement, and to regulate the stress events.

From these various experiences a great deal has been learned about the theoretical and methodologic problems involved in psychosomatic research. We wish to present in this communication some general statements about these problems, as an introduction to a fairly large series of reports concerning several years past, and still on-going, researches.*

In presenting a discussion of our conceptual model of psychosomatic processes within a broad framework, we realize that it is only one of many possible ways of viewing the total organism. Ours has developed from a series of past experiences and pilot studies on anxious subjects during which we have become aware of the many difficulties inherent in deriving feasible empirical studies from theoretical ideas. No matter how broad or inclusive the initial conceptualization, in practice only segments of biologic and psychological functions can be observed, measured and analyzed. Consequently, in the remainder of this paper we will present first an over-all theoretical scheme and then the necessarily more limited experimental program derived from it.

II

In part, the present extensive research program was undertaken because we felt there was a need for a methodologic model based on tenable theory, applicable to general problems of psychosomatic research. If such a model were fruitful in the study of a single affective state, it might be utilized in studies of other affects and perhaps eventually lead to the formulation of general laws. In the present research we chose to study anxiety because of its great importance in the economy of human existence.

Anxiety has a special role in the adjustive processes of the human organism, both as an indicator of stress and as a precursor of further stress response.[6] We believe that anxiety is a signal portending that organismic adjustments are being made to present or expected stress in the dynamically

---

*This is the first of a series of publications and expresses the basic theoretical and methodological problems with which the research program began. It is intended to provide the background for subsequent papers describing detailed techniques and results.

interrelated somatic, psychological and behavioral processes. At higher levels of anxiety, as in the holocaust of war or unexpected catastrophe, equilibrium becomes so disorganized that adequate behavior, psychological efficiency and somatic functions are profoundly disturbed. However, milder anxiety is of great significance as a signal of threat to the organism, for it precedes or accompanies active preparation for adjustment and hence may lead to facilitation of functioning at all levels.

Psychologically, the defensive responses may be seen in such maneuvers as counterphobic activity, magical, ritualistic behavior or thought, withdrawal, or character alteration. Thus, anxiety in some past time may be responsible for the development of psychiatric syndromes and personality deformations. Threatening recrudescence in the present, it may intensify the previous defenses or evoke new types of defenses, for free anxiety is one of the most unendurable afflictions of man. As a signal of danger, anxiety is accompanied by a host of interrelated somatic processes which are in the nature of activities preparatory to emergency action. Often these are patterned in individual ways which derive from the subject's early learning. Whatever the later stimulus, the personal pattern is evoked and recognized. With decrease in psychological defenses and lessened control, anxiety mounts and the somatic responses tend to become less discrete and patterned and more diffuse, global and undifferentiated. Similarly, the same dedifferentiation of function can be seen in cognitive, conative and behavioral processes as the defensive utilization of the anxiety breaks down.

Free anxiety is an affect, and as such it is objectively experienced by the subject and reportable by him to an observer. Such anxiety is experienced as an inexplicable foreboding of danger or disintegration. As an emotional experience it is necessarily conscious and pressing. We are less concerned here with the condition termed "unconscious anxiety" or with the study of affects which are not reportable. Anxiety can best be defined by the existence of a particular emotional experience. It is relatively meaningless to speak of "unconscious anxiety," meaning by that phrase an affect which would be present *if* some defense were weakened or some mode of action prohibited. Unfortunately, much psychosomatic research has been based on assumed affects which were only vaguely implicit in unconscious and underlying processes expressed only indirectly in symbolic form. Still, as we found in our paratrooper studies, the state in which anxiety is nascent or latent may be related to certain chronic states of somatic activity, and this problem does require study in its own right. What we mean to suggest here is that research in this area requires a clear and consistent definition of anxiety, which should have its referent in emotional experience, rather than being an inferred psychological state from symbolic processes or from physiologic concomitants.

In the same paratrooper studies, it was also found that anxiety could be categorized into at least two types, shame and guilt, each with seemingly different correlates in physiologic measurements. There seemed to be evidence that these two modalities were associated with at least varying quantities of physiologic disturbance and possibly qualities as well. However, the distinction between types of anxiety is properly made in terms of the parameters of personality discoverable in the subject. We believe it important to define different qualities of anxiety in terms of the time of onset and the life history of the individual, the ego structure, and specific conflict areas. Such research, attempting to describe various qualitative aspects of anxiety and their possible relations to qualitatively different physiological states, is necessary and important. However, for the subject himself, anxiety is phenomenally unitary in the sense that he experiences dread and foreboding no matter what its origin or history. Therefore, for our present purposes, we tentatively conceive of anxiety as being a monistic affect and attempt, through the study of personality structure, to tease out such differences as may exist in its qualities.

Before we pass to other considerations, it should be noted that free anxiety, having any degree of intensity and duration, is a neurotic phenomenon. However, it is part of a general biologic process which, at lower levels, is represented by the apprehension and state of alerting or vigilance evoked by minor or short-lived dangers that every human being needs to preserve his life. Anxiety exists when the stress is excessive and the ego controls inadequate.

III

The research workers at this Institute have had considerable experience with various aspects of human anxiety under conditions of severe life-stress in combat and lesser life-stress in paratrooper training; they have studied patients with chronic states of neurotic anxiety, induced acute emotional responses in anxiety-prone individuals, and have evoked anxiety in healthy persons in contrived laboratory experiments. From these experiences a series of general principles and operational concepts has been derived which led to the design of our present and ongoing experimental studies.

1. *The Principle of Organization.*

We speak of organization in designating any vital or systematic whole, whether it be a morphologic structure, a functional process or a theoretical concept. Organization is a term usually applied to systems composed of parts or variables which have numerical values. Living systems or conceptual systems are dynamic, since they change through time.[12] Although some systems are composed of arbitrarily selected variables, others consist of variables whose association has been empirically derived.

It is generally accepted that biologic and psychologic—and perhaps social—systems are regulated by integrative or homeostatic processes which function to maintain equilibrium within the boundaries of the healthy and adaptive physiologic range of organismic functioning.[4] When the integrative determinants or essential variables of a system are strained to a critical point, new or emergency adaptive processes are activated, often with a sacrifice of some functions of the original system. Then, through a "step-function" or a "jump-state"[1,17] a new system of organization develops which increases the system's chances of survival or maintenance of organization. Anxiety may be the principal function of a new organized and integrated system. If anxiety serves only as a signal, the life of the new system may be temporary, and reversibility to the previous organization is a probability. In other situations anxiety may remain chronic, that is, neurotic, and the system remains irreversible. Psychiatrists are well aware of this stability of such an organization as evidenced by the difficulty encountered in treating patients with chronic anxiety.

As the determinant of a system, anxiety maintains components or processes of organization involving total behavior in the social environment, cognitive and conative functioning and physiologic actions, all of which are adaptive under conditions in which anxiety exists, for as long as it remains. The total system is involved with the environment in that external influences or internal disturbances acting on the anxiety system may augment its component activities or stimulate behavior of the organism to remove itself safely from the dangerous stimulus to which it is highly sensitive, or to attack in attempting to destroy the danger. Thus, even if interest is centered on anxiety as an organization with its multiplicity of component parts, transactions that involve environmental parameters are always present.[15] The total social and interpersonal setting in which the observed subject lives and moves should therefore be taken into account, either by recording its changes or by controlling its constancy as much as possible.

2. *The Disparity in Time Between the Stimulus and the Total Anxiety Response.*

(a) Anxiety persisting long after the application of a stimulus or after a cue has been "forgotten": In some earlier experiments we stimulated an area of the human brain above the sphenoid bone in the midline in the general location of the hypothalamus through a basal electrode inserted in the nasopharynx.[9] We recorded action potentials from the stimulated area and from the surface of the skull for some time after the cessation of the stimulus. Not only was the basal area excited, but large bursts of cortical excitatory waves followed within a few seconds. Then, gradually, there was a decrement in frequency and amplitude of responses from both the basal and cortical areas. The smooth path of decline was interrupted within a period as long as eight minutes by bursts of excitation in the basal area followed by cortical responses which finally disappeared, and for a short period the basal area responded spontaneously without cortical activity. Thus the basal area behaved like a condenser. The human subjects suffered intense anxiety at the moment of stimulation and experienced milder bouts of anxiety at the recurrent periods of basal discharge. The corresponding phenomenon in life is a sudden burst of anxiety in response to a crucial situation or a wounding remark with vigorous attempts at recovery of equilibrium by trying to "put it out of mind." This fact notwithstanding, the person will experience, against his will, upsurges of anxiety of lesser degree for a long time, often with involuntary conscious recall of the original provoking experience.

(b) Behavioral and physiologic disturbances may persist after the affect of anxiety has subsided. During the war we observed profound alterations in behavior, serious physiologic changes and cognitive and conative disturbances in subjects whose anxieties had dwindled to endurable quantities.[10] Long after the stimulus was over, regressive behavior, posture and speech persisted, suggesting that an initial precipitant could influence the total anxiety process even though the emotion of anxiety was no longer experienced.

(c) Anxiety may appear long after the stimulus cue. Psychiatrists and psychoanalysts are aware of the fact that real life situations or therapeutic interpretations, even those not consciously recallable to memory, may evoke, after a variable latent period, some or all of the manifestations of anxiety. It may be difficult to determine the crucial stimulus responsible for the anxiety response even in persons under continuous observation because of the time lag between stimulus and response. In the "end-phenomenon" described in the analysis of a paratrooper training program,[3] anxiety often appeared after the stress of training was over.

3. *The Components, Parts or Subsystems of Anxiety.*

When we consider the anxiety process as an organized system composed of subsystems, the essential parts of the process should be identified in order that they may be subjected to rigorous experimental analysis. Empirical data have accumulated to indicate that humans have a wide variety of "personal" responses associated with anxiety. Some report sweating, tachycardia, hyperpnoea, diarrhea, "butterfly" sensations, etc., as habitual somatic indicators of anxiety. Others describe purely subjective sensations located "in the head" or "in the mind." Still others indicate disturbances in psychologic functions such as concentration, memory, perception, decision, etc. And some reveal anxiety by behavioral signs of restlessness, manic behavior or patterns of flight in panic.[2]

The study of anxiety as a process is thus complicated by the wide range of variables implicated at one time or another as specific or general patterns. Isolation of one or two variables may seem expedient for the sake of simplicity of experimental design, but we believe that the atomistic view of man is misleading and that a larger view, if not entirely molar, is now more productive.[7] Even so, there is a limit to the number of variables that can be studied as components of anxiety because of the limits of endurance of the subject, the interference of systems of measurements and the available skills. Therefore, it is essential to test in combination those variables, suggested by empirical data to be most significant, that come closest to representing the total range of responses.

Obviously, our choice of variables may be erroneous even though suggested by experience or logic. These errors could only be determined through the process of testing—which is one of the prime purposes of the research. We need to determine the significance or lack of significance of dependent variables within the anxiety system in order to drop those that are unaltered during change in anxiety and to discover new and more significant ones, located most closely to the central process of anxiety.

4. *The Relationship of Subsystems to the Central Process of Anxiety.*

Our conception of anxiety as an organizing process confronts us with problems of spatial and temporal relations between the "central state" and its peripheral parts. We recognize that anxiety is a function of the central nervous system and that human anxiety, by our definition, is even more dependent on central nervous functions in that it appears only after the development of consciousness, self-discrimination, concept of future time, and capacity for communication. At the same time, we may view anxiety as a system of psychosomatic organization without reference to any morphologic location or limitation to specific organ functions, particularly when the system of anxiety is viewed in transaction with other psychological organizations, in interpersonal transactions and in group behavior. But when we focus on the internal operations of anxiety, we are in a nexus of psychosomatic functions of organ units and systems. Organization then becomes identical with structure-function of the central nervous system, the endocrine systems and their great outflows.

Aside from estimation of degree and kind of anxiety, we became interested in three large subsystems. The first involves the perceptive system through which cues are received, augmenting or decreasing anxiety, and which, in turn, is seriously affected functionally in the presence of anxiety. The second involves the reciprocal functions between the hypothalamic-pituitary hormones and their target peripheral glands, such as the adrenal cortex, the thyroid, the gonads, etc. The third involves the direct sympathetic outflow integrated and controlled by the hypothalamus innervating the visceral organs, the adrenal medulla, thus liberating endocrine substances from various glands and at the nerve synapses and endings.

The combined effect of nervous and endocrine stimulation, in turn, may involve the function of such organs as the cardiovascular, respiratory, gastrointestinal system, liver, spleen, adrenal medulla, sweat glands, other smooth muscles, secretory organs, distribution of blood supply, etc. In fact, the activities of these structures are associated in vital metabolism and are subject to many local as well as general influences. They are less certain to be construed as essential participants in a stress response the more distantly they are located anatomically or in a functional chain of events. Therefore, we should choose as our significant variables functions as close to the central state as possible. Size of pupil, skin resistance, bowel peristalsis, etc., as symptom indicators common to many types of disturbances, are less important for our theoretical concepts of stress response than pituitary or hypothalamic functions and their immediate neighbors in the sequential chain, which are more important for understanding system mechanisms.

5. *Principles Involving Temporal and Quantitative Relationship Among Subsystems of Anxiety.*

When sequential relationships between parts of the anxiety organization are analysed, several principles should be taken into account.

(a) *Resiliency:* Biologic systems vary in degree of resiliency in individual systems and at various ages. In infants, physiologic responses shoot to hypermaximal degree quickly in response to minor stimuli. In old age, responses are slow, rarely reach the maximum and decline in intensity gradually. For example, a virus infection may be accompanied by a hyperpyrexia in the infant and no fever or even a subnormal temperature in the aged. Most estimates of homeostatic resiliency at the biologic level have been only partially successful.[5]

In all systems there is a period of inertia followed by an over-action of function far beyond that of the resting level. Then there is an overreaction in the opposite direction followed by a period of damped oscillations within successively smaller ranges until decrement into the basal range is complete. The prototype of this resiliency may be observed during a blood sugar tolerance test.[14] The blood sugar mounts to a high level until finally insulin effects a reduction of sugar to considerably below the resting level, followed by another rise and then gradually a decline to pre-test levels. Without considering exactly which hormones are concerned with the opposing direction of circulating sugar, the elasticity of the system is demonstrable. A variety of enzyme systems is involved.

Many other examples could be given of this ubiquitous biological process. One other is the effect of cold on the victim of "sun-stroke" with its subsequent hyperpyrexia. The immediate therapeutic response is a rapid fluctuation between varying degrees of hypothermia and hyperthermia despite the constancy of the body surface temperature.

(b) *Mechanisms maintaining stability among subsystems:* Within the nervous and enzyme systems stability within physiologic ranges is kept constant by processes of reciprocal excitation and inhibition. There is a mechanism to maintain plasma adrenocortical steroids at relatively constant levels, which exemplifies this fact. This is true in spite of considerable apparent variations in the rates of peripheral utilization and metabolism of such compounds. This is possible because variations in blood steroid levels themselves influence the amounts of such steroids subsequently released into the blood by cortical tissue. The feed-back operation of this servo-mechanism functions through the pituitary.[18] The pituitary adrenocorticotrophic hormone has been shown to play an important role in the control of the rate-determining reaction for cortical steroid release. While it appears probable that ACTH release is mediated to a large degree through hypothalamic factors, and while it is true that many of the factors controlling ACTH release are not understood, circulating corticosteroid levels have nevertheless been shown to determine the rates of ACTH release.[16] The greater the deviation of blood corticosteroid level from the homeostatic norm, the greater the associated effect on ACTH release.

(c) *Hierarchy of Responses:* In our paratrooper studies we found a general pattern of sensitivity; some reactions would be evoked quickly with minimal degrees of stress while others required maximal quantities of stress. We could distinguish a hierarchy of stress-sensitivity among biochemical variables in that eosinophil levels dropped quickly in response to all stress situations.[3] At the other extreme, hippuric acid excretion was extremely stable under stress, while Glutathione was intermediate in sensitivity between these two measures. We found another type of hierarchical response indicating that activation of different systems may occur in meaningful sequences. Thus, the blood level of amino acids rose prior to change in hippuric acid. In some subjects, anxiety was experienced only after biochemical indices were elevated for some time, and in others the reverse order held.

An interpretation of the meaning and economics of the hierarchy of responses is apriori extremely difficult. At this time we can only mention a few possibilities, since adequate interpretation would depend on future experimental findings. (1) Differences in timing of response may be due to inherent differences in sensitivity or latency of the individual variables within the total anxiety organization, or differences in central thresholds.

(2) Some variables, particularly in metabolic processes, may serve as donors for others and need to build up a significant quantity before another substance can be produced (i.e., glycine into hippuric acid). (3) Variables may respond in chainlike fashion, each one tipping over the stability of the next process in a mechanistic sequential chain. (4) Early idiosyncratic conditioning may result in specified responses of certain variables before others that have not been conditioned. (5) Other processes in the complicated homeostatic activities may influence timing of responses, although not of themselves directly involved in an aspect of the anxiety organization which we are observing. For example, adrenaline liberated through discharge of the hypothalamic-neural mechanism probably potentiates the peripheral utilization of adrenocortical hormones and may also further activate the production of ACTH.

IV

From the previous discussion of anxiety as an action system possessing a function and an organization, we have indicated some assumptions from which hypotheses may be derived. Since our research is focused on the psychosomatic organization of anxiety, we decided to study the component parts and their relationship to the central state and to each other. As psychosomatic research, this involves the isolation of specific functions represented by the variables of affect, psychological performance, central nervous system activity and endocrine secretion.

We propose to measure the activity of a sample of significant variables or subsystems of the anxiety organization as accurately as possible within the limits of present methods. We hope that each sample could serve as a representative or an index of activity of one of the essential psychosomatic subsystems of anxiety: affect, psychological performance, central nervous system and hormonal activity. However, since we are investigating the human psychosomatic organization, working with the intact person without harming him, limitations are imposed on our goal of measuring processes as close to the central state as possible. Thus for our sampling of significant variables we often must be satisfied with indirect indices spatially remote from central functions and often temporarily delayed in appearance. However, for each variable we hope to obtain some notion of its significance, latency, sensitivity to stimuli, resiliency, relationship to other variables, and position on a sequential chain.

We had hoped that we could isolate for each variable a cycle of reciprocal excitation and inhibition, involving a central and peripheral process. But for this there is required the operation of a negative feed-back which decreases the activity of an excitatory process. When anxiety is associated with an increase of ACTH, there results an increment in plasma hydro-cortisone which in turn decreases the output of ACTH. Thus, measurement of hydrocortisone gives some idea of the activity of the hypothalamic-pituitary system. Likewise, intravenous infusions of ACTH could presumably influence the level of plasma hydrocortisone to different degrees, depending on whether the adrenal gland had been activated by anxiety.

Anxiety may be liberated or augmented when vulnerable conflicts are verbally explored or when psychological defenses are temporarily weakened or undercut. The result is vigorous attempts to re-establish defenses against anxiety or creating new ones which may be successful in varying degrees.

Perception and decision may be considered as a cycle in that perception of significant cues influences decisions, which, in turn, modifies further perception; however, feed-back is not automatic but requires information from the environment regarding the accuracy of decisions. Experimentally, the subject can be failed or passed by the observer, but the subject's own level of confidence is no criterion of accuracy or speed of decisions.

Such cycles can be measured by tapping in on them at one pole—measuring anxiety, hydrocortisone or decision time and accuracy. They may be disturbed by methods applicable to one focus, such as introducing anxiety-producing thoughts, making accurate decisions impossible or injecting ACTH, at the same time that anxiety and all other variables are also measured. These measures may give one a good grasp of the significance of variables and their spatial and temporal relationship.

Time relationship is an even more complicated problem, as has been indicated in the preceding section. To ensure measurement of variables in relation to each other, it became necessary to introduce the principle of simultaneous measurements. These are often not possible. Measurements of heart rate, movement, affective state, etc., can be continuous, but psychological performance, circulating hormones, urinary output, etc., can be measured only periodically. We attempted to get as close as possible to simultaneity, at least in a relative sense.

Furthermore, a limited time had to be set for each experiment to obviate the distress of long immobility for the subject. Therefore, in order to observe relationships among subsystems, some of which had a long cycle of activity, long latent period or slow recovery rate, and others of which were fast-acting, one must utilize successive blocks of time to span the total spectrum. Correlation of values at any of several short periods of sampling time would give quite different results; for this reason, it is necessary to conduct experiments observing several variables at different successive blocks of time, moving, as it were, from the earliest phases of responses step by step to the later. If feasible, the experiment itself could extend in several stages from a short time to increasing lengths of time until all systems had recovered completely from the stimulus and had again resumed basal levels.

Our experiments are oriented to give information regarding level, variability, and change as a response to the applied disturbance. They enable us to determine conventional correlations between two or more variables. With successful research into new statistical methods, it is hoped that the pattern of simultaneous response of all variables to a disturbance applied to a single system may be appropriately described.

If patterned groupings could be determined with reference to several types of somatic responses or to anxiety, or if temporal patterns of response of subsystems could be isolated, they would of necessity require correlation with essential personality differences. We assume that significant personality groupings could be found to encompass the content of psychosomatic categories. The important question is how such categories will be defined, especially as to the meaning of the more superficial versus the deeper elements of personality.

For this purpose each experimental subject from our hospital population is carefully studied psychiatrically. In addition, detailed notes are taken of the patients' spontaneous responses in the experimental interviews and their interactions with the psychiatric interviewer who discusses the patients' reactions twice in each experimental day. A follow-up interview is conducted after the total experiment is completed. In addition, nurses' notes and the therapist's material are available, thus providing us with extensive psychiatric data from which to view personality in categories or groupings at various levels of abstraction, which can be correlated with patterns of anxiety organization either in total or in part.

V

The experimental program undertaken to discover the transactional relationships among several selected aspects of human functioning in the state of anxiety starts with four broad questions: 1. When the level of free anxiety is altered, what concomitant changes occur in each of the other variables? 2. When the existing level of any given variable is influenced experimentally, what concomitant changes, if any, occur in free anxiety? 3. When the existing level of any given variable is influenced experimentally, what concomitant changes, if any, occur in variables other than anxiety? 4. When a change occurs in any variable, such as anxiety, what are the sequences and relative degrees of change in other variables?

In the present studies the functions sampled include affective variables, ego functioning as measured in a perception-decision task, physiologic measures such as cardiac and respiratory rates and percentage time of somatic movements, and biochemical indices of pituitary, thyroid and adrenocortical endocrine functioning. Each is chosen on the basis of existing knowledge to sample a separate area of functioning believed to be of importance in the total anxiety state. Clearly, many more measures could have been made within each of the areas, and many could have included, as well, areas at present unrepresented.

The nature of the experiment, and the theoretical conception upon which it is based, obviously require the utilization of a number of investigators from several disciplines, each proficient in a variety of special techniques. Not all available disciplines are represented, nor could all of the potentially important variables be measured. The particular variables chosen necessarily reflect the particular knowledge, interests and backgrounds of the members of the present group.

THE VARIABLES STUDIED

In later reports the rationale, methods of measurement, and findings obtained in each of these areas of evaluation will be presented in greater detail, but in the interests of an over-all picture we should describe them briefly now.

1. *Affective variables.* Although in earlier research anxiety was observed and rated as a single affect, in the present studies the approach is broadened to include anger and depression and an over-all estimation of the total emotional response. We do this not only in the interest of completeness, but also because anxiety is so often intermingled with other types of emotional responses in the stress situation. By rating all three, observers are forced to discriminate anxiety, anger and depression and to discover the signs by which each is distinguishable. The emotional ratings are based on a specially devised evaluative interview and on the continuous observation of the subject by observers behind a one-way-vision screen during the entire experimental period.

2. *Perception and decision.* A simple task involving the judgment of the relative size of visual forms is used as a measure of the subject's ability to distinguish and judge visual stimuli. Of particular interest is the relationship between the accuracy of such judgments and the time required to make them.

3. *Physiologic measures.* Heart rate, respiratory rate and general bodily movements are measured throughout the experiment as indices of disturbance at a physiologic level.

4. *Hormonal measures.* Plasma hydrocortisone and serum protein-bound iodine are assessed as measures of adrenocortical and thyroid activity. Urinary hydroxycorticoids are also determined as an additional estimate of the status of the adrenal cortex.

CHOICE OF SUBJECTS

We attempt to use subjects with free anxiety, since we are concerned with the changes of functioning in an individual already at a relatively high level of disturbance and who, in principle, should show greater changes under stress. However, in ours, as in most clinical settings, it is hard to find patients with any high degree of anxiety which is not quickly subdued by neurotic defenses. Therefore, subjects are chosen who are believed to be most prone to become anxious, a supposition based on the past history of the subject (especially recent) and on the ascertainable weakness of defenses. Even so, it is often found that the experimental intervention stimulates greater defensiveness, often by virtue of implying therapeutic significance to the situation.

All subjects are chosen from a known population in which considerable information is available about the particular personality, major conflict areas, and type of anxiety of each person. Subjects are selected who can be available for the four-day period required by the experiment and who are capable of enduring this degree of restraint. Since our interest is not only in establishing the general patterns of response among the several variables, but to discover whether there might be types of response patterns, related perhaps to enduring personality characteristics, working with known subjects becomes a principle of central importance. In the design of such research the decision often must be made between the extensive study of a relatively few individuals, in which individually organized findings can be understood, but which may not give much basis for discovering more general principles, and, on the other hand, the study of large numbers of individuals, each of whom is unknown except for a narrow segment of data which he yields. In the present researches we try to stay between these two poles, studying sufficient subjects to have some conviction of representativeness and at the same time knowing each one sufficiently well to have a basis for understanding idiosyncratic patterns.

A further and important consideration is that each subject be studied for a sufficient period so that changes in response through time might be seen. Here again we stand between two possible experimental designs, the one in which a larger number of subjects is studied in a particular situation on a single occasion, thus giving little basis for judging within-subject variability, and the opposite pole of studying a few subjects through extended periods of time, as in the therapy situation, during which considerable within-individual variation can be observed, but of necessity limiting the number of subjects that can be studied and consequently knowledge about the variation between subjects. Having the experimental procedure extended in time also allows for the comparison of change within a subject in terms of his own levels of functioning. Using "self-controls" in an area where considerable difference among people is to be expected is, we believe, a necessary procedure.

EXPERIMENTAL DESIGN

In terms of the various theoretical assumptions, a number of pilot experiments were run in which different variables and conditions of testing were explored. Certain considerations became manifest. The repeated measurement of a number of variables over a period of days limits the choice and frequency of the measures to be used. For example, though one might in principle want more points of measurement of a particular biochemical index, the number of blood samples required from a single subject might produce a severe anemia. Interesting variables cannot be used because of interference with other testing procedures. Thus, test methods have to be chosen which can be used within a single experiment on the same subject without interfering one with the other, without requiring excessive time or unusual conditions for administration, and which can be done repeatedly without earlier testing directly affecting the results of later testing.

The general experimental plan evolved includes four continuous days of testing. The first of these is a pre-experimental day in which the subject is brought to the experimental room and run through each of the procedures. This day is designed to acclimate the subject to the experimental setting and test procedures. The three subsequent experimental days consist of periods before, during and after an experimental intervention (stresss stimulus), which differ in each section of the study. Although the measurement of each variable yields different amounts and types of information— heart and respiratory rates are recorded continuously throughout each of the days, while the evaluation of perceptual functioning depends on a test given once in the "before" and once in the "after" periods—each of the major periods of the experimental day is viewed as a single unit within which all measures are conceptually "simultaneous." The value of each variable for the entire period, whether based on the mean of a number of measures or in a single measure, is taken to represent the level of functioning in that system for that period.

A central event on each of the experimental days is a stress stimulus condition which is intended to induce change in some aspect of the total system. This event, describing the "during" period, separates the measures made before and after on each of the three experimental days. Thus, it is possible to compare the amount of change in each variable separately and jointly as a function of the inducing stimulus. The effort is made to increase the intensity of the experimental stress on each of the three experimental days in the hope that different threshold responses for the several variables can be exposed.

In the over-all plan the experiment is to be divided into four studies, each involving a different stress stimulus designed to affect the functioning of each of the systems in turn. Different groups of subjects, matched in their anxiety proneness, are to be used for each of the conditions. These involve (1) increasing anxiety itself by use of a stress interview designed to confront the subject with unconscious or unacceptable material and to challenge certain defenses; (2) affecting perception and decision-making by a procedure impugning the accuracy of the subject's perception; (3) disturbing the adrenocortical system through the intravenous injection of ACTH. In each of these different experiments the same basic design is used and the same measures of affect and other functioning made before and after the experimental intervention. Clearly, each of these stimulus situations differs; some, like ACTH, can be regulated for the entire duration of the experimental day, while others, like the stress interview, may often have short-lived or even quite unpredictable consequences. Still, we are hopeful that using the same basic evaluative design—three days of pre-post measurement in a number of selected variables—and changing the inducing force so that its point of application represents in turn each of the different systems, may provide an approach to the questions raised earlier and may determine a model for experimentation in the psychosomatic field.

REFERENCES

1. Ashby, W. R.: Design for a Brain. New York, John Wiley, 1952.
2. Basowitz, H., Korchin, S. J., Oken, D., Goldstein, M. S., and Gussack, H.: Anxiety and performance changes with a minimal dose of epinephrine. Arch. Neurol. & Psychiat. (In press)
3. Basowitz, H., Persky, H., Korchin, S. J., and Grinker, R. R.: Anxiety and Stress. New York, Blakiston, 1955.
4. Cannon, W.: The Wisdom of the Body. New York, Norton, 1939.
5. Freeman, G. L.: The Energetics of Human Behavior. Ithaca, Cornell University Press, 1948.
6. Freud, S.: The Problem of Anxiety. New York, Norton, 1956.
7. Grinker, R. R.: Psychosomatic Research. New York, Norton, 1953.
8. Grinker, R. R. (editor): Toward a Unified Theory of Human Behavior. New York, Basic Books, 1956.
9. Grinker, R. R., and Serota, H. M.: Studies on corticohypothalamic relations in the cat and man. 1:579, 1938.
10. Grinker, R. R., and Spiegel, J. P.: Men Under Stress. Philadelphia, Blakiston, 1945.
11. Haufmann, E.: Psychological approaches to the study of anxiety. In: Anxiety (Hoch, P. H. and Zubin, J., Ed.). New York, Grune & Stratton, 1950.
12. Lillie, R. S.: General Biology and Philosophy of Organism. Chicago, University of Chicago Press, 1945.
13. Persky, H., Grinker, R. R., and Gamm, S.: Correlation between fluctuation

of free anxiety and quantity of hippuric acid excretion. Psychosom. Med. *14*: 1, 1952.

14. SOSKIN, R. AND LEVINE, R.: Carbohydrate Metabolism. Chicago, University of Chicago Press, 1952.

15. SPIEGEL, J. P.: A Model for Relationships Among Systems. *In*: Toward a Unified Theory of Human Behavior (Grinker, R. R., Ed.). New York, Basic Books, 1956.

16. SYDNOR, K. L. AND SAYERS, G.: Blood and pituitary ACTH in intact adrenalectomized rats after stress. Endocrinology *55*:621, 1954.

17. TOMAN, J. E. P.: Stability vs. Adaptation. *In:* Anxiety and cerebral excitability. Arch. Neurol. & Psych. *75*:534, 1956.

18. WIENER, N.: Cybernetics. New York, John Wiley, 1948.

19. WOLFF, H. G., WOLF, S. G. AND HARS, C. C. (editors): Life Stress and Bodily Disease. Vol. 29, 1950. Proceedings of Association for Research in Nervous and Mental Diseases. Baltimore, Williams & Wilkins, 1950.

Special thanks are due the publishers of the A.M.A. Archives of Neurology and Psychiatry for permission to reprint this article by Roy Grinker, et al., which appeared in volume 76, 1956, of the latter journal.

The Structure of Anxiety

KURT GOLDSTEIN

IN THE PAST THE PHENOMENON OF ANXIETY was the special interest of the philosopher in relation to the problem of the existence of man. Here the names of Pascal, Spinoza, Kierkegaard and, recently, Heidegger have to be mentioned particularly. Anxiety became the central problem of psychiatry, especially since Freud stressed its paramount significance for understanding neuroses and psychoses. According to the general trend of Freud's psychology, he put in the foreground the causal explanation of anxiety and stressed the significance of definite events in previous life to which the anxiety of a patient could be traced.

My contribution to this symposium is concerned primarily with the *structure of the phenomenon we call anxiety.* My restriction to this aspect of the problem is not at all simply determined by the consideration that other writers will treat the question of the contents related to the anxiety condition, but by the conviction that only a *clarification of its structure and the distinction from other,* in some respects similar emotional states, *will enable us to understand the onset of anxiety under definite conditions.*

The observation and treatment of thousands of brain damaged patients who were under my care during and after the First World War* served as material particularly suited to characterize the behavior we call anxiety. The psychophysical condition in which anxiety occurs is much easier to observe here than in neuroses and psychoses. It was possible to study not only the physiologic processes but also what was going on in the individual in the state of anxiety. Starting from such well studied material I hope to bring the discussion down to a concrete basis.

There would be no better way of getting to the core of our problem than by demonstrating the behavior of such a patient. Because that is not possible, I have to restrict myself to a description and count on your imagination. If we observe such a patient, he appears, in his customary way of living, not much disturbed. He is a little slow; his face is rather immobile or rigid. His attention is directed very strictly to what he is doing at the moment: listening to you, writing, etc. Confronted with tasks in various performance fields, he gives often about normal responses, but at other

---

*See Goldstein, K.: After-effects of Brain Injuries in War. New York, Grune & Stratton, 1948.

times he fails completely in tasks which seem to be very similar to those he has performed before quite well.

Careful examination reveals that he fails in tasks which demand for their fulfillment the use of a special *mental capacity,* which in him is impaired because of the brain damage. We call this capacity "abstract attitude."† This attitude is necessary when we have to make a choice, to do something voluntarily, to shift from one aspect to another of the situation, etc. As much as the patient is able to react in direct response to a stimulus or a situation (as we say, in "concrete" behavior), he fails when thinking, deliberation, or choice (the "abstract" attitude) are necessary for his reaction.

For our problem here, it is particularly important that we define abstract attitude as the *presupposition for giving to oneself an account of what one wants to do and what one is doing.* Due to the defect in this respect, the patient is unable to realize the failure and why he fails. But simply stressing the occurrence of failure or success would not give a correct picture of what we observe in the two situations.

A man who, when confronted with a task he can solve, looks animated, calm, in a good mood, well poised, collected and cooperative, appears dazed, trembles, perspires, becomes agitated and is evasive, even aggressive when confronted with a task he cannot solve. I have called the state of the patient in the situation of success an *ordered* condition, and the state in the situation of failure a *disordered* (catastrophic) condition, because all performances are somewhat disturbed. We can produce this condition experimentally by demanding from the patient something, which, as we know from our investigations, he will not be able to do. How is it understandable that failure in seemingly unimportant tasks, such as a simple problem in arithmetic, can bring an individual to a state of total disorder? There must be something else, some more serious incapacitation, which produces this disorder. The explanation is as follows: as I have stressed on several occasions, my observations have brought me to a definite concept concerning the driving forces in organismic behavior. I came to the conclusion that the interpretation of behavior as the effect of various isolated instincts cannot be correct and that all behavior, normal and pathologic, becomes understandable only if one considers it as an expression of *one basic* organismic trend, the trend to *realize as much as possible all its capacities, its nature.** The state of full self-realization of the individual goes along objectively with order and subjectively with satisfaction: wellbeing, the

---

†K. Goldstein and Scheerer: Abstract and Concrete Behavior. Psychological Monograph, Vol. 53, No. 2, 1941.

*Cf. Der aufbau des Organismus, Nijhoff-Haag, 1934 (Engl. trans.: The Organism: A Holistic Approach to Biology. American Book Co., 1939. P. 35).

experience of what we may call realization of oneself in existence. Anything which hinders self-realization essentially brings the organism to disorder and catastrophe, subjectively experienced as anxiety.[†]

Because the patients, due to the defect in abstract attitude, are not able to judge whether or not a situation is dangerous for self-realization, they easily come to disorder and a state of anxiety. The dependence of the onset of anxiety upon the impairment of abstraction explains why normal subjects do not so easily develop anxiety in a situation of failure, and why, when it does occur, it occurs because of an awareness of the danger of a failure for their self-realization. Let me illustrate this with a simple example of the behavior of a subject who is not able to answer questions in an important examination. If the outcome of the examination is not particularly important, the person may feel somewhat upset, but he will take it calmly, trying to come to terms with the situation by using his wits and thus bringing it to a more or less successful solution. This shows not only that he reacts reasonably well with the use of abstract attitude to the failure but that his self-realization is not endangered. It is far different, however, when passing the examination is of great significance for this person; for instance, when failure may hinder his professional career, marriage for love, etc. Now, with self-realization seriously in danger, catastrophe may occur, with severe anxiety and inability to answer questions which, under other circumstances, could be answered without difficulty.

Here, too, we see that what produces anxiety is *not the failure itself,* but the *danger which it presents in relation to the individual's existence. Hence, anxiety is related to a situation which endangers our self-realization. It is not simply the effect of inability to cope with the task, but of the danger to self-realization which the failure brings about.* That is the specific danger experienced in anxiety. This origin of anxiety makes it understandable that the danger situation must not be a real one; anxiety can set in if the individual imagines that the situation may disturb self-realization.

Our concept of the structure of anxiety demands a clarification of the following point: certainly, catastrophic conditions and so also anxiety are connected with an object, an event (outer or inner). But the observation of brain injured subjects shows that the individual comes to a state of anxiety *without being aware of the objective course;* due to damage of an abstract attitude, he is not able to give himself an adequate account of anything. Asked what was the cause of his disorder, he cannot answer.

From our concept that anxiety is always an expression of inability to come to terms with the world in the form of self-realization, it follows

---

†*Ibid,* p. 291 and Zum Problem der Angst. Aerztliche Zeitschr. & Psychotherapy II, 1:409-437, 1927.

that anxiety is always an *expression of a present condition,* never simply a repetition of a previous state in which anxiety occurred. The latter cannot be, because states of disorder cannot be remembered as such. They certainly can have an after-effect on the functioning of the organism, but this consists of a decrease of the threshold for occurrence of anxiety, not in an after-effect of previous contents.

When the condition we have characterized occurs, anxiety *always* sets in. From our observation we cannot agree, for instance, with the theory of tracing anxiety back to a previous event, e.g., the trauma of birth, whereby recalling it gives to a new event the character of anxiety. If, at birth, the infant has anxiety—and I am not at all sure about this—then anxiety originates here *in the same way as later,* namely, by the inability of the organism to cope with the situation in his trend of self-realization (here in the form of the trend for survival). The same is the case in all other conditions in which anxiety occurs.

Our conclusion concerning the nature of anxiety is in agreement with the interpretation of anxiety by such philosophers as Pascal, Kierkegaard, and Heidegger. In their opinion anxiety represents an emotional state which does not refer to anything definite. They say, the *individual in anxiety has no object;* the state of anxiety is the experience of being faced with 'nothingness.' I would say, *"of not being able to have any object."* In anxiety the individual experiences the *breaking down and dissolution of the world and himself;* he experiences the loss of existence.

Our concept of the structure of anxiety could be considered correct only if we distinguish strictly between anxiety and another emotional state which is very often confused with it: *fear.* Superficially, fear may have many of the characteristics of anxiety, but it is an *intrinsically different condition, as a phenomenologic analysis shows.*[*] In the state of fear we are confronted with an object with which we have difficulty in coping because it may endanger our existence. But we can meet the object. We are conscious of ourselves as well as of the object; we can deliberate as to how we shall behave toward it. We can try to remove it or we can intentionally flee from it.

The assumption that we are dealing with *qualitatively different conditions in anxiety and fear* is supported by the fact that we use two different words, "fear" and "anxiety," and that these words are not interchangeable. The distinction between the two conditions is more definite in German than in English. One speaks of *Angst* and *Furcht.* The different relationship of the two conditions to the experience of an object is reflected in such

---

[*]Kurt Goldstein: Human Nature in the Light of Psychopathology. Cambridge, Harvard University Press, 1940.

expressions as "Ich fürchte etwas" and "Ich ängstige mich." (I fear some-thing, I am anxious.) That means that, *in our experience, fear is related to an object,* while anxiety is an inner state, without object; it concerns only me.

If fear, in contrast to anxiety, is related to the experience of an object, what is it that *makes an object capable of inducing fear?* Is it something inherent in the object itself that we fear? Of course not. An object that at one time arouses interest, or is met with indifference, at another time may evoke the greatest fear. In other words, fear must be the result of a specific relationship between individual and object. What is it, then, that leads to fear? *It is the experience of the possibility of the onset of anxiety. What we call fear is the experience of impending anxiety.* Some characteristics of the objects indicate to us that anxiety *may* occur.

Because the person in a state of fear is not yet in a state of total disorder, but only envisions it or its possible occurrence, he is not disturbed in his judgment concerning the outer world, as is the person in a state of anxiety. On the contrary, driven by the tendency to avoid the onset of anxiety, he attempts to establish special contact with the outer world. He tries to see the situation as clearly as possible and to react to it in an appropriate manner. Fear is conditioned by and directed against very definite aspects of the environment, which have to be recognized. Fear sharpens the senses, whereas anxiety renders them unusable; fear drives to action, anxiety paralyzes. We can escape anxiety only by avoiding situations which might result in anxiety.

From our explanations it follows that to feel anxiety it is not necessary to be able to give oneself an account of one's acts; to feel fear, however, presupposes that capacity. Correspondingly, the observation of our patients with defect of abstraction shows that they have anxiety but, due to their mental impairment, they do not know fear. The difference between anxiety and fear finds its expression in different reactions of the individual in both conditions. Anxiety makes impossible any active interference on the part of the individual in anxiety, even an attempt to reduce it.

But also under the condition of permanent catastrophe, as in the brain injured, *changes in the behavior of the patient occur which we call protective mechanisms.* Failure in a simple task can cause a patient suffering from epileptic fits to fall into a state of unconsciousness. Of course, resorting to unconsciousness is hardly a suitable protection against a catastrophic situ-ation, since it completely abolishes contact between the patient and his environment. Other means, however, can be very helpful, e.g., the patient may withdraw in order to prevent a number of stimuli from reaching him; he may lack awareness of the defect; he may like to be in familiar rooms where everything is arranged in a definite way; or he may show extreme orderliness in every respect (space, time, etc.). It is a very simple order which allows living on a low level of existence only and a restriction of freedom with an enormous shrinkage of the world and of the personality of the individual.* A particular characteristic of such behavior is that the patients always try to do something which they *can do*. Indeed, all this can take place only if the life of the individual, deprived of so many relations with the outer world, is protected by his environment and the people around him from the breaking in of dangerous stimuli.

Since abstract attitude is not fully developed, the child shows a behavior similar to the brain-injured. He is very frequently confronted with tasks with which he cannot cope and which menace his existence. Thus, anxiety certainly plays a great role in the life of the child. However, it is diminished through safeguards which the adult arranges and which save the child from shocks he could not stand. Furthermore, anxiety in children is reduced through a peculiarity which we must consider carefully, the more as it also plays a certain part in the adult's overcoming of anxiety. This peculiarity is the extraordinarily strong and general *tendency to action* and the urge to solve given tasks, which belongs to the nature of the child. Thus, the pleasurable surprise when the conquest of a piece of the world has succeeded replaces the experience of shock. This drive is so strong that the child not only fails to draw back from the impending anxiety situation, but possibly goes out of his way to seek it: "Little Johnny went out to learn how to creep." Not to be afraid of dangers which could lead to anxiety—this represents in itself a successful way of coping with anxiety, and with that represents the essential difference between a normal child and a brain-injured adult. Especially through this tendency to action does the child manifest itself as an early stage of the normal adult, in contrast to the patient.

As the child grows into the world of the adult, its behavior becomes more even and "ordered." The more it becomes fitted to its environment, the more its "wondering" decreases, but it never disappears completely. The adult is affected anew by surprise and anxiety, as he is always faced with new outer and inner situations.

It is a fact that the normal person, in his conquest of the world, *undergoes, over and again, such states of shock*. If, in spite of this, he does not always experience anxiety, it is because his nature enables him to bring forth creatively situations which insure his existence. Thus, the disproportion between his capacity and the demands of the environment, which may lead to catastrophic failure, is averted to a certain degree in average life. As

---

*See "The Organism," pp. 35-66 for details of their behavior.

long as this secure state is not essentially shaken, and the existence is not endangered, the shocks are not experienced as anxiety.

Just as in the brain-injured person, the normal adult has the *urge to diminish his anxiety,* but to a much lesser degree. As an expression of this urge, we find in the adult the tendency toward order, norms, continuity, and homogeneity, in principle similar to the behavior of the brain-injured patients. But apart from this, the normal is determined by his urge (already inherent in the child) for new experiences, for the conquest of the world, and for an expansion of his sphere of activity in a practical and spiritual sense. His behavior oscillates between these two tendencies, and is influenced sometimes more by the one, sometimes more by the other. The outcome of the two tendencies is the cultural situation.

But in no way could one claim that this "ordered" world, which culture represents, is the product of anxiety, the result of the desire to avoid anxiety, as Freud conceives culture to be sublimation of the repressed drives.* This would mean a complete misapprehension of the creative trend of human nature, and at the same time would leave completely unintelligible why the world was formed in these specific patterns, and why just these forms should be suited to procure security for man. This becomes intelligible only if one regards them as expressions of the creative power of man, and of the tendency to effectuate a realization of his nature. Only when the world is adequate to man's nature do we find what we call security.

This tendency toward actualization is primal; but it can effect itself only in conflicting with, and in struggling against, the opposing forces of the environment. This never happens without shock and anxiety. Thus we are probably not overstating the case if we maintain that these shocks are essential to human nature, even to all organic life, and if we believe that life must, by necessity, take its course *via* uncertainty and shock. Even though the tendency to reduce uncertainty, to standardize the environment, may have its correspondence in certain formal peculiarities in science, art, and religion, one cannot emphasize too strongly that it is impossible to regard the contents of cultural products as the expression of uncertainty and anxiety.

Where anxiety, as the mainspring for the activity of an organism, comes into the foreground, we always find that something is upset in the nature of that organism. Or, to put it another way, that organism is normal and healthy in which the tendency toward self-actualization is acting from within, and overcomes the disturbance arising from the clash with the outer world and inner conflicts, not out of anxiety but out of the joy related to self-

---

See Goldstein: "Human Nature," p. 111.

realization. How often this most perfect form of actualization is a fact, and whether it exists at all, we leave open to question. In any event, even life in its most perfect manifestation must pass through disturbances. The creative person who ventures into many situations which expose him to shocks will find himself even more often in anxiety situations than the average person. Individuals differ as to how much anxiety they can bear. For a patient with brain injury, the amount is very low; for a child it is greater; and for the creative individual, it is greatest.

The capacity for bearing anxiety is the manifestation of genuine courage,* where ultimately one is concerned not with the things in the world but with the threatening of existence. *Courage, in its final analysis, is nothing but an affirmative answer to the shocks of existence, which must be borne for the actualization of one's own nature.* This form of overcoming anxiety requires the ability to view a single experience within a larger context, that is, to assume the "attitude towards the possible," to have freedom of decision regarding different alternatives. Thus, it is a characteristic peculiarity of man.

We do not have time to consider the various *concrete situations* where anxiety occurs. I think it would not be difficult to show how they all become understandable if one analyzes them from our point of view. Then it will become apparent which role the particular conditions in infancy, in neurosis, and in normal life play in the development of anxiety and why these conditions are suited to produce anxiety or to bring into the foreground fear, etc.; further, why protective or defense mechanisms occur under certain conditions. Our discussion of the structure of anxiety and fear could not give more than a characterization of the methodologic procedure to acquire an understanding of all these phenomena. I would like to mention a few details: the infant knows only anxiety, no fear. The protective mechanisms he develops originate passively, as in the brain-injured. Both are due to the lack of abstraction at this age. With increasing maturation, particularly development of abstract capacity, beside the passive development of protective mechanisms, active, voluntary "defense" mechanisms are built. The defense mechanisms should be distinguished from the protective mechanisms. They have a different origin and have to be treated differently in therapy.

The neurotic's symptoms are particular expressions of protective and defense mechanisms originating as protection against anxiety. The patient will be less restricted by the abnormal behavior belonging to these mechanisms the more he is able to bear conflicts and danger. In psychotherapy he learns what is more important for his self-realization: the security which the protective mechanisms bring about or the greater freedom which goes along with some suffering, due to the impossibility of eliminating all conflicts.

---

*Human Nature, p. 113.

Indeed, to make this evaluation it is necessary that he see clearly the conflicts and face them, in other words, that he react to them with *fear*, not with *anxiety*. To help the patient in this direction seems to me *one of the main tasks of psychotherapy,* and success in this respect is one of the most important presuppositions of improvement. This shows how significant the clear distinction between anxiety and fear is, not only for theoretical clarification but also for our procedure in practice.

To change anxiety into fear becomes thus the most important endeavor in psychotherapy.* Here the significance of transference† in the transition period would have to be discussed. Its development, which Freud has stressed as so essential for successful treatment of neuroses and psychoses, is important according to my experience also in treatment of organic patients.

Let me conclude with some general remarks. The emotion we call anxiety can be understood only if we consider the phenomena in the frame of reference of the total organism and its basic trend toward self-realization. In anxiety we meet this striving for realization of the self in the most primitive form: a lowering of the existence and a shrinkage of the nature of the individual. So to say, only survival is guaranteed. Indeed, this also can be achieved only with the help of the "other." Without that the individual would not be able to survive.

Fear allows a somewhat higher level of existence; it makes it possible to come to terms with dangerous situations and guarantees some higher degree of self-realization, although not the highest. Even in this condition the individal may sometimes have to be satisfied with the feeling of being freed from distresses and pain and with some release of tension. This is the condition we call pleasure. Pleasure may, under certain conditions, occur as a state of respite, but it is a phenomenon of standstill, akin to death, excluding realization in a higher degree.‡ That is all that can sometimes be achieved by therapy.

But there is in fear an element which has some positive value, insofar as it activates the creative power of the personality. We no longer feel simply release, pleasure; we experience as always in use of the totality of our capacities another emotion, which we call *joy,* which goes along with the possibility of a higher form of self-realization. While pleasure separates

---

*See Goldstein, K.: "Health, Disease and Therapy," Amer. J. Psychotherapy 8:745, 1954.

†Concerning the problem of transference, see Goldstein, K.: The concept of transference in treatment of organic and so-called functional nervous diseases. Acta Psychotherapeutica, Intern. Congr. f. Psychotherapy, 1954 (Karger, Basel).

‡Goldstein, K.: On emotions. J. Psychol. 31:37, 1951.

us from the world, in joy we experience existence of ourselves and others.

Joy also is not without some danger, but we accept the danger. That occurs with the help of *courage* by which we affirm the shocks of existence as a necessary part of it, and with that we become able to reach higher degrees of self-realization. In this form of self-realization man not only searches for *security alone* (not even predominantly), but exerts his *creative activity and enjoys the beauty and colorfulness of life.*

From these remarks it becomes apparent that we have to *separate anxiety from all other emotions because it alone has a negative character.* All others have some positive significance for the existence of man, but their analysis warns us not to overlook the fact that they have an ambiguous character. They mirror the complexity and ambiguity of man's nature.

Anxiety and Stress in Warfare

ALBERT J. GLASS

THIS PRESENTATION will focus upon various aspects of anxiety in military personnel who are subjected to the hardships, hazards and other stresses of warfare. Anxiety is herein operationally defined as a subjective mental state of dread or apprehension which occurs when an individual is unable to cope with or reasonably control his environment. Because war imposes similar danger and deprivation rather uniformly upon its participants at any one time and place, it provides almost laboratory conditions for the observation of anxiety associated with situational stress. It is believed that these observations can contribute to the further understanding of anxiety which may arise out of the more subtle vicissitudes of everyday life.

For military personnel the stress of warfare begins during the training phase—the transition from civilian to military life.[1] In this change, relationships with family and friends are abruptly severed and the freedom of choice and action, so highly prized in our culture, is sharply curtailed. Overt resistance to this new regimen produces only further restrictions and social as well as self-disapproval. A successful adaptation requires satisfactory interpersonal relationships with fellow trainees, gratification from newly acquired physical and military accomplishments, or the surrender of immediate self needs for the more abstract goal of group and community welfare. A majority of newly inducted men achieve adequate adjustment to the training environment, which is more or less incomplete or delayed, during which time there are varying degrees of anxiety and resentment. Only a small minority resort to overt escape from military control. In a somewhat larger group there is persistent inability either to cope with deprivations and frustrations of the new environment or to flee illegally from the situation. This failure of "fight or flight" produces manifestations of anxiety which, if not disabling, cause considerable psychic and somatic discomfort and constitute a medical problem of some magnitude.

After completion of the training period the new soldier receives his first duty assignment with an operational unit. Prior adjustment difficulties in training may be resolved or continued, depending upon the effectiveness of integration into the new organization. This process is determined by multiple considerations, such as the level of morale in the unit, leadership qualities of noncommissioned and commissioned officers, job assignment, distance from home, social and recreational opportunities, and even climatic conditions. With the passage of time there is usually an increasing identification with the military group and a greater ability to tolerate the exigencies and restrictions of military existence.

Probably the most frequent cause of anxiety in warfare comes from uncertainty of future events. Obviously it is difficult to deal adequately with an environment which is unpredictable. While some apprehension of what may lie ahead is present upon entry in the services, and may persist during assignments in the United States, it becomes raised to a conscious and disturbing level when the serviceman is alerted for shipment to a potential overseas combat area. Here the individual is not subjected to an actual traumatic situation, but faces the chronic threat of an unstructured danger. Anxiety from this source cannot be discharged by action other than desertion, and must be passively endured. Perhaps the most successful defenses against such anticipatory fear arise from within a group of men assembled for shipment. Confronted by a common menace, they figuratively move toward each other for mutual support. Feelings of anxiety are ventilated and accepted. Humor is introduced which aids in reducing tension and rumors of the unknown destination are widely discussed. In effect, the group creates, at least temporarily, a secure and structured world. The efficacy of this group defense is particularly evident in units of high morale whose members have successfully withstood common hardships and deprivations in training and maneuvers. These organizations achieve such a marked degree of group identification that there is an intense desire to remain with the unit even when medical or administrative considerations offer legitimate reasons for being stationed in the United States. On the other hand, so-called casuals who are sent overseas as individual replacements do not have the benefit of previously established group sustaining mechanisms, and are more apt to exhibit anxiety symptoms.[2] For this reason there was developed in the Korean campaign a system of dispatching replacements for overseas assignment in groups of four men who had been friends or buddies during the training phase.

At the port of embarkation, anticipatory anxiety reaches a high level and often produces various tension symptoms for which medical aid is anxiously sought. However, once individuals leave the United States aboard ship or plane, it is rare for anxiety manifestations to be brought forth for medical attention. Under these circumstances, the die is cast since it is understood by all that wartime convoys will not evacuate patients or turn back from their course.

After arrival at overseas destinations, noncombat units soon establish a relatively structured function and environment which may be monotonous, but is predictable and stable. For combat troops, however, anticipatory anxiety continues to be a psychological burden. Following exposure to battle, apprehension is no longer associated with the dread of unknown danger, but is now dependent upon previous combat experience. If battle was of a minor nature with few or no nearby casualties, or consisted of a rapid advance against only scattered enemy opposition, these "remote miss"[3] events inspire confidence in one's ability to cope with the combat situation, and may even be associated with feelings of pleasurable excitement due to mastery of a feared task. As a result there is a considerable lessening of anticipatory fear relative to the next combat engagement. On the other hand, intense battle episodes associated with the sight of maimed and mutilated casualties is a "near miss" experience and the cause of severe residual fear, particularly if the participant finds himself helpless to cope with the situation by aggressive or evasive action. This helplessness in the face of danger is responsible for heightened apprehensiveness at the prospect of similar catastrophic feelings of anxiety in future combat, and is akin to other post-traumatic phobic reactions. Being wounded is often such a "near miss" event when associated with helplessness and terror, and also sharply increases the anticipatory anxiety level upon return to combat duty. This psychological stress component of battle injury is intuitively understood by other combat personnel, for after an individual has been wounded on two or three occasions, it is generally agreed that he has had "enough" and even though returned to duty as physically qualified, he is usually reassigned to a noncombat position.

It should be recognized that combat is not a constant process but occurs intermittently as battle episodes of from one to seven days. Units cannot fight continuously but must be periodically withdrawn for one or more days of rest, food, absorption of replacements and resupply. After 30 to 60 days of fighting, units are removed from combat for longer periods of weeks. Even defensive or static warfare is not continuous. There may be intensive fighting on patrol actions or during episodic enemy assaults, but there are more frequent occasions of slight or desultory harrassing enemy artillery action.

Between periods of contact with the enemy, residual apprehension is an unspoken but commonly understood stress. The often quoted statement of World War II that "every man has his breaking point" refers more to the length of time that residual apprehension can be borne rather than the number of combat days endured, which are too variable in type and intensity to serve as an adequate measure of stress. The deleterious effect of chronic residual apprehension is exemplified by the "Old Sergeant Syndrome" of World War II.[4] This type of psychiatric casualty occurred in the veteran combat soldier who had performed excellent or superior function for 200 to 300 days of actual battle. These men gradually came to be less and less able to cope with the uncertainties of battle and finally began to exhibit ineffectual behavior even during the preliminary stages of combat. When interviewed after medical evacuation, they exhibited little or no anxiety but seemed downcast and self-condemnatory, using such phrases as "I'm all burned out," "I'm no good anymore," "I'm all beat up," "I'll only get the men killed." They recognized a steplike increase of residual apprehension following severe battle episodes and could contrast their present state with previous confidence during combat.

Levels of anticipatory anxiety not only aid in setting the pattern for initial behavior in battle, but produce psychiatric casualties and behavioral abnormalities prior to participation in combat. These psychological disorders become apparent on moving forward to the combat zone, or prior to the onset of battle. They are characterized by anxiety and its somatic representations, with none of the elements of physical fatigue or the drawn appearance of one who has been through a terrifying experience. Often they are not considered to be cases of "genuine" combat fatigue or may be referred to in derogatory tones by line personnel, or categorized by division psychiatrists as "character and behavior disorders."[5]

It is pertinent to examine the methods by which personnel are enabled to resist anticipatory anxiety before or between combat periods. It has already been stated that one such defense can arise spontaneously from within the combat group which provides emotional support and the promise of aid and protection in the event of need. In addition, there are certain mental mechanisms that are commonly employed by combat personnel to ward off the distressing effect of anticipatory fear. Among such defenses are the following:

1. *Fatalistic Attitudes.* Here are included conscious efforts to quiet the gnawing apprehension of future danger by placing responsibility for the determination of later events upon luck or fate. By this reasoning, since one cannot control his destiny in warfare, conceding that the worst eventuality, even death, can occur, it is logical to discount or not be alarmed by the painful warnings of fear. Rationalizations of this type may be of considerable comfort during overseas movement or prior to actual combat. They are represented by such statements as "If the bullet (shell) has your name on it, you've had it, otherwise there is nothing to worry about," which is a socially acceptable viewpoint and can be verbalized and shared with others. After combat experience this approach is of less benefit, for then it is not the abstract concept of death that is feared but rather a recurrence of ill-defined but intense feelings of impending catastrophe during which one is helpless.

2. *Myth of Invulnerability or Immortality.* This well-known defense employs a subconscious mechanism of denial. Here the omnipotence of the individual will not tolerate or conceive of discontinuance, as in death or mutilation. One is cloaked by a protective feeling of "it can't happen here." Such a defense may be quite effective prior to combat and even during initial phases of battle, particularly in young men. However, "near miss" experiences that include wounding or the sight of mutilated bodies rudely shatter this omnipotent shielding and may produce the opposite idea that each shell "seems aimed at me."

3. *Superstition and Magic.* In this traditional defense mechanism the individual appeals to supernatural powers for aid. It is a far more individualized belief than fatalism, and therefore not so readily communicated and shared with others. Various objects may be invested with magical powers, particularly articles that have been in one's possession for a long time, such as a cigarette lighter, pictures of loved ones, a watch, religious medals, an old coin or a favorite weapon. Also, the company of a particular buddy or group may be considered "lucky" protection. This defense may be of help before and during combat, and is reinforced so long as "near miss" experiences do not occur.

4. *Religion.* In times of stress, religious faith is a commonly used means of maintaining a structured and predictable world. It has been frequently observed that truly devout persons employ religious faith as a successful defense against anxiety before and during combat. However, individuals whose faith is lukewarm or only belatedly acquired for the purpose of divine protection during combat, merely utilize religion as another magical device and obtain corresponding results. Their plight is illustrated by Bill Mauldin,[6] the well-known World War II cartoonist, who portrayed one of his typical unshaven combat veterans in a difficult combat situation appealing to a nearby British Indian soldier with the request, "Know any good Moslem prayers? I don't wanna miss any bets." Group prayer conducted prior to a combat engagement has been noted by some line officers to have an excellent calming effect upon anticipatory tension.

5. *Apathy.* This is a subconscious defense mechanism for resisting anticipatory anxiety which is utilized by combat veterans between battle episodes. Such an adaptation accomplishes an isolation of the individual by the blocking of disturbing thoughts from within or stimuli from without during a time when there is no realistic combat danger. However, apathy rapidly disappears with the whine of incoming shells. Between combat episodes such individuals give the impression of a blunted or absent affect and exhibit little emotional response to ordinary environmental change. This state is usually associated with, and no doubt facilitated by, physical fatigue from

lack of rest and the strenuous activity of recent fighting. A vivid picture of apathy between combat phases is portrayed by Ernie Pyle,[7] who wrote, "For days and nights they have fought hard, eaten little, washed none, slept hardly at all. . . . They are young men, but the grime and whiskers and exhaustion makes them look middle-aged. In their eyes as they pass is not hatred, not excitement, not despair, not the tonic of their victory— there is just the simple expression of being there as though they have been doing this forever, and nothing else."

In considering the problems of anxiety during active combat, it should be recognized that our knowledge of behavior under battle conditions is incomplete.[5] The very nature of the organized confusion of combat makes adequate observation a most difficult task. Also, information from combat participants is less than reliable. Retrospective accounts of subjective feelings and actions in battle are subject to error due to an almost inevitable distortion of events, in order that battle experiences are made meaningful to oneself and structured for the purposes of communication.

Probably the most objective data upon behavior during battle was obtained by S. L. A. Marshall[8] by his technique of debriefing company-size units shortly after their withdrawal from combat. In the presence of other members of the group, corrections and additions of the individual's account of the recent battle engagement were facilitated. Marshall was able to piece together a more complete and accurate record of individual and group behavior under fire than was possible by the remembrances of any single participants. From the above data and studies of combat psychiatric casualties it is believed that the following assumptions can be made: 1. Danger does not necessarily induce fear or anxiety. In a minority of combat personnel, danger evokes a useful type of tension or alertness which facilitates perception, enhances evaluation, and mobilizes the body mechanisms for sustained action. 2. Only when an individual is helpless in the face of danger, either because of internal incapacity or adverse circumstances of the battle situation, is there produced the manifestations of anxiety. There are many occasions in combat when, because of external conditions such as heavy shelling or "near miss" experiences, persons are temporarily unable to move or function appropriately in battle. As a consequence there are brief periods of anxiety which subside with resumption of effective activity. These incidents are responsible for residual apprehension following combat, which occurs in most persons. A persistent inability to cope with the battle environment produces psychiatric breakdown or other type of non-effective behavior, or severe anticipatory fear of future combat.

From the foregoing it is evident that stress in combat can be divided into two major types: (1) External conditions which make it difficult or impossible for the soldier to control or master the battle situation, including such events as an intense shelling, overwhelming enemy superiority in numbers and weapons, and unexpected air attacks. In brief, external stress includes circumstances that increase the intensity, duration and unpredictability of the battle situation. (2) Circumstances which inhibit or lower the ability of combat participants to respond appropriately to the battle environment. There are a number of such internal stresses, namely, (a) increased level of residual apprehension; (b) lowering of physical capacity by fatigue, lack of food and intercurrent illness; (c) extreme climatic conditions; (d) difficult terrain; (e) inadequate combat training and experience; (f) insufficiency of weapons, ammunition and other necessary supply items; (g) faulty leadership; (h) isolation from the group due to failure of communication, lack of group cohesiveness or disruption of the combat unit by heavy casualties; (i) psychological trauma of viewing the mutilated bodies of friends and buddies with whom there has been strong identification. From the above list it is clear that there are many causes for temporary failure in combat adaptation. Usually, non-effective behavior or psychiatric breakdown is produced by multiple precipitating events which include elements of both external and internal stress. It should be obvious that the prevention of combat psychiatric casualties can only be directed toward the correction of internal stress, since the degree of external stress is determined by the enemy.

The disabling manifestations of anxiety that occur in combat situations also have not been clearly delineated. It seems fairly certain that the clinical syndromes exhibited by psychiatric casualties in relatively safe medical facilities have been altered and reorganized from their original state. Certain abnormal anxiety states in combat are known. One such manifestation is the "Gung Ho" reaction recently described by Harris et al.[5] Here the combat participant, unable to tolerate helplessness and anxiety, manifests a primitive, aggressive pattern of behavior, and with a "fearsome expression" rushes towards the enemy without regard for personal safety. Rarely is such an adaptation successful. A typical example of this response was displayed by a veteran sergeant during the Korean campaign who found himself and his artillery unit being infiltrated by the enemy, who attacked with small arms fire. He desperately attempted to move and salvage his guns but, frustrated and unable to proceed, he openly went after the concealed enemy with only a pistol. Fortunately he was knocked out by a fellow-soldier and dragged to safety. Subsequently, he could not remember his anger, helplessness and the necessity to do something about the situation.

Another well-known manifestation of anxiety in combat is "freezing" in one's foxhole with inability to move forward or to the rear. Dissociative type of behavior is not uncommonly seen by the battalion surgeon and division psychiatrist. Here, in relatively safe areas the individual is confused, misinterprets reality, and is seemingly still in active combat as he claws the ground to gain protection. Others may remain mute and retarded in a manner reminiscent of catatonia. These syndromes may continue from one to three days but it is difficult to determine if they are present under actual combat conditions. Certainly they do occur after the engagement or when there is a lull in the fighting. Most cases of psychiatric breakdown in battle exhibit trembling, dejection or apathy and verbalize their inability to continue. Again, these manifestations are not particularly noted during active combat but rather after the acute phase of battle or at a time when medical evacuation is possible.

It is quite probable that the manifestations of anxiety in combat are at least partly determined by what is permitted by the battle situation and what is accepted by the group as sufficient reason for medical evacuation. For example, bizarre or dissociative type reactions are not observed during patrol action, but may occur when the group has attained the safety of its own lines. Similarly, precipitous flight from the combat area does not occur when such exposure is hazardous. Psychiatric casualties from veteran combat units usually exhibit little in the way of bizarre symptomatology. An inability to control behavior during combat and the frank admission of failure have come to be regarded as an acceptable end state or "breaking point." None of the above data should convey the impression that non-effective behavior or psychiatric casualties can be eliminated by a desperate combat situation, or banned by group pressure, but only that the form or type of such failure can be influenced by outside forces.

Regardless of the type of military stress, anxiety associated with warfare presents the following unique features:

1. Except for the acute phases of combat psychiatric breakdown, anxiety during warfare conditions is most apt to be expressed or experienced as somatic discomfort. It is likely that psychic distress or disability is regarded as a sign of weakness instead of a valid excuse for nonparticipation in social obligations. The type and pattern of anxiety-induced bodily symptoms are strongly influenced by what is accepted as an illness from a medical stand-point, or suggested by popular disease entities. For example, psychogenic gastrointestinal symptomatology was common in World War II,[10] perhaps stimulated by an increased incidence of peptic ulcer during this conflict. During the Korean campaign the widespread knowledge of herniated disc pathology was probably a major reason for the frequent complaint of low back syndromes by military personnel.[11] Perhaps the most convincing

evidence of suggestibility in production of somatic symptoms occurred in World War I[12] when desultory shelling in a rear or holding combat position caused the alarm of "gas" to be sounded. That day a large number of soldiers were evacuated as gas casualties and the influx continued for eight days, reaching 500 cases. The divisional gas officer failed to find any clinical evidence of gas inhalation. The patients presented vague complaints of chest pains, coughing, husky voice, tingling or burning of the throat and indefinite eye symptoms. "Gas neurosis" was a well-known psychiatric entity in World War I. Similarly, the "syndrome of cold feet" accompanied the large incidence of frostbite in the first winter of the Korean campaign.[13]

2. Past experience has demonstrated that it is difficult, if not impossible, to predict efficiently the minority of individuals who become disabled by anxiety under military stress conditions.[14-17] The identification of personality types who are vulnerable to stress was a fond hope of military psychiatry which has not been realized in practice. The small degree of success that was obtained by such predictive efforts proved to be only slightly better than chance. Reasons for errors in psychiatric selection, aside from inevitable inaccuracies in personality evaluation, are due to a host of variable circumstances in a stress situation which cannot be predetermined. Among such variables are the morale of the unit support by buddies, differences in the intensity of combat or deprivation, quality of leadership, and type of assignment. Psychiatric prediction is most effective when made only for brief time periods such as the training phase, where the environment is relatively constant.

3. Persons who exhibit marked anxiety and unadaptability in one type of military stress, such as training, do not necessarily have similar difficulties in different or even more stressful situations such as combat.[18] Conversely, excellent adjustment in training or in a United States assignment is not guarantee of good performance in combat.[17]

4. Casualties that are evoked by the anxiety of stress situations are best treated near or at the scene of environmental trauma.[19] Hospitalization and the complete removal from external stress almost invariably result in a fixation of symptomatology and phobic avoidance of potential traumatic situations which then may become further generalized and prevent participation even in usual tasks and responsibilities. This principle was first learned by trial and error during World War I, for the treatment of combat psychiatric casualties. It was relearned in World War II but extended to include psychiatric problems that arose during the training period. As a result, World War II saw the establishment of army mental

hygiene consultation services for trainees and division psychiatric services for combat troops.[20] During the Korean campaign, peripheral psychiatric treatment facilities were further extended to serve most major posts and stations in the United States, in addition to training camps, overseas garrisons and combat.

SUMMARY

In this report anxiety is operationally defined as a dread or apprehension which occurs with an inability to adequately cope with the environment. Major military stress situations which produce anxiety are outlined, and various defenses that are employed by military personnel to prevent or resist anxiety are discussed. Anxiety secondary to the stress of warfare was noted to have the following characteristic features:

1. It is mainly expressed as somatic symptomatology.

2. Vulnerable personality types or specific predisposition to military stress have not been demonstrated.

3. Individuals who exhibit anxiety under one type of stress situation do not necessarily have similar difficulties in other stressful circumstances.

4. Therapy of psychiatric disorders secondary to the anxiety of military stress is most effectively accomplished by peripheral treatment facilities which operate near or at the site of environmental trauma.

REFERENCES

1. MENNINGER, W. C.: Psychiatry in a Troubled World. New York, McMillan, 1948. Pp. 58-68.
2. MENNINGER, W. C.: op. cit., pp. 333-334.
3. JANIS, I. L.: Air War and Emotional Stress. New York, McGraw-Hill, 1951.
4. SOBOL, R.: Anxiety repressive reactions after prolonged combat exposure—the "old sergeant syndrome."
5. HARRIS, F. G., MAYER, J., AND BECKER, H. A.: Experiences in the study of combat in the Korean theater. WRAIR Research Report 43-55, Walter Reed Army Medical Center, Washington, D.C. November, 1955.
6. MAULDIN, B.: "This Damn Tree Leaks," The Stars and Stripes, Italy, 1945. P. 24.
7. PYLE, E.: Here is Your War. New York, Holt, 1943. Pp. 247-248.
8. MARSHALL, S. L. A.: Men Against Fire. New York, Morrow, 1947.
9. GLASS, A. J.: Combat Psychiatry and Civilian Medical Practice. Transactions and Studies of the College of Physicians of Philadelphia. Vol. 23, No. 1, June, 1955.
10. MENNINGER, W. C.: op. cit., pp. 153-163.
11. DODGE, P. R. AND CLEVE, E. A.: Backache. Symposium on Military Medicine, Supp. issue, Surgeon's Circular Letter, Far East Command, September, 1951.
12. Neuropsychiatry in the World War, Vol. 10, U.S. Army Medical Department, Washington, D.C., U.S. Government Printing Office, 1929, pp. 318-320.
13. GLASS, A. J.: Psychiatry in the Korean Campaign. U.S. Armed Forces M. J. 4:1563-1583, November 1953.

14. AITA, J. A.: Efficacy of the brief clinical interview method in predicting adjustments. Arch. Neurol. & Psychiat. *61*:170-176, 1949.

15. EGAN, J. R., JACKSON, L., AND EANES, R. H.: Study of neuropsychiatric rejectees. J.A.M.A. *145*:466-469, 1951.

16. BRILL, N. Q., AND BEEBE, G. W.: Follow-up Study of Psychoneuroses: Preliminary Report. Am. J. Psychiat. *108*:417, December 1951.

17. GLASS, A. J., RYAN, F. J., LUBIN, A., REDDY, C. V. R., AND TUCKER, A. C.: Psychiatric Prediction and Military Effectiveness. Part I, U.S. Armed Forces M. J. *7*:1427-1443, October 1956; Part II, 1575-1588, November 1956. (Part III *in press*.)

18. PLESSET, M. R.: Psychoneurotics in combat. Am. J. Psychiat. *103*:87-90, July 1946.

19. GLASS, A. J.: Psychotherapy in the combat zone. Am. J. Psychiat. *110*:725-731, 1954.

20. MENNINGER, W. C.: *op. cit.*, 253-254.

Anxiety and Values

ROLLO MAY

IN THIS PAPER I shall try to show that the distinctive quality of human anxiety arises from the fact that man is the valuing animal, the being who interprets his life and world in terms of symbols and meanings, and identifies these with his existence as a self. As Nietzsche remarked, "Man should be named the 'valuator'." It is the threat to these values that causes anxiety. Indeed, we would define anxiety as *the apprehension cued off by a threat to some value which the individual holds essential to his existence as a self*. The threat may be to physical life itself, i.e., death; or to psychological life, i.e., loss of freedom. Or it may be to some value the person identifies with his existence as a self: patriotism, the love of a special other person, prestige among one's peers, devotion to scientific truth or to religious belief.

A classic and dramatic illustration of this fact is seen in the remark of the unsophisticated Tom, whom Wolf and Wolff* studied in their significant work on anxiety and gastric functions at New York Hospital. You may recall that Tom and his wife lay awake all one night worrying whether Tom's job in the hospital laboratory would last or whether he would have to go back on government relief. The next morning the gastric readings for anxiety were the highest of any encountered in all those studies. The significant point is Tom's remark: "If I couldn't support my family, I'd as soon jump off the end of the dock." The threat which underlay this great anxiety in Tom was not that of physical deprivation—he and his family could have gotten along on relief—but was rather a threat to a status which Tom, like so many men in our culture, held even more important than life: the ability to fulfill one's role as a middle class provider for one's family. The loss of this status would be tantamount to not existing as a person.

We see similar examples in the area of sex. Sex gratification in itself, of course, is a value. But at every turn in dealing with patients in psychotherapy one notes that the physical gratification itself is only a small part of the question, since a person will be thrown into conflict and anxiety when rejected sexually by one partner, but not by another. Obviously other

---

*Wolf, Stewart, and Wolff, H. G.: Human Gastric Function. New York, Oxford University Press, 1943.

82

elements—prestige, tenderness, personal understanding—give the sexual experience with one a value the other does not have. It is no doubt fair to say, incidentally, that the less mature the person, the more the simply physiologic gratification itself carries the value and the less difference is made by *who* gives the gratification; whereas the more mature and differentiated the person, the more such other factors as the special relationship to the other person determine the value of the sexual experience.

Death is the most obvious threat cueing off anxiety, for unless one holds views of immortality, which are not common in our culture, death stands for the ultimate blotting out of one's existence as a self. But immediately we note a very curious fact: some people *prefer to die rather than to surrender some other value.* The taking away of psychologic and spiritual freedom was not infrequently a greater threat than death itself to persons under the dictatorships of Europe. "Give me liberty or give me death" is not necessarily histrionic or evidence of a neurotic attitude. Indeed, there is reason for believing, as we shall indicate later, that it may represent the most mature form of *distinctively human* behavior. Nietzsche, Jaspers and others of the more profound existentialists, in fact, have pointed out that physical life itself is not fully satisfying and meaningful until one can consciously choose another value which he holds more dear than life itself.

What is the origin of these values, the threat to which results in anxiety? Obviously, the infant's first value is the care, nourishment and love it receives from its mother or parental substitutes; a threat to these, being indeed a threat to the infant's existence, gives rise to profound anxiety. But as maturation proceeds, the values are transformed, becoming a desire for approval by the mother, for example, "success" in the eyes of parents or peers, and, later on, status in cultural terms; and ultimately in the mature adult the values become the devotion to freedom, to a religious belief or to scientific truth. I do not mean this as an exact maturation scale; I mean only to illustrate roughly that maturation involves a continuous transformation of the original values identified with one's existence, the threat to which causes anxiety; and that in the normal human being these values take on an increasingly symbolic character.

Now, it is an error to think of these later values as *merely the extension* of the original value of preserving mother's care and love. Capacities emerge in the developing person which render him a *new* gestalt; on the pattern of emergent evolution, the maturing person continually develops new capacities out of the old, new symbols, values in a new form. To be sure, the more an individual's anxiety is neurotic, the more he may be actually trying to satisfy year after year the same values he held at earlier stages: he still, as we know in so many clinical cases, repetitiously and compulsively

seeks mother's love and care. But the healthier the person, the less his
values as an adult can be comprehended as a sum of his previous needs
and instincts.

The most important emergent capacity in the human being is self-relatedness. It begins somewhere after the first few months and probably is fairly
well developed in the child by the age of two. Thereafter, the values of
love and care take on a new character: they are not simply something
received, but are reacted to by the child with some degree of self-awareness:
he may accept the mother's care, defy it, use it for various forms of power
demands or what not. A patient at a clinic reported that he had learned
at an early age to put his hands against the wall and push his high chair
over so that his parents would catch it. The value involved here was not
self-preservation, that is, being saved from hitting the floor (he had his
parents so well trained that this contingency never arose); the value gained
was rather the satisfaction and security involved in his power to force
his parents to sit on pins and needles, ready to jump to his aid.

We can see how the value of love also develops a new characteristic
when we observe that in the mature person—the adult with a degree of
autonomy—some choice, some conscious affirmation, some self-aware participation, is necessary in loving and accepting love if the experience of love
is to yield full satisfaction. The value then lies as much in being able to
give to the other person as to receive; and such a mature individual may
well experience his most severe anxiety if his opportunity to give love to
the partner is threatened.

Thus, in understanding the origin of values, the threats to which, as
we have seen, cause anxiety, we must avoid two errors. The first is the
error of not relating the value to the early needs for love and care; but the
second error is thinking that the matter is *just* that and overlooking the
fact that emergent qualities in the person make the value threatened at
each stage of development really new.

Let us look now at this distinctive capacity for self-relatedness of the
human being, a capacity which is crucially significant for understanding
human anxiety. It is man's capacity to stand outside himself, to know
he is the subject as well as the object of experience, to see himself as the
entity who is acting in the world of objects. This unique quality which distinguishes man from the rest of nature can be described in many ways:
Goldstein terms it man's capacity to transcend the immediate, concrete situation and to deal with "the possible." Mowrer, following Korzybsky, calls
it the human being's time-binding quality: "the capacity to bring the past
into the present as a part of the total causal nexus in which living organisms behave (act and react) is the essence of 'mind' and 'personality' alike."

Howard Liddel points out that his sheep can keep time for about 10 minutes, his dogs for about half an hour; but the human being can keep time into the distant future—he can plan for decades or centuries; and, we should add, he can worry about this future and suffer anxiety in anticipating his own eventual death. Whatever terms are used, the capacity we are here describing, which emerges somewhere in the first two years of life, underlies our capacity to use symbols as tools, to talk and to reason. It makes us the historical mammals who are not only pushed by history, as all organisms are, but who can also "look before and after" and, by understanding the past, mold and to some small extent influence the future. As Lawrence Kubie has indicated, neurosis has its source in the distortion of these symbolic functions as a result of a dichotomy between conscious and unconscious processes which starts early in the development of each human infant.*

What is important here for understanding anxiety is that man, the symbol-maker, interprets his experience in symbolic terms and holds these symbols as values, the threats to which give rise to profound anxiety. The understanding of anxiety can thus never be separated from ethical symbols, which are one aspect of the human being's normal milieu. Through his distinctive social capacity to see himself as others see him, to imagine himself empathetically in his fellow man's or stranger's position, the person can direct his decisions in the light of long-term values, which are the basis of ethics and therefore the basis of ethical anxiety.

I use the terms "symbols" and "values" incidentally, in the sense of their being the *quintessence* of experience. They are a boiling down of the most real relationships and satisfactions; and thus a threat to a symbolic value can have tremendous anxiety-arousing power.

An individual's values and, therefore, his anxiety, are conditioned by the fact that he lives in a given culture at a particular moment in the historical development of that culture. This is by no means just because the person happened to grow up among others and therefore reflects their opinions, but because it is the essence of man's nature to interpret his values

---

*It was Adolf Meyer, so Sullivan suggests, who held that the human being operates on a hierarchy of organization, and that the physiologic functions should be seen subordinate to the integrating functions and particularly to man's capacity to use symbols as tools. I think that it is very important in experimental work with human beings, in anxiety or other areas, to *define the context* of the particular person being studied; to ask, that is, what symbolic meaning does he give the situation, and what are his values in the experiment at that particular moment? Or if the experimenter is isolating a particular reaction from the self-aware human being, this too should be made evident and defined. For the real meaning of neurophysiologic data as well as data of other sorts will be understood only as it is seen in the context of the self-aware person, that is, the person as valuating.

in the context of his relation to other people and their expectations. Tom, who believed he had to be a self-supporting middle-class male, was validating himself by values that have been dominant in Western society since the Renaissance. As Fromm, Kardiner and others have pointed out, the dominant value since then has been competitive prestige measured in terms of work and financial success. If you achieved this, you felt yourself a person and your anxiety was allayed; if you did not, you were subject to powerful anxiety, and you lost your sense of being a self, like Willie Loman in "Death of a Salesman," who, in the words of the playwright Arthur Miller, "never knew who he was."

A curious fact, however, has emerged in the last decade or so: this dominant competitive value has apparently been reversed. David Reisman, in his studies in "The Lonely Crowd," points out that young people rarely have the goal of competitive success any more; they want, not to be first in school but rather to stay somewhere in the middle. *Mirabile dictu,* then; the dominant value becomes not getting ahead of the next man but being like everyone else—that is, conformity. One now validates himself by fitting into the herd; what makes you prey to anxiety is to be different, to stand out. This development obviously is part of our special social problems these days of anti-intellectualism, witch-hunts, suspicion of the original and creative person, and the general tendency to avoid anxiety by assuming the protective coloring afforded by looking like everyone else.

These contemporaneous cultural values of conformity, adjustment to the "radar type" of person who reflects his signals from the crowd around him, are related to the prevalence of loneliness in our day, about which Sullivan and others have written. Loneliness is a special form of anxiety; as Freud, Rank and others have suggested, all anxiety may be, at bottom, separation anxiety, and thus loneliness—the awareness of separation—may be the most painful *conscious* and *immediate* form of anxiety. As all of us observe, loneliness is a common experience of those who conform, for while on one hand they are driven to conform because of loneliness, on the other validating the self by means of becoming like everyone else reduces their experience of personal identity, making for inner emptiness and thus causing greater loneliness.

Shall we say that in this shift from competition to conformity, the dominant value and hence the locus for the genesis of anxiety, since the Renaissance, has changed? Certainly one of the clearest reasons for the prevalence of anxiety in our culture is the fact that we live in a time when almost all social values are in radical change, when one world is dying, as social scientists too numerous to mention have demonstrated, and the new one is not yet born.

But is there not a more specific explanation which underlies *both* the value of competitive success, dominant from the Renaissance until recently, and its apparent present opposite, conformity? Do not both arise from the same cause, namely, modern Western man's disruption in his relationship to nature, including human nature? Since the Renaissance, Western man has been infatuated with the goal of gaining power over nature; as Tillich points out, he has gradually transformed the broad concept of reason of the seventeenth and eighteenth centuries into technical reason in the nineteenth and twentieth centuries, and he has dedicated himself to the exploitation of nature. Ever since Descartes' dichotomy in the seventeenth century between subjective experience and the objective world, Western man has progressively sought to see nature as entirely separated from him, and he has thought he could best study nature by making it entirely objective and impersonal. The deep loneliness and isolation this entailed was already sensed by Pascal, who said, "When I consider the brief span of my life, swallowed up in the eternity before and behind it, the small space that I fill or even see, engulfed in the infinite immensity of spaces which I know not, and which know not me, I am afraid and wonder to see myself here rather than there; for there is no reason why I should be here rather than there, now rather than then."

But since modern men were *successful* in validating themselves by power *over* nature for several centuries, the loneliness and isolation inherent in this situation became widespread only in the recent twentieth century. Particularly with the advent of the atom bomb, sensitive laymen as well as scientists began to experience the loneliness of being strangers in the universe; and it has made many Western men, like Pascal, afraid. Our contemporaneous loneliness and anxiety thus go deeper than alienation in relation to ourselves and our society; they stem also from our alienation from the natural world.

Several straws in the wind show the movements in our society toward recovering an indigenous relation with nature. Modern physics is one such movement. As Werner Heisenberg says, the essence of modern physics is that the Copernican view that nature is to be studied "out there," entirely separate from man, is no longer tenable; nature cannot be understood apart from man's subjective involvement, and vice versa. The West's new interest in Eastern thought points in the same direction. Oriental thought never suffered our radical split between subject and object, between I-the-person and the world "out there," and therefore escaped the special Western brand of separation from nature and consequent loneliness.

I mention these somewhat speculative points because I wish to emphasize strongly that to understand modern Western man's anxiety we must see him in his historical position as the heir of several centuries of radical splitting of subject and object, and consequent disrupted relation with nature.

A central implication of this paper is that we must *differentiate neurotic anxiety from normal anxiety*. Indeed, I believe that without a concept of normal anxiety we are unable to discern the neurotic form. If, as we have said, anxiety is the reaction to a threat to values one identifies with his existence, no one can escape anxiety, for no values are unassailable. Furthermore, values are always in process of change and reformation. The only apparent escape—albeit a self-defeating one—from the anxiety that goes along with transformation of values is to crystallize one's values into dogma. And dogma, whether of the religious or scientific variety, is a temporary security bought at the price of surrendering one's opportunity for fresh learning and new growth.

Normal anxiety is anxiety which is proportionate to the threat, does not involve repression, and can be confronted constructively on the conscious level (or can be relieved if the objective situation is altered). *Neurotic* anxiety, on the other hand, is a reaction which is disproportionate to the threat, involves repression and other forms of intrapsychic conflict, and is managed by various kinds of blocking-off of activity and awareness.

Actually, neurotic anxiety develops when a person has been unable to meet normal anxiety at the time of the actual crisis in his growth and threat to his values. Neurotic anxiety, that is to say, is the end result of previously unmet normal anxiety.

Normal anxiety is most obvious in the steps in individuation which, as Rank pointed out, occur at every stage in one's development. The child learns to walk and leaves the past security of the pen; he goes off to school; at adolescence he reaches out toward the opposite sex; later, he leaves home to earn his own living, marries, and eventually must separate finally from immediate values on his deathbed. I do not mean that these events are necessarily actual crises, though they are *potential* ones; I mean rather to indicate that all growth consists of the anxiety-creating surrender of past values as one transforms them into broader ones; it consists of the giving up of immediate security in terms of more extensive goals, death being the final step in this continuum.*

This transforming of values, and meeting the anxiety related thereto

---

*Hence, Paul Tillich holds that normal anxiety is synonymous with the "finiteness" of man. Each human being knows he will die, though not when; he anticipates his death through self-awareness. Facing this normal anxiety of finiteness and death may, indeed, be an individual's most effective incentive to make the most of the months or years before death cuts him down.

is one side of creativity. Neitszche well says, "Valuing is creating; hear it ye creative ones! Without valuation the nut of existence would be hollow. Hear it, ye creative ones!" In Goldstein's phrase, man as the valuator is, in the very act of valuing, engaged in molding his world, making himself adequate to his environment and his environment adequate to himself. This interrelation of transforming of values and creativity indicates why creativity has always been considered, from the myth of Prometheus on down, as unavoidably connected with anxiety.

I wish to underline three implications for therapy in this discussion.

First, the goal of therapy is not to free the patient from anxiety. It is, rather, to help him become free from neurotic anxiety, but to help him meet normal anxiety constructively. Indeed, *the only way he can achieve the former is to do the latter.* Normal anxiety, we have seen, is an inseparable part of growth and creativity; the self becomes more integrated and stronger as experiences of normal anxiety are successfully confronted. Hence the famous saying of Kierkegaard: "I would say that learning to know anxiety is an adventure which every man has to affront if he would not go to perdition either by not having known anxiety or by sinking under it. He therefore who has learned rightly to be anxious has learned the most important thing."

Second, our discussion implies grave questions about the use of drugs to relieve anxiety. (We except the rare cases in which anxiety, if not relieved, itself would lead to more serious breakdown, or needs to be relieved to the point where psychotherapy is possible). The harmful effect of the general use of drugs for normal anxiety is obvious, for to wipe away the anxiety is in principle to wipe away the opportunity for growth, i.e., value transformation, of which anxiety is the obverse side. By the same token, neurotic anxiety is a symptom of the fact that some previous crisis has not been met, and to remove the symptom without helping the person get at his underlying conflict is to rob him of his best direction-finder and motivation for self-understanding and new growth.

Third, this discussion implies that there is an inverse relation between the soundness of an individual's value system and his anxiety. That is, the firmer and more flexible one's values, the more he will be able to meet his anxiety constructively. But the more the person is overcome by anxiety, the more his values will diminish in strength. Thus, the patient's arriving at sound values is, in the long run, an integral part of his therapeutic progress. This does not relieve the therapist of his responsibility to help the patient in the technical process of slow, steady uncovering of the roots of his conflict; indeed, this has to be done in most cases *before* the patient is able to arrive at his own enduring values.

The criteria for mature values follow from the distinctive characteristics of the human being we discussed earlier; mature values are those which transcend the immediate situation in time and encompass past and future; transcend also the immediate in-group, and extend outward toward the good of the community, ideally embracing humanity as a whole. The more mature one's values are, the less it matters to him whether his values are literally satisfied or not. The satisfaction and security lie in the *holding* of the values. To the genuine scientist (or religious person, for that matter), security and confidence arise from his awareness of his devotion to the *search* for truth rather than the finding of it.

Anxiety Problems Within Cultural Settings

_____KENNETH E. APPEL

BEHAVIOR IN THE HUMAN BEING can scarcely be conceived, much less understood, without considering the cultural context. Forces from without (nurture) and forces from within (nature) stimulate the organism, and both modify and pattern the personality.[1]

The individual tries to acquire material which the environment refuses to give; on the other hand, the environment, society, or culture tries to force material that the individual tries to reject. Neuroses are thus frustrated goal-directed (motivated) activities representing noneffective "adaptation to stress and conflict."[2] If the individual cannot cope with the conflict, anxiety defense mechanisms develop.

Three types of anxiety may be indicated: ego anxiety, id anxiety, and superego anxiety. Ego anxiety might be thought to exist in the man who exhibits typical symptoms toward the beginning of the end of his working career. Restlessness, tension, apprehension, sleeplessness, loss of appetite appear apparently without reason. Investigation shows that a junior is moving up, with energy and judgment, and the threat of displacement is in the offing—the physiology and unconscious mind react to the situation before the conscious self recognizes and evaluates it. This is becoming more and more a cultural anxiety in our society. Medicine has prolonged life and maintained physical and intellectual vigor beyond the traditional years; yet, concepts from outmoded medicine and outdated ideas of industrial usefulness are creating new cultural, "mental," and economic problems—conflicts and anxieties which our society has not yet learned to solve. Premature retirement, a sort of cultural Alzheimer's Anxiety, is a new condition which calls for new psycho-socio-economic solutions.

Instinctive or id anxiety might be illustrated by the persistent, handicapping apprehension of the stenographer whose elevator got stuck in a burning building, or the man whose parents died when he was under six years of age and who was shifted to relatives, whose older sisters finally reared him without male influence, and who had many illnesses in growing up, chiefly of a respiratory sort. He had a sort of permanent fund of anxiety or lowered resistance in his personality. To stresses, whether of an economic, professional, or business nature, he had an anxious set, which might be called instinctive anxiety. His physical or mental state cannot be properly evaluated from time to time nor treated adequately without considering the cultural as well as the medicinal condition through which he has lived.

Superego anxiety is the background of many unidentified tensions and unspecific somatic disorders. It is related to the general atmosphere of the aggressive, competing, struggling, aspiring United States of the twentieth century. (Can I succeed? Can I survive? Will I attain prestige, power, success, things, status, comfort? Will I outdo myself, my parents and the Joneses? Can I keep my head above water with the energy and effort it entails?) The level of aspiration and drain is pretty strenuous. The fear of failure, of falling, of submersion, dependency, humiliation, and extinction *is* a cultural phenomenon which may be involved in any headache, palpitation, indigestion, insomnia. The aspirations, goals, standards, and values of a society determine, among other things, muscle tensions and illness.

This is the cultural setting of much disease. A number of years ago, Halliday pointed out that the indices of psycho-social illness—infertility rate, peptic ulcer, suicide, exophthalmic goiter, diabetes, and hypertension—are rising,[3] while Lawrence Frank speaks of "society as the patient."[4]

Superego anxiety exists at times in professional men in religion, the clergy, and the priests, who are supposed to live by more than human standards. It may arise in the cultural setting of the man brought up with a sensitive, conservative, conscientious, clerical background, involved in a broker's business inherited from the other side of the family. Realistic necessities in this area of cultural values and modes may paralyze the nepotist, as we have seen not infrequently.

Anxiety has different origins according to competent thinkers. Anxiety and fear perhaps are evolved from the "startle reflex" described by Landis and Hunt.[5] According to Goldstein, anxiety is the experience of the organism in a catastrophic condition. For Freud, anxiety is the threat of breakthrough of erotic or aggressive impulses and is perceived as a danger signal. The symptoms and inhibitions are developed to avoid anxiety. Rank, Adler, Jung, Alexander, Horney, Fromm, Kardiner, and Sullivan pointed to anxiety origins in the trauma of birth and separations, inadequacies and inferiorities, and break-through of the irrational, hostility and aggression, helplessness, isolation, taboos blocking the child's relaxation or pleasure patterns, social and self-disapproval. Mowrer's theory is that fear of social punishment, withdrawal of love and approval are repressed, and that the associated fears and guilt, when repressed, become neurotic anxiety; he thus developed a guilt theory of anxiety, as opposed to an impulse theory. To complete this array of assumptions, the existentialists, from Kierkegaard to Tillich, speak of anxiety as being involved in actualizing any possibility, in creativity, the realization of selfhood, of the inevitability of anxiety, its confrontation in the development of individuation; freedom and responsibility as goals of personality, and anxiety as inherent in the possibility of freedom. Anxiety is the reaction to the threat of nonbeing, to the threat of meaninglessness in one's existence. The capacity to bear anxiety is a measure of selfhood.

The profusion of diversity and conflict of theories is enough to cause a kind of cultural anxiety among psychiatrists and analysts themselves. It might almost seem, in other words, that they create anxiety to cure it. Furthermore, there are cultural conflicts and anxieties among psychiatrists, psychoanalysts, and social workers, and among different schools of analysis. There are professional castration threats that reinforce indoctrination and membership in certain groups. Anxiety exists in the cultural relations of psychiatrists, psychologists, and psychoanalysts, of a kind and in a proportion that do not exist among biologic scientists and practitioners of medicine. There is no Boston and Philadelphia anemia but there *are* different types of psychiatry and analysis in different cities of the country. No wonder the public is often confused. Historic and legitimate reasons for some of this exist, of course, which could be interpreted to the public, but the variety of formulations certainly does not warrant the dogmatism that exists in some thinking. The variety indicates a heuristic richness which can stimulate investigation and research and can offer a variety of tools for the alleviation of disorders of personality.

What relevance does all this have to anxiety within cultures? We are beginning to study with profit the culture of the hospital community where the different goals of the various groups of personnel may conflict to the detriment of the patient. Reflection on the state of psychiatric thinking and training indicates that the cultural homeostasis in psychiatry is under considerable strain and that it might be profitable to study more objectively the cultural climate of our own discipline with the concept of university education in mind.

Cultural conflicts and tensions are not confined to psychiatry. Other branches of medicine are showing cultural changes. There is a cultural contrast between those who tend to stick to the structural, the anatomic, the physiologic and pathologic and pharmacologic, and those who are stressing the social aspects and functions of medicine. The public is becoming increasingly involved and concerned in this conflict.

Cultures as customs, beliefs, practices, and expectations are conditions of experience as well as physiology and structure. They modify not only ideas but feelings, preferences, physiology, and behavior.

Cultural attitudes influence human growth and development. One of my patient's earliest memories was of crying, pain, and hunger. Her pediatrician belonged to the obsessive self-confident culture that controlled physiology and feeding by rules and edicts opposing the humanitarian cultural feelings of the mother, who deferred to authority. The patient remains in middle life subject to hunger pains and continual doctoring. Indigestion, pain, hunger remain. Only the crying has changed; it appears in stomach disturbances and reinforces them.

Parents of extreme Prussian culture impressed their rigid rules of performance and cleanliness on eliminative processes too early. "Duty" was the word for defecation. The strands and straps of constriction were drawn so tight that only a psychosis of hate, symbolic destructiveness, and appeasement could and did finally break the parental hold.

Cross cultural contacts may be the source of anxiety and psychosis. A girl brought up in the isolation of wealth and snobbishness could not marry a man who "worked" because a gentleman does not work. Biologic and social frustration developed pressures issuing in psychosis where only in phantasy, revery, and delusion could her natural urges be fulfilled and released from the domination of parental culture. Another girl burst similar bonds of isolation and overprotection in a reversal of training—dashing into unconventionality and promiscuity.

Conflict of religion and economic culture is not infrequent. A man was brought up under strong maternal and religious influence. Kindness, fair play, deference were virtues cultivated in him. When his college friends carried him into competitive business, he collapsed because he did not have the aggressiveness to compete and survive. It took five years before he could catch his breath, reorganize his resources, and take his part in society as a contributing member.

A man and a woman showed similar problems. Both grew up in the tradition of large families—the children looking after the parents in their ageing. Their children, much fewer in number, came into contact with the active hurrying, independent, achieving culture of thriving, alive America. Individualism was accentuated. Parents were left alone except for financial contributions. Both the man's and the woman's frustrations and hostilities moved into self-disappointment, self-dissatisfaction, self-castigation—or melancholia.

The overprotection and overdirection of a pietistic, religious culture, closely knit, did not prepare a gentle, young girl for her contact with a lively spontaneous, wholesome extraverted group in another city. Her feeling of difference was accentuated into delusions of reference and persecution. She had illusions, on looking into a mirror, of seeing herself as a howling hyena with horrible fangs. Ten years of psychotherapy were required to help her rescind her hostilities and distortions and move into friendly relations with for her a new and distant culture.

An extreme case of cultural constriction was a 33-year-old woman brought up in an extraordinarily pietistic sect in the mid-west. The cultural and familial rigidities, taboos, and phobias sound almost unbelievable. Work was to be her life. Only boy-crazy girls went to high school. She was told not to speak to boys and men except the few relatives who visited the family. She was hired out as a family helper and was warned against any but the most formal contacts with the male members of the household. Recreation, amusement, socialization were taboo. "I get tired and feel exhausted. Sometimes it takes my appetite and sleep. I am trying to keep from becoming too mentally depressed. Have been fighting a losing battle for years." Why she was not severely depressed or psychotic was difficult to understand. Her anxieties seemed to be reactions to cultural pressures rather than to intra-psychic echoes of childhood traumata. There had been a continued struggle against external conditions. She always maintained a grip on reality and finally, with support from her therapist, was able to shake herself loose from sick reality and move constructively into a new, more wholesome reality. One is sometimes tempted to enter deep psychotherapy fascinated by intriguing patterns in psychopathology. By moving in on a comparatively direct plan of reinforcing and guiding constructive impulses she was salvaged both mentally and vocationally. She was advised to move hundreds of miles from her home and culture—to Philadelphia, where she took a practical nursing course and established herself on her own, developing satisfying social and recreational activities with religious affiliations of a less extreme form. Therapy can often be appropriate and effective only if it considers the external cultural and environmental attitudes and relationships.

Anthropology brings to attention the relativity of culture—rules, regulations, customs, beliefs, expectations, taboos, rewards, acceptances, punishment. The Balinese woman wears no clothing above the waist. In America, technically, such behavior violates the mores. However, fashion makes certain accommodations between extremes of instinct and restriction; a certain suggestive approach to the Balinese is found unofficially interesting and attractive to a significant portion of the population.

The relativity of culture could bring to mind the relativity of concepts and formulations in psychiatry. Unfortunately, one often finds in this profession the protectiveness of absolutes and controlling conformities, which one thinks of as signs of immaturity in patients.

Among the Marquesans there is little breast feeding, since it is believed this tends to make the children anxious and insecure. In the Alorese there is absence of genuine security and affection of the mother for the child; the adult appears as rather disorganized, with much submerged hostility.

This is in contrast to the Navahos who, being accepted and loved as children, develop secure and confident personalities.[6]

Halliday points out the increase in obsessiveness in western cultures, and believes this is related to repressive child rearing in infancy. Carothers speaks of the rarity of psychoses among preliterates. Among the Debuans paranoid conditions are culturally dominant.[7]

In our culture manics seem to be decreasing. Carothers in Africa believes manics far outnumber depressions. Hysteria has changed its manifestations greatly since the times of Charcot and the early days of Freud. It has been said that the ratio of obsessive conditions to hysterical was greater in the last World War than in the first. Psychoneurotic reactions decreased during the stringencies of German war camps. Faris and Dunham believed that schizophrenics came chiefly from slum areas, while manic-depressives came from upper levels. Redlich studied the incidence of psychoses and neuroses in different socio-economic classes in New Haven. The incidence of psychoses increased as the socio-economic scale decreased, while the incidence of neuroses diminished. Methods of therapy show a cultural distribution— psychoanalysis is used by the upper economic classes; physical methods more by the lower economic brackets. Psychoanalysis is much more prevalent in American psychiatric thinking and practice than in England, France, or present-day Germany. It is not used in totalitarian countries.

Margaret Mead[8] notes that anthropology can throw "light upon an understanding of human psychodynamics, check tendencies to read our own special local social forms into theories, and broaden our views of the many potentialities which each human being has for constructing viable ways of life." And, finally, the goals of psychiatry and anthropology have something in common in "constructing, out of our insights, cultures in which human potentialities will have fuller play."[9] Viewing the formulations, concepts and theories of psychiatry and psychoanalysis in the broader perspectives of anthropology will help us develop sharper outlines and deepen our insights. Perhaps too we will be able to overlook some of our parochial perspectives, eliminate some of our defensiveness and hostilities, and join in a collaborative *eros* or *agape* for the benefit of our patients and the survival of mankind.

REFERENCES

1. HALLOWELL, A. I.: Culture and Personality. Inventory Paper for Wenner Gren Foundation International Symposium on Anthropology. New York, June 1952.
2. MASSERMAN, J. H.: Dynamic Psychiatry. Philadelphia, Saunders, 1955. P. 123.
3. HALLIDAY, J. L.: Psycho-social Medicine—A Study of The Sick Society. New York, Norton, 1948.
4. FRANK, L.: Society as the Patient. New Brunswick, Rutgers University Press, 1948.
5. MAY, R.: The Meaning of Anxiety. New York, Ronald Press, 1950. Pp. 46, 201 ff.
6. ABRAMS, H. R. AND HALLOWELL, A. I.: Anxiety and its relation to the culture patterns and personality development among primitive peoples. Conference on Psychiatric Education, Cornell University, Ithaca, June 1951.
7. SCHERMERHORN, R. A.: Social Psychiatry in Mental Health and Mental Disorder (A. M. Rose, ed.). New York, Norton, 1955.
8. MEAD, M.: Social Anthropology and Psychiatry in Dynamic Psychiatry (Alexander & Ross, eds.). Chicago, University of Chicago Press, 1952. P. 240.
9. ——: Ibid, p. 433.

Part III: SPECIAL PROBLEMS:
STRESSES and TECHNIQUES in LATER LIFE

Pregnancy and Childbirth*

HENRIETTE R. KLEIN

ADMITTEDLY IT WOULD BE IMPOSSIBLE to attempt to discuss the many problems, and their multiple forms of expression, associated with pregnancy and childbirth. I have decided, therefore, to limit my discussion to two general problems, one related to the pregnancy period and one related to the postpartum period, using these two examples to illustrate the type of problem encountered and to indicate the rationale for planned psychotherapy during these periods.

I. PROBLEMS DURING PERIOD OF PREGNANCY

Pregnancy is a topic about which everyone and anyone has opinions, impressions, prejudgments, and convictions, which are similarly encountered among those undergoing the pregnancy experience.

Whatever the attitude of the gravid woman toward her pregnancy, the processes involved in childbearing and the emotions mobilized inevitably constitute a threat at some level to the pregnant woman. This may be manifested as realistic concern about the foetus, as anticipatory fears about the delivery, as somatic complaints, complaints of uneasiness or fears; or, conversely, it may be manifested in complete denial of concern.

Whether the pregnant woman expresses concern about the foetus or about herself, these fears are mutually substitutive. They differ in frequency, intensity and duration, depending upon their derivatives and the previous level of adaptation and they vary, also, in their susceptibility to resolution.

Feelings of guilt and fear of punishment indicate their presence through a variety of attitudes. Fear of harming the foetus during intercourse, refusal to admit any preference for the sex of the unborn infant, and concern about a maimed child are familiar expressions of this. One patient voluntarily gave up smoking because she decided this might injure the baby's lungs. Frequently an "undesired" pregnancy is inaccurately equated with being a "rejecting" or "bad" mother, with subsequent fear of punishment to self and foetus.

---

*Round Table—Annual Meeting of the American Psychiatric Association on May 1, 1956.

In a study[1] of a group of primiparas, multiple prejudgments and fixed ideas about childbearing were found. Sometimes, irrespective of what was told them, these women maintained stereotyped attitudes concerning, for example, when coitus should be discontinued, what might influence the unborn infant through the eating of specific foods or having specific thoughts, or how to ward off bad luck by not buying clothes for the infant before birth. Notions about hereditary patterns for delivery were frequent: some felt that if their mothers had had easy deliveries so would they, and vice versa. One frightened young woman felt that she could not expect to have an easy time not only because of the unfavorable experiences of her mother and sisters but also those of her two sisters-in-law. Patients frequently mentioned difficulties experienced by their mothers or sisters in relating worries and fears. Identification with the mother was especially striking. Stories they had heard from or related to their mothers were not readily changed. One patient wondered, when her baby was born dead, whether something had been wrong with the umbilical cord because the putative father was a sailor and "had a lot to do with ropes." One believed that if she had a permanent wave during pregnancy she might be electrocuted. Another believed that an x-ray was taken because "you're more apt to get things when you're pregnant." Another patient, after discussing at length what she heard about birth marks being caused by maternal impressions, stated that she did not believe any of this; she went on to say, however, that she would not get any clothing for the infant until after it was born because her sister said that "some accident might happen." Still another thought that if one craved expensive out-of-season food, the child might have a birth mark, but that if the same food were in season, the baby would not be so injured.

One patient explained her reticence to mention anxieties by stating that to express or admit anxiety was to make it operative. Similarly, a primipara who expressed the fear that the baby might be defective because of certain hereditary factors refused to continue any discussion of the subject. Another said she did not want to talk about her feelings for the baby; "if you make too many plans you are sure to be disappointed."

Taboos, rituals and magical explanation of childbearing represent cultural devices to express and to cope with fear; they also operate circularly by reinforcing the original fears.

PSYCHOTHERAPY DURING PREGNANCY

Depending essentially upon the adaptive level of the woman, the pregnancy processes and its representational effectiveness may mobilize, release, or reinforce previous fears. The pregnancy may become a conveyor belt for closely related fears now expressed in and through the pregnancy.

Recognition of these subtle fears is the first step in treatment. Since fears felt interchangeably as concern about self or foetus may not be expressed as direct complaints or symptoms, it is important to provide the pregnant woman with information and reassurance as early as good rapport is established. The psychiatrist or any member of the obstetrical team must be alerted to the subtle and disguised expressions of fear and guilt, frequently expressed as mild mood shifts, restlessness or uneasiness, concern about personal health or viability of the foetus, or silence and refusal to face problems.

Our knowledge of the sources of these representational fears and their reinforcement indicates what methods should be employed to combat them. It is essential that the pregnant woman be given an opportunity not only to gain accurate information about pregnancy and her physical health but to give expression to fear and guilt as well. Obstetrical centers where planned delivery programs include discussion and meaningful contact with the pregnant woman report that, when properly treated, such fears are transitory.

Therapeutic emphasis in this period should be geared toward elimination of fear-born feelings so that there may be increased self-esteem, pride in the creative process, and emergence of love, tenderness, and affection, allowing a constructive emotional experience. Other psychotherapeutic goals should be ancillary to those aimed at a successful pregnancy. Treatment in this period should not encourage disturbing search for basic conflicts or underlying fears and guilt, nor should it allow such feelings to intensify. Except when these feelings are so acute as to require emergency measures, psychiatric treatment should aim at being reparative, to help the woman cope with the pregnancy and childbirth. It should not introduce a probing analysis.

This discussion far from covers the general problem of anxiety during pregnancy: I have restricted myself to this brief outline of the manifestation of anxiety and general therapeutic procedures.

II. Problems Related to Breast Feeding of the Infant

We turn now to the problems related to the postpartum period. I shall discuss only one phase of the postpartum period, the matter of breast feeding, an experience frequently equated with maternal devotion, acceptance of the infant, and so on. How maternal a mother is or how to interpret what she says or does as an indication of maternal strength has been a matter of opinion subject to the bias of tradition-bound concepts of how a mother ought to feel and behave toward her children. Since the kind of mothering afforded any child is a crucial factor in the child's emotional growth and social integration, the value of aiding the emergence of maximum welfare feelings toward the infant is self-evident.

How much of the desire to breast feed comes from the mother and how much from social and medical pressures, must be carefully assayed if one is to obtain a factual picture of what motivates the new mother in her attempts or decision to nurse. Early patterns of competitiveness with siblings, identification with her mother, a need to be in control, nursing to assuage fears or as an expiatory measure for controlled aggression may well motivate some mothers' desire to breast feed, just as a strong desire to "mother" may motivate others.

The inhibiting factors of fear and guilt may discourage not only the erotic pleasure from breast feeding but the very desire to nurse. Where the fear and guilt are of an intensity that can be assuaged, the mother may be able to nurse with pleasure and success. However, unless some objective attempt is made to evaluate the new mother's feelings and attitudes before prescribing or encouraging breast feeding, certain difficulties are inevitable. Nor are there sufficient studies of the human lactating mother to justify such strict injunctions.

In a study[2] of mothers who were in a hospital division where nursing was mandatory, the group necessarily included some who had wished to nurse and some who were violently opposed to it, although all had carried out the standard nursing act during their hospital stay. Two-thirds of this group were seen again after a nine-month lapse of time, thus providing the opportunity to explore further their previously expressed attitudes. Some stated that they would not have nursed except for hospital insistence: these had discontinued at once upon leaving the hospital. Although some gave as explanation for discontinuance of breast feeding their having to return to work or having insufficient milk, half stated quite frankly that they discontinued because they "did not wish to nurse." Of those who had said originally while in the hospital that they did not wish to nurse, without exception all had given it up once they were discharged from the hospital and thus free to make such a decision.

Our data raise many questions about the meaning of breast feeding to the mother, the variability in the gratification it provides, and the significance of the presence or absence of the desire to nurse. The assumption that a normal mother would want to nurse in itself contributes a social pressure and may operate as a factor which overrides the personal preference of the lactating mother.

Psychoanalysts have observed that analyzed patients are inclined to nurse or attempt to nurse their infants. Does the fact that allied topics have been analyzed allow the mother to be freely motivated in this direction or do certain interpretations constitute a form of indoctrination, even though the analyst may have expressed no specific judgment? It may well be that some analyzed women hold themselves to the alleged ideal of a nursing mother.

The assumption that the experience of nursing might stimulate further desire to nurse was not borne out in our sample. Those who had said, while in the hospital, that they did not want to nurse did not change their attitude or behavior, even after having had the breast feeding experience with the infant. Not one of these had continued to breast feed her baby: all of these stated, a year later, that they did not plan to nurse any babies they might have in the future.

Until thorough hormonal and psychodynamic studies of the lactating mother are available, the injunction that mothers should breast feed cannot be based on well-established facts. Indeed, there is possible harm in the current emphasis on breast feeding in situations where it goes counter to the mother's emotional needs, whatever the individual biologic or physiologic derivatives.

I have restricted my discussion to two topics: (1) the problem of anxiety during pregnancy and (2) the operation of fear and inhibition as expressed through breast-feeding attitudes. These two themes have been used merely to illustrate the many factors operating at these various periods in time and to indicate how a further psychodynamic formulation may direct and determine the course and the role of psychotherapy.

REFERENCES

1. KLEIN, H. R., POTTER, H. W. AND DYK, R. B.: Anxiety in Pregnancy and Childbirth. New York, Hoeber, 1950.
2. POTTER, H. W. AND KLEIN, H. R.: Some implications of breast feeding: a study of nursing mothers. Presented at the 110th Annual Meeting of the American Psychiatric Association St. Louis, Mo., May 6, 1954.

Psychotherapy of the Aged

JACK WEINBERG

MAN'S INORDINATE STRIVING for orderliness is exceeded only by nature's capacity to achieve it. No matter where man's eye falls and what he perceives, he sees natural phenomena of both matter and form in exquisite relationship to each other. The orderliness of the universe, the harmonious relationship existing between its component parts is reflected also in the inner structure of the various parts. For no matter whether the part is large or small, animate or inanimate, it is composed of still smaller elements, each related to the other in an orderly fashion and each contained within a certain boundary. No wonder, then, that man, seeing all of the above, is impressed by its design and particularly by its meaning—the meaning that there must be an order to things. And it is obvious, too, that for a natural phenomenon like himself to survive he must adhere to the observable laws of nature—orderliness, containment within certain boundaries, and a capacity for transactions with other elements or systems.

Manifestly, man recognizes that the existing harmony and inter-relationships in the world about him and within him bespeak an inter-dependence between them; the loss of any of the components or systems calls for a new adaptation and adjustment to the whole. The observation of these phenomena plus man's own life experiences, from infancy to maturation in a complex society, make it quite apparent to him that he cannot exist isolated from other interacting individuals. Certainly he can manage to do so for a given period of time, particularly when there is hope that the isolation will at one point end; but he cannot manage, however, if the isolation is not self-imposed and is a threatened end in itself with no hope of an amelioration. This is precisely the trauma of later life in our culture.

The gradual isolation of the aging organism into a state of aloneness is the great tragedy of aging. Isolation, of course, is a result of a number of factors. There is the reality of the dispersal and death of members of the family and meaningful friends. Each loss is attended by a need for a re-arrangement of the equilibrium which had been set up by the organism for a comfortable functioning. Each loss disrupts the interdependent relation-ship that had been so useful. Each loss, too, liberates within the organism an energy (libidinal cathexis) hitherto invested in some meaningful object which now is unattached and is in search of a new object. But there are no takers. There is no replacement of family and there are no bidders for the friendship of the aged. When the aging organism attempts to re-establish equilibrium by attempting to reinvest the freed libido to new objects in the environment, it meets a wall of resistance. Having lost erotic values to the ravages of time and productive values to our exacting economy, the aged are further rebuffed by our cultural attitudes towards them.

Excluded from living in the homes of their children, often retired from jobs merely because of age and thus cut off from the occupational interests which have absorbed their creative energies for so many years, older people tend to become increasingly isolated. We have to some extent overcome the hazards of their inability to rely financially on their children through social security measures and the tremendous elaboration of insurance devices. But the gap which severs dependent relations between the generations makes it impossible for the aged to rely emotionally, as well as financially, on their children. Whereas in other cultures parents would expect not only to live with their children but to receive their continued respect and devotion, older people in our doing, nature-mastering, future-oriented society can expect to be told that they are old-fashioned, their opinions out of date, and their capacity to give helpful advice based on lifelong experience strictly limited. With our impatient march into the future and our restless pursuit of change, the wisdom of an older generation is not likely to count for much. Space does not permit an inquiry into the complicated effects of this required separation between the generations on individual personality structures or on behavior disturbances in the individual; however, some observations are pertinent here.

Aging is one of the developmental phases in the life span of the individual. It is developmental in the sense that it is not a static phenomenon which comes at the end of the organism's existence, but is rather a fluid state, influenced by one's physiology, psychology and economies, and the socio-economic and cultural environment in which it lives and whose attitudes the organism embraces, applies to itself, and reacts to accordingly. To be sure, one out of one ages; yet it is the above-mentioned variables that to my mind bring the aging process at varying rates and in a varying way to different individuals regardless of their chronologic years. These become self-evident truths when one is engaged in the clinical practice of psychiatry related to the aging. However, even self-evident truths, possibly because they are so self-evident, must be subjected to investigation and scientific validation.

Since we postulate that aging is one of a series of developmental phases, we must determine the specific traumata of this period. Each phase in the individual's development, in its quest for adequate adaptation, has some aspects which are common to all; yet each phase also has some problems which are unique to it and it alone. We probably cannot go far amiss if we were to state that the specific trauma of old age is aging. However, a definition of the latter almost defies description. One immediately encounters endless philosophical and scientific description of the end result of aging but not of the process itself. It is no easy task, of course, to assess a process even under the most favorable circumstances. It becomes particularly difficult to do so in the area of human behavior. The human being reacts to stimuli, internal and external, interacts with others about him, and constantly finds himself in a transactional field of infinite possibilities, all of which call for observational powers of no mean proportions and objective recording which may become outmoded at the very moment of transcription. Recognizing all of these difficulties we must nevertheless strive for an evaluation and assessment of the processes attendant to later life, if not in their entirety, at least some aspects of them.

In the area of intrapsychic adaptation and economy the following idea has become apparent to me clinically, difficult though it may seem to validate experimentally: The physician dealing with the clinical problem of the aged must keep certain criteria in the foreground of his thinking if his judgment and, consequently, his therapy are to be correct and effective.

1. Man, no matter what his age, is heir to any of the disease processes that organic matter is susceptible to in its attempts at adaptation. Neuroses, therefore, can and do make their appearance with astonishing frequency in later life.

2. The understanding of the psychological disease entities in old age depends, as it does in any age, upon the knowledge and understanding of the premorbid personality structure and its historical development. For whether the disease is organic or functional, the psychological picture will depend not so much on the site of the lesion as on the premorbid character structure.

3. All symptom formation has inherent in it a protective quality.

The first two criteria are self-explanatory; the last needs further amplification.

Physicians are wont to look upon symptoms as undesirable phenomena, signs that something has gone wrong within the organism in its quest for homeostatic equilibrium, something to be "rid of." However, one must not lose sight of the fact that symptoms have a function to perform that is often useful and protective in nature. As psychiatrists, we conceive of all symptoms as defense maneuvers on the part of the ego in its attempts at adaptation to an ever-changing internal and external scene. Psychologically, one is really afraid of only one disease: the dissolution of one's ego boundaries, with a subsequent loss of identity, intactness and oneness. It is to guard against such an eventuality that pathologic defenses in the form of symptoms appear as last-ditch efforts against a complete break.

The ego, of course, is that institution of the personality which perceives internal and external stimuli, integrates them and allows for unified action. It is the compromiser between our instinctual drives, our appetites and hungers, with all of their irrational demands upon the organism, and the moral, ethical and cultural forces which are opposed to the chaotic expression of these drives. It is the ever-watchful, alert guardian whose job it is to protect the individual against utter and complete dissolution in the face of whatever vicissitudes may befall him. Furthermore, it is its function to maintain a psychic homeostasis which it will do at all costs short of a psychosis. Yet, even in the latter it attempts to restore order where order, as the normal person sees it, is lacking. The more flexible and plastic the ego, the more integrated the individual's behavior. Added to the above, it is good to remember that the ego may be flexible in certain areas of adaptation and rigid in others. Thus, one may be able to adjust and change with the times in a vocational choice and yet be rigid and stereotyped in the social outlook.

Adequate ego function is dependent on a number of factors. Freedom from physical disease or crippling greatly enhances the chances for good adaptation, for the less the organism is disturbed by pathologic stimuli the more ego energy is available for external adaptation. The converse is true for the phenomenon of loss of interest in the outer world and what goes on about one, when one is ill. Furthermore, the ego's proper functioning depends on the element of hope. A man will endure the greatest pain if he has the hope that eventually the suffering will come to an end or that the future will be brighter. The child who gives up many of his dependent gratifications for responsible achievement does so out of the clear knowledge that not only will his own concepts of what he is to be like be met thereby, but also because of the fact that every progressive step will bring approval and love from his parents or the meaningful people about him. Approval and love from others, the yearning for them and the hope for their realization, are important ingredients in the person's drive for the maintenance of the self. Since this hope diminishes with age, since the hope for a better tomorrow is a mirage in the twilight of life, the danger to the psychological balance of the organism is great. The imbalance is augmented by the fact that the aging process diminishes the energy reservoir available to the ego and that organ destruction within increasingly and disproportionately forces man to look inwardly to internal pathologic symptoms.

The threat of organ destruction within plus the welling up of heretofore unacceptable but controlled impulses and the deterioration of the individual's socio-economic status tax the adaptive capacities of the ego to the utmost.

To master the threat of dissolution of its boundaries and to ward off any break with reality, the adaptive capacities of one's character will go through all sorts of contortions in symptom or defense formation. The symptoms that arise with aging have a uniqueness characteristic of that period in our life. They indicate that there is a waning of power and they tend to indicate that the organism is trying to maintain itself by giving up certain powers in order to maintain or preserve others more essential to its unity. In general, the symptoms that form in later life may be divided into three categories: exclusion of stimuli, conservation of energy, and regression. The defense maneuvers of conservation of energy and regression are fairly clear and have been dwelt upon by many others. I would like to explain, however, what I mean by the exclusion of stimuli, a very common defense in later life which most physicians usually ascribe to organic changes.

I have stated before that it is the function of the ego to perceive and integrate internal and external stimuli. Since the aging process curtails one's capacity to deal with the multitude of stimuli that clamor for attention in our complex society, the organism begins to exclude them from its awareness. This may best be illustrated by the following example. We often hear someone make the remark, "My grandmother doesn't see too well, but what she shouldn't see she sees only too well." Or "My father doesn't hear too well but that which he shouldn't hear, he hears all right." A remark of this sort is really an observation which can be classified as being scientific in nature. It implies that the afflicted individual is capable of selection and that the defect is not really organic. For were it organic in nature the person suffering from it would probably be unable to hear a particular tone or to see in a particular direction, etc. However, organically affected organs do not exclude certain ideas and permit others to pass their perceptive threshold. It is my conviction that the aging organism, having at its disposal a lowered psychic energy supply and being unable to deal with all stimuli, begins to exclude them. This is true of all sensory stimuli except possibly for those of the olfactory nerve.

The infant also is faced by the same overwhelming stimuli with little ego development to help it cope with them. However, the very young can and do take refuge in sleep to allow for a gradual exposure to the clamor and the integration of them. Then too, they have the help of supportive figures who are ever ready to supply ego judgment and strength to the struggling new organism. Both of these elements are not available nor are they acceptable to the aging organism; hence, the exclusion.

Though it may be argued by some that the mechanism of exclusion of stimuli is identical with the familiar mechanism of denial, it is my feeling that it is quite different. Denial to me implies that a stimulus has been perceived, has been cathected to and invested in, with cathexis being then withdrawn. But exclusion of stimuli, in this instance, is an unconscious blocking out of stimuli with an investment of energy only in that which becomes emotionally pertinent.

To meliorate the arising pathology, the psychiatrist's role is a triple one. The first is his relationship with the patient. In 1951 I stated it as follows: "From time immemorial man has struggled with the irrational forces underlying emotional disturbances. Everything conceivable has been tried by those who have been called upon to treat human beings. Psychiatrists have gone a long way from the days when, through incantation and prayer, man tried to placate and drive out the evil spirits. We have attempted brain surgery and shock treatment, long-term psychotherapy, short-term therapy, individual psychotherapy, group-therapy, various drugs, heat and cold, fire and ice, music, socio-drama, hydrotherapy, occupational and recreational therapy, total push to total regression; all have been tried, and to all have been ascribed healing powers by those who promulgate their favorite means. The confusion resulting from all of the claims becomes no confusion when one realizes that all of the above therapies have a common denominator. The common denominator is, of course, the therapist and the patient, the interpersonal relationship between them . . . . For no matter what the treatment may be (and there are, of course, valid and intrinsic values in all of the above-named methods), it is nonetheless the awareness on the part of the patient that in the therapist he has an individual who is ready to understand, willing to give and to help, which is beneficial."

What I said then holds true today and certainly coincides with the thinking and experience of many clinicians. All recognize the enormous importance of the relationship and the role played by the psychiatrist. The need is for an enthusiastic, optimistic approach which is genuine, an active participation in the relationship which depends as much on its quantitative aspects as it does on the evaluation of its quality. The psychiatrist working with the aged must free himself of his feelings of being bound by formalistic approaches to therapy. He must be willing to venture out and try out modifications of traditional techniques. Certainly, the psychoanalytically-trained psychiatrists who have reported on their therapeutic success with the aging cited their more active role, were ready to do away with the couch and allowed themselves to enter more freely into a relationship with the patient.

Second, the psychiatrist must be aware of the nature of the pathology. The outstanding characteristics of senescence which threaten emotional health are physical decline, loss of erotic values, loss of supportive figures, social and economic insecurity and the gradual contraction in the flexibility and plasticity of the adaptive mechanism. The decrement in personal, physical and emotional assets and the absence of hope (a vital ingredient for ego integration) for a better tomorrow greatly endanger the adaptive capacities of the ego. To master the threat of dissolution of its boundaries the ego will utilize all of its previously learned defenses and add some new ones to its repertory. The major defenses employed by the ego in later life are those of regression, rigidity and the exclusion of stimuli.

Regressive symptoms are easily discernable phenomena and I need not elaborate upon them. However, few recognize in rigidity the dynamic principle of a defense. We live in a highly complex, ever changing world demanding of us constant readaptation. To master new situations requires the greatest efficiency and integration of the ego. The decreased efficiency of the ego in the elderly almost always calls forth anxiety when readjustment is necessary. To avoid anxiety the aging person will cling to automatized and familiar patterns of behavior no matter how faulty they may be. He reacts to new situations as to some danger with peevishness, irritability and hostility. Change is regarded with paranoid suspicion and fear and the individual will cling to behavior which has heretofore given him the nearest approach to mastery of his environment. This, then, is the familiar conservatism of the aged.

The third defense maneuver of the aged, which may be called upon first, is the exclusion of external stimuli which, by their confusing diversity, may upset the homeostasis of the psyche as set up by the ego. This is particularly true of the sensory system. The diminution of visual and auditory acuity in the aged are notable examples. Yet, there is something selective about the two, which can be explained only on the basis of the exclusion of some stimuli when energy to perceive, interpret and cope with new stimuli is at a low ebb. And, as I have indicated above, exclusion of stimuli seems to me to differ from denial.

All of these defenses are dynamic mental processes rather than fixed habit patterns with organic substrata, and are therefore not beyond therapeutic reach. The therapeutic goal, then, is first, to understand the symptom, then to modify, alternate or work for the acceptance of some of them without resigning necessarily to further deterioration.

Last, it is the therapeutic function of the psychiatrist to manipulate the environment in which the older person lives. This may range from the education of the family, friends and those who are entrusted with the care of the aged as to the needs of the patient and the meaning of the symptoms to a dogged gnawing at the conscience of society for a better emotional climate for our aging population.

Current Therapeutic and Psychotherapeutic Concepts for the Geriatric Patient

L. Z. COSIN

THERE CAN BE NO DOUBT NOW that the rapidly increasing expectation of life in the younger age groups has been precipitating a crisis. We must be in a position, however, to define the problem in numerical terms before we can proceed to solve the psychiatric, medical and welfare problems of geriatric patients. In this, the importance of the coordinated multi-disciplinary approach cannot be underestimated.

Nearly ten years ago I was able to evaluate some of the clinical and pathologic uses in fairly precise numerical terms, thanks to the help I received from the great statistician and epidemiologist, Professor Major Greenwood. Much of this approach is described in the "Analysis of Geriatric Care" (Proceedings of the Royal Society of Medicine, 41: 333-336). Briefly, we found that the incidence of acute pathologic processes of patients over sixty admitted to a chronic sick hospital was far higher than had been thought to be the case. Moreover, many elderly patients with acute disease that was reversible with a better medical approach could have been left with minimal medical diagnosis and care for an indefinite in-patient period; in many of these cases a far more active approach was necessary and sometimes essential to facilitate their return to the community. A superficial medical prognosis might then decide that the physical disabilities of the elderly and chronic sick were sufficiently gross to necessitate an organized nursing service for permanently bedfast patients. From this concept has arisen the need to provide beds for custodial care, but when some patients receiving custodial care recovered spontaneously no clear administrative decision to withdraw this facility was made as a matter of policy. As a result, all over the world, a peculiar mixture of patients with diverse diseases and varying degrees of disability, in large part due to a combination of institutional and domiciliary neglect and in small part to the after-effects of an acute or progressive pathological process were, and are, found to be occupying custodial care beds.

The effects of any disability, however, cannot be accurately assessed in terms of pathology only, for an inaccurate prognosis of the possibilities and results of rehabilitation would result. A more accurate prognosis can be obtained by what I term the "Dynamic Quadruple Assessment." The

110

assessment is dynamic because it must be related to a life situation which is constantly changing, rather than to a pathologic process expressed in static terms. The four assessments are the pathologic, the psychological, the sociologic, and finally the assessment of the residual physical disability. Without this approach we become appalled by the numerical size of problems and may be misled into building vast structures of no functional value whatever.

ORGANIZATION OF THE GERIATRIC SERVICE

The organization of the Geriatric Service in the Oxford area is based upon the functional solution of problems occasioned by the dynamic quadruple assessment of each elderly patient whose need has been declared by his own doctor.

Briefly, the basic desiderata for the program for handling the problem of medical and mental ill-health in the geriatric patient consists of the following:

1. The assessment unit, where the dynamic quadruple assessment can be worked out by a multi-disciplinary team approach, and where, with skilled integration of the various therapeutic disciplines, the patient is helped to adjust to the experiences and treatment he will be offered.

2. The physician, nurse, biochemist, pathologist, electroencephalographer, dietician, occupational therapist, physiotherapist, and their aides must be available on the active treatment unit where the biochemical, medical, surgical and nutritional problems can be expertly handled. Where the regular daily intake of patients is not large, or has been stabilized as a result of long and experienced usage, the assessment unit and the treatment unit can be amalgamated. It must not be forgotten, however, that two functions are being performed in such a unit.

3. A rehabilitation annex, where physical improvement and sociologic adjustments are achieved in a period of weeks or months.

4. A very small nursing unit for the few permanently bedfast cases will replace the usual large custodial care program.

5. A ward for "confused patients," to which I shall refer later.

6. A housing program for different groups of patients whose functional needs may vary considerably. The housing need may be normal as part of the resettlement scheme, it may need to be modified for groups with severe physical disabilities, or it may need to be modified for the confused and demented patient. But we are finding it less and less necessary to segregate the large majority of confused patients on a permanent basis.

7. Follow-up service for treatment. It is essential to provide an efficient

medical, psychiatric and social follow-up service for those patients discharged from the in-patient part of the service. Many patients can be discharged after a relatively short stay because efficient out-patient treatment can be organized, especially as far as physiotherapy is concerned. It is understood that medical care is given by the patients' own practitioner. For the confused and demented old person, however, the day hospital is one of the solutions.

8. The day hospital. So many old people will continue to live and die at home in the family groups that, as Sheldon has shown, incomparably the greater burden will not be borne by hospitals at all. In fact, it is very desirable to attempt the further reduction, wherever possible, of accommodation for the elderly not in need of the fully organized and increasingly expensive hospital facilities.

The increased number of admissions of old folk to chronic sick hospitals and mental hospitals, while small as a percentage of the elderly population, is due in part to a failure to provide facilities in a field of preventive medicine.

The geriatric unit, exploring this, is finding more and more examples of patients who can be discharged to their own homes for greater or lesser periods of time, so that care by the family in selected cases can be supported by the community and local authorities until it is desirable for medical or sociologic reasons to readmit the old person to hospital on a permanent or temporary basis.

I had found previously, at Langthorne Chronic Sick Hospital in London, that the admission of elderly patients for a temporary period of assessment, treatment of organic disease, and rehabilitation resulted in an increased willingness on the part of families to continue to care for their old people, as long as they were offered the following advantages:

1. A limited responsibility for a period of time that could be suspended after joint consultation and agreement of the family, the general practitioner, and the geriatric unit's doctor and medical social worker.

2. Intermittent periods of freedom for the family by readmitting the patient so that summer holidays and rest periods could be available.

3. In certain selected cases the day hospital regime has proved very helpful in afford methods for treating the patient and relief of emotional stress in the family group by removing the patient from the family during the daytime and returning him home to sleep in the evening. During the daily hospital stay the patient received physiotherapy in the form of the appropriate remedial exercises to enable him to get about with less pain and greater comfort, and incidentally to prevent accidents at home. More important still, the patient received occupational therapy, which is a well recognized form of treatment for the confused or psychiatric

patient at any age. As a result, much nocturnal restlessness can be prevented and quiet nights obtained for relatives and the patients.

SOCIAL WORKER'S FUNCTIONS

The nursing staff's somewhat rigid discipline toward the patient and his disease should not be equalled by a similarly rigid discipline of the social case worker's approach to his problems. For thus his problems will remain problems, and a sense of static frustration replaces the dynamic hopeful approach we all expect from such a worker. Her chief contribution to the rehabilitation program must be her understanding of human relations, her permissive nonrigid approach to their settlement, and her powers of integrating the various therapeutic techniques with which her patients will be helped to achieve a greater or lesser degree of independence in the community. The medical social worker must be available to investigate the difficult situation apparent even before the patient enters the unit as an in-patient.

The function of the social worker is to assess the needs of the patient in a community or family setting before admission to the unit, and also to assess the environment situation from which the patient came, so that an accurate assessment of the situation can be prepared, in order that appropriate adjustments to it can be discussed and agreed upon.

In this way the social worker will be helping to create and perpetuate conditions under which the physician's work can be rendered more helpful and healing.

The social worker can also help to elicit positive motivation in the patient, and to help the family group or community to reaccept the handicapped patient.

NURSING

Consideration must be given to the "social climate" of the hospital or the ward unit in which assessment, treatment, and rehabilitation is attempted. While it is necessary to utilize the ward for the first "active treatment" and assessment stages of the rehabilitation program, we must be aware of the rigid outlook and the tendency toward an authoritarian and nonpermissive atmosphere, sometimes encouraged by the nursing staff.

With certain exceptions the very nature of acute pathologic disease from which patients of all ages suffer necessitates the strict application of nursing techniques based on sound epidemiologic and bacteriologic practice. Because these techniques are often left to the nursing staff to be organized and performed, it is not surprising, but no less unfortunate, that the discipline of a whole ward unit tends to become stereotyped into a rigidly organized pattern of work which is offered to patients and subordinate staff alike. This approach tends to spread to medical staff, administrators, and even architects who carry out the planning or alteration of ward units. The patient then tends to become surrounded by all too solid evidence of the extensive degree of his dependence upon personalities other than his own, to accept the all too firmly stressed need for dependence associated with the nursing techniques for the bedfast patient, and to lose initiative and the will to join wholeheartedly in the rehabilitation program.

It is essential, then, as one of the most important therapeutic techniques offered the patient, to introduce a far more permissive atmosphere into the ward unit without disturbing the efficiency of nursing care.

A hospital ward orientated toward the restoration of independent motivation needs a permissive regime which will create a social climate that will allow the patient to live in hospital with a feeling that things are not undertaken against him in a quasi-punitive way, though this should not be allowed to deteriorate into unlimited freedom.

A permissive atmosphere presupposes the readiness of people in charge not to take anything for granted; it presupposes their intellectual and emotional readiness to have their decisions questioned by the patients individually, or collectively, so that the group can live in a permissive climate willingly accepting the limitations imposed by their life situation, not only accepted out of loyalty to the group but also because they are in receipt of sympathy or kindness from the authorities.

1. Combined Assessment and Active Treatment Ward

This consists first of a small active treatment unit of eight to ten beds in the center of the various ward facilities. These comprise the head nurse's office, utility rooms, kitchens, and piped oxygen and suction. The duration of stay in these beds can be measured in a few days or weeks while biochemical homeostasis and pathologic resolution is approached or achieved in 70% of the patients admitted.

The main bulk of the beds, however, is provided in the more peripheral part of the ward unit and will be used for the convalescent patients. Here a less rigid routine is envisaged, although the medical and nursing supervision and technical level of treatment and investigation is the same as in the small number of intensive treatment beds.

A large dining and sitting room will provide far more social activities for the improving patients, while group occupational therapy, group physiotherapy, and the more frequent visiting by friends and relatives will assist the milieu. It is here also that physical rehabilitation can be begun and the clinical psychologist and medical social worker commence their all important work.

2. REHABILITATION AND LONG STAY ANNEXES

As a result of recent legislation in Great Britain the responsibility for elderly people who are ill rests with the Health Service, and for old people who are "well" with the local municipal authority. This left an obvious gap, since many old folk are infirm or "frail ambulant," and when the responsibility of their future care cannot be clearly defined a joint residential home, usually close to the geriatric unit, is provided. This has variously been called a "rest home" or "half-way house." Its name is immaterial, but its function is important.

In the residential annexes and the rest homes the attempt is made to provide a housing project instead of an institutional plan. I feel that the size of the basic family group is usually the number of people who sit around a dining table. Although families are smaller than they were, we have struck a compromise between the administration's needs to save a few cents by providing for large numbers, and the basic sociologic concept of the synthetic family group by having units of eight or nine in an annex comprising no more than 50. These numbers may seem ridiculously small, but as many patients tend to pass through these units in the course of a year either to their own homes or to the municipally owned homes there seems no need to overcentralize and complicate our sociologic problems. I have found that it is possible to maintain the status of the group when two or three confused patients are matched with five or six infirm or "frail ambulant" patients. If the proportion of confused is increased this situation tends to become unstable and may disintegrate with much disturbed behavior and considerable personal unhappiness in the more stable patients and the staff.

3. THE INDEPENDENT UNIT

Attached to one residential annex or half-way house in Oxford we have a very simple building consisting of 11 single small rooms with central dining room and kitchen.

At each end of the single story building is a toilet and bathroom. Thus, groups of patients of either sex in their seventh, eighth, and ninth decades can be housed under medical and nursing supervision, each in a single bedroom.

Each patient is responsible for the cleaning and tidiness of his own room but there is every encouragement for the more robust patients to help their frailer companions. There is little daytime nursing supervision and no nursing attention at all at night, for if we consider patients of 80 years of age and over to be fit to return to the family group or to their single rooms to live alone, then by definition they must be capable of washing, dressing, feeding, cleaning, and cooking a meal for themselves if necessary, while still under the beneficient supervision of the administrator and the occupational therapists.

Residents in the independent unit plan one meal a day and draw the stores from the administrator; later, they may have the option of going out and buying their needs from nearby shops. After preparing the meal, they are required to eat it and finally wash up and clear away the dishes.

Individual patients in need of adequate dietetic knowledge to feed themselves properly are sent to the independent unit, where, with the help of the dietician and the administrator they prepare their own food. The period of residence in the half-way house or independent unit varies between 14 days and about 100 days.

4. The Night Hospital

This program is varied in certain circumstances whereby patients in the independent unit are allowed to go out to full or part-time work so that they can return at night to a therapeutic social environment closely integrated with the medical care program. In this way they can obtain the advantage of gainful work while still maintaining a link with the helpful supervision of the geriatric unit. The medical social worker then helps them to find suitable lodgings to live in, and maintains contact.

We thus see the provision within a hospital unit for the final fruition of the multi-disciplinary coordinated therapeutic approach; here under minimal but adequate medical and nursing supervision, dieticians, medical social workers, occupational therapists, and physiotherapists, assist the final stages of the resumption of physical independence to patients in a therapeutic community. This restoration of individual initiative then facilitates his return to organized help in the community and eases family burdens.

Sociatry,* the Social Atom and Death

J. L. MORENO

THE GODS AND IMMORTALS whom men have cherished for millennia have lost a great deal of their former prestige. The prevailing view is that of a single appearance of man on the world stage and of his ultimate death. But the view of man's progress through the universe may change. It may give way to some form of reincarnation or immortality. The idea of immortality may not be entirely a figment of the human mind; I believe that in the future it will become fashionable again and find new attraction for the philosopher and the dreamer. We have been thrown down from the heavens and have a hard time to keep midway between heaven and hell.

One of the basic concepts which sociometry has developed is that of the "social atom." Atom is derived from the Greek *atomos,* "the smallest thing." The term was introduced into scientific language by Democrites; he used it to indicate the smallest particles in the physical universe. However, the physicists have no priority on the word; many words introduced by early philosophers describing such physical phenomena as gravitation, atom, attraction, and saturation have a poetic-symbolic character; they are metaphors for psycho-social experiences and thus belong rightly in our social science vocabulary.

Sociologists have used the term "socius" in a vague way for a long time. It has never meant anything specific until sociometry redefined it. The individual was usually thought of as the center of the social universe, of the family as the next larger unit, then the neighborhood, the village, etc.; from the point of view of surface experience sociologists tacitly accepted a scale starting with the individual and ending with the entire social universe. We sociometrists challenged this view. The social atom, not the individual, is the smallest social unit. It was discovered when the first sociometric geography of a whole community was charted (1932). The social atom is defined as the configuration of interrelated individuals, near or distant, who are emotionally related to each other at the time. The individuals may not be the same people with whom a person is "officially" related to and who are in turn "officially" related to him, but they are always individuals to whom he has a feeling relationship. It is like an aura of attractions, rejections and indifferences, radiating from him and

*See my definition, this book, page 1.

117

towards him, resulting in a tele structure. The social atom functions as one unit. The atoms change from time to time in their membership, but there is a consistency about their structure, the way our bone structure has a certain consistency. An individual has from birth on a ready structure of relationships around him: mother, father, grandmother, friends, neighbors, and so forth. The volume of the social atom is in continuous expansion as the individual grows up. It is within it that we live most concretely.

But the telic consistency of these social atoms changes as we get older, especially the ability to replace loss of membership. The social atom is changing intermittently and easily as long as we are young and more resourceful. When one individual member goes out of it, another individual fulfilling a similar role takes his place. As one friend steps out, the old friend is rapidly replaced by a new one; social repair seems to take place almost automatically. However, rarely more than *one* steps in to replace him. It is as if the central individual cannot sustain emotionally two or three of the same kind. There is, simultaneously, a continuous pull from millions of other social atoms, equally craving for replacements. The total effect is as if the emotional economy of the social atom operates in accord with an unconscious postulate—to keep the social atoms in equilibrium, or "sociostasis." Thus, a certain range of emotional contacts always exists and remains fairly constant. Their frequency of emotional exchange tends towards balance. Because of the constancy of emotional contacts the "emotional expansiveness" of an individual can be measured.

As we grow older replacement of lost members in significant roles takes place with greater difficulty, just as repairs are more difficult to our physical organism in the course of aging. It is the phenomenon of "social" death, not from the point of view of the body nor in the individual sense of the psyche. It is not how we die from within but how we die from *without*.

The "death trauma" takes many sociatric forms. A man or woman of sixty may be related to twelve or fifteen individuals, so many women and so many men, of various age levels representing various interests, in such roles and in such counter-roles. Social death throws its shadow upon such a man or woman long before physical or mental death. An individual may begin to lose the cohesiveness of his social atom for various reasons: (a) loss of affection, coming in and going out; (b) replacement by another individual not as well suited; (c) death. The death of an individual member is usually a more persistent loss, the shock coming from it rarely considered in its full significance at the time. If we happen to survive the ones we love or hate, a little bit of us dies with them as we feel the shadow of death marching from one person of our social atom to another. The people who move in to replace them do not always substitute the lost ones, since the very fact of substitution itself represents a certain loss. Therefore, from childhood on, we feel the meaning of death through the networks of our social atom long before it actually comes with the signs of physical and mental disability. It may be that sociometrists will find the objective pre-determinants for social death, a syndrome quite different from the sub-jective perceptions held by the people involved in the social atom. Then it should be possible to find remedies against the social death shock.

It is probable that the minute shocks coming from social death experience pave the way to pemature aging, old age sickness and physical death. Old people should learn not to give in to this curse; they should find friends, someone to love again. They should first try to restore the youth of their social atom. It is at times easier to treat the social atom disorders by sociatric devices than to treat physical and mental complaints. The idea that love and spontaneity is for the young only, that old people should prepare themselves for death, is an antiquated cruelty. A new breath of hope should come to geriatrics, the science of old age, from the recognition that we do not live only within ourselves, but that there is a "without" of the self which is highly structured and responsive to growth and decay. Death is a multidimensional event; it has also a social reality. The death of one person is connected with the death of many others. The people toward whose death you are sensitive and who are sensitive toward yours make up the last social atom you have. We are all surrounded continuously by people with whom we die. Physical death is something negative—we don't experience our own, the other fellow does, the fellow who is a member of our social atom. But social death is a *positive* force. Death is among us, like birth. Just as the infant, to an extent, pushes himself into birth, we push ourselves *and each other,* into death, often prematurely. Fear spreads like an emotional contagion through our social atoms and pushes its members gently toward death. We can observe how birth progresses during pregnancy, from conception on; similarly, we can observe how death progresses, from its conceptions in the social atom, the first people whom we have experienced as dying, and the little shocks we received from it. When we know more about the processes going on in the social atom of individuals, we may invent means of repairing its disorders. Perhaps in time a new profession will develop whereby, among other things, the sociatrist will treat socio-atomic disorders.

The case may be referred to of twelve individuals who were each sensitive to the other's death expectancy. They were all physicians, and their respective social atoms crossed and overlapped. One pioneered in coronary thrombosis. Five of the group succumbed to this very ailment, the other six lived in fear of it. At this writing two of them have died from it while three have recovered from an actual attack; the balance of the group are increasingly worried. The first thing they read in the morning newspapers are the obituaries and they all frequently go for physical checkups. We sociometrists are aware, of course, that the psychosocial networks are more important than printed matter; all kinds of news travels through them—including death notices.

Another case concerns nine air pilots. As the protagonist, who was one of them, was enacting on the psychodrama stage shocks from death threats, a scene suddenly occurred to him which he felt more keenly than even the death of his grandfather and a younger brother. He acted out, simultaneously with the other eight candidates, how he was undergoing a physical checkup. These copilots were all total strangers to him. He had seen them for the first time in the examination room, but they arranged to keep in touch with each other in the future. He wrote to them and they wrote back, but after a while his own letters returned from each one of them in succession, stamped "missing in action." These new and rather incidental members of his social atom were apparently dead. As he was reenacting the situation on the stage, he said, "There but for the grace of God, go I." The eight men were not quite dead yet; they were beckoning to him to follow.

The life of men extends beyond their physical atom through their social atoms. A man dies when his social atom dies. Physical and individual death are not the end of life; they can be viewed as functions of an older unit, of the socio-atomic processes in which they are both embedded.

BIBLIOGRAPHY

CARPENTER, C. R.: Concepts and problems of primate sociometry. Sociometry *8*: 56-61, 1945.

EISSLER, K. R.: The Psychiatrist and the Dying Patient. New York, International University Press, 1955.

JENNINGS, H. H.: Experimental evidence on the social atom at two time points. Sociometry *5*:135,145, 1942.

——: Sociometry and social theory. Am. Soc. Rev. *6*:512-522, 1941.

——: Individual differences in the social atom. Sociometry *4*:269-277, 1941.

MEAD, M.: Some relations between cultural anthropology and sociometry. Sociometry *10*:312-318, 1947.

MORENO, J. L.: Organization of the social atom. Sociometric Rev. *1*:11-16, 1936.

——: The two sociometries, human and subhuman. Sociometry *8*: 1945.

——: The social atom and death. Sociometry *10*: 1947.

——: Psychological Organization of Groups in the Community. Fifty-seventh Yearbook on Mental Deficiency, 1933.

Biodynamic Therapy in the Aging—An Integration

_____JULES H. MASSERMAN

Concepts of Senility

If, in accordance with the three preceding papers on aging, we try to define "senility," we recognize that making this concept personally meaningful entails difficulties greater than those presented by other psychiatric entities, the primary phenomena of which we have all experienced. For example, in our dreams and fantasies we have all felt the primal solipsism, the all-encompassing pervasiveness, the autistic logic and the thalassic affect of the schizoid state, and can therefore approach what a "schizophrenic" tries to regain in his atavistic flight from inimical reality. Or we have all railed against "fate," and in over-compensation have become appealingly melancholic, regressively helpless and anaclitically demanding—hence, we know how a "depressive" feels. At other times we may have tried to rationalize our failures and reassert our status by attributing our difficulties to specially important and influential enemies—and thus for a little while we may have become grandiose and "paranoid." As to delirious reactions, most of us have had acute illnesses with their accompanying temporary cripplings and transient confusions, but we have likewise had an eventual return to reasonable physical strength, intellectual capacity and renewed confidence. But here is the rub: in contrast to such reactions, none of us will admit to having been irreversibly and hopelessly _senile,_ and therefore we find it most difficult to reconstruct from our own experiences what the elderly must feel. Instead, our concepts of the role and treatment of the aged are secondarily indoctrinated, and have varied greatly with time and culture.

In fact, from a comparative psychological standpoint, there is a tremendous range evident even in prehuman animal societies. For example, red deer cherish and protect elderly cows and bucks, since experienced survivors can lead the herd to remote trails and pasturages. In contrast, predatory beasts like wolves turn their aged out of the pack hierarchy and exile them to fend for themselves. I wonder which is closer to our own particular culture?

Certainly, in human societies, the evaluation of the aged depends upon the particular mores of the group. In the peaceful and esthetic Finnish Golden Era (as idealized in the Kalevala mythology), the elderly were honored and even romantically cherished because they knew all the ancient songs that filled the universe with grace and glory. In Hellenic times also good gray Homer was revered both as a wise man and as a poet, and the Elders of the city governed through the Senate. But quite another pattern is exemplified by colonies of Labrador Eskimos, in which, if the communal food supply becomes insufficient for all during a particularly hard winter, the patriarch is expected to wander away from the village and quietly freeze to death. Since the eldest son respectfully accompanies him part way on this last journey to say goodbye, the oldster may feel that he is still an especially honored member of his community and will, therefore, in a wishful fantasy immanent in all of us, be rewarded in some more pleasant land beyond the bleak horizon.

In our modern American culture the epitome of the acceptable senior citizen is, on the whole, significantly different from the examples cited, though it borrows subtle components from all of them. Thus, the typically successful "retired American" is generally pictured in our advertising arts as a well-to-do and peripatetic playboy. His wife is not dowdy or gray— she has interestingly platinum blonde hair and displays a remarkably well preserved figure. And the two of them—provided, of course, they subscribed in time to the selflessly offered largesse of the Rugged Individualist Retirement Insurance Company—can travel gaily about the country rootless as to place or family, fishing or golfing with well-preserved tan and vigor anywhere from the Golden Coast of California to the Enchanted Keys of Sunny Florida. Insofar as the middle-aged in our country can look forward to fitting in with this peculiar fantasy, they may be fairly serene; in fact, the Cornell Study by Street and Thompson of some 2,000 older people indicates that 5/6 of those in the upper economic brackets who can achieve a reasonable facsimile of this particular goal, remain content. Regrettably, most Americans cannot achieve it.

There is another striking statistic as to the current extent of the problem: in 1910 there were 10 workers who remained at their jobs throughout their lives to every 1 who "retired," whereas this year the proportion is only 5 to 1. It is estimated that by 1962 there will be twenty million people over 65, mostly jobless, in our country. What will happen to them will actually depend less on their individual problems than on the future attitudes of their families and of society. Mass institutionalization is obviously socially unjust, economically catastrophic* and medically indefensible. As to the

---

*Gov. R. E. Meyner of New Jersey reported to the Federal Council on Aging (1956) that "today in the United States, our payments to persons over 65 total 6 billion dollars a year. Estimates are that by the year 2000 the cost of federal Old Age and Survivors Insurance will be 20 billion dollars annually—a figure which would play havoc with our future national economy if we are not prepared to deal with it."

latter in particular, Cosin estimates that 9/10 of the commitments for senility in Britain are a result of failures on the part of the family or society to provide for economic or medical emergencies, and that the aged are among the very few who are sentenced to life imprisonment for being poor and temporarily sick.

PROBLEMS OF ADAPTATION

It is against such social and economic realities that the "psychodynamics of aging" must be understood. Nor can one make a complete distinction between the actual disabilities of aging (i.e., diminished ability to perceive, differentiate, abstract, and evaluate the environment, and to respond in a properly versatile and efficient fashion) and the reaction of the *individual-in-his-milieu* to such impairments of both capacity and opportunity. Permit me to cite from my own experience two prominent and therefore widely appreciable examples of how the aging person may react to his repressed but sorrowful recognition of his inevitably waning powers to control his private world.

The first is the case of a famous violinist—perhaps one of the five greatest in recent history. As a virtuoso he had developed consummate grace and authority; indeed, his almost incredible technique and tone control may have approached the limits of human central nervous and musculo-skeletal function. Then, in his late sixties, he suffered a mild concussion in an automobile accident, and after his hospitalization he began to recognize once and for all that his mastery of his instrument must now decline. His staccato was no longer as crystalline, his trill as vibrant, his phrasing as well modulated, or his intonation as precise. Of course, so great was his remaining skill that few discerned these changes, but he could no longer dedicate himself to the ideal of perfect artistry. And so, even though he continued his concert career and was still better than most, he was in continuous travail of soul because he could no longer masterfully interpret the music he loved. Therefore, despite his wealth, fair general health, and the continued respect and love of his audiences, he gradually changed from a vibrant, creative, happy man to a stooped, tense and tragic figure of premature "senility."

Another poignant example is furnished by one of my most revered teachers, Adolph Meyer. Let me first relate two anecdotes pointing up the acuteness of his thinking and the subtle wit with which he was normally endowed—a humor which often consisted of apposing opposites in a disconcertingly and unforgettably penetrating fashion. The first story concerns one of his seminars on what he called psychobiology, in which he almost literally included everything in the universe as seen from his peculiarly pragmatic and humanistic standpoint. It so happened that one day we were discussing the experiential roots of knowledge, and he was expounding an essentially Lockeian position, to the effect that, beneath the vagaries of words, analogies and abstractions, mutual understandings were nevertheless possible because they arise from communal experiences. For instance, he said, if you see this table and call its color "brown," and I see it as "brown," there can be no misapprehension as to what "brown" is. So, also, if you see it as "oblong' and call it such, I know what you mean, since I, too, see it as "oblong." And again, if I touch it, and say it is hard, and you touch it and agree it is "hard," from then on all "hard" things in sense or experience are abstracted by both of us as objects or stresses difficult to penetrate. Thus we attain mutual comprehension and communication.

I was then a young man as naive as I am now, but less cautious—and so at this juncture I interposed what I thought was a basic epistemologic question. "Dr. Meyer," I said, "I am still not quite clear as to the finality of this derivation. Is it necessarily so, even if we describe some object with the same words, that we have had the same experiences? Take again this eternally troublesome philosophers' 'table.' We both look at it and call it oblong, but for all I know you might see it as oval, and for all you know I might be seeing it round, though we both agree to call your oval 'oblong' and my round 'oblong.' So also, when we both touch it and call it hard, for all I know I am feeling it 'prickly' in your private sensorium, and you're feeling it as what would be 'soft' in mine—but again we have agreed to call your soft 'hard,' and my prickly hard. What still troubles me, then, is that even with apparent identity of description there is still no certainty that even the sensory roots of our individual experiences are the same—or, for that matter, even comparable. How, sir, do we get around this basic solipsistic dilemma?"

There was a momentary pause after this brashness, and then I was given another lesson in the relative value of metapsychology as compared with more earthy wisdoms. Said Dr. Meyer, twinkling just a little: "Dr. Masserman, there is an old Swiss proverb that you ought to learn. In fact, it might help you a great deal. The proverb is: 'Where it doesn't itch, don't scratch!' " Ever since then I have been able to join in a great many scientific discussions with less pruritus and more appreciation of everyone's need for glib and seemingly impregnable explanations of the unexplainable.

On another occasion Dr. Meyer attended a seminar on the topic "What is essential in a psychoanalyst?", held some years ago at an A.P.A. convention, with Stanley Cobb presiding. Various people with various dialects had already spoken lengthily and sometimes not a little pompously, mainly to the effect that a psychoanalyst must possess one virtue above all, to wit:

integrity. Dr. Meyer, who had not been scheduled to speak, had sat through all of this discussion apparently lost in his own thoughts. When invited to comment on the proceedings he at first refused, but at the chairman's polite insistence he eventually got up, stroked his beard, and proceeded in his customary deliberate, imperturbable manner somewhat as follows: In view of the fact, he said, that the Hippocratic Oath pledged *all* physicians to "integrity," the speeches that evening had seemed a little redundant up to then unless the psychoanalysts wished to differentiate themselves from the rest of the medical profession.

This point made, he went on to develop what he thought truly characterized the analysts of the day—though, as will be seen, he did it in a manner few understood at the time. Stroking his Van Dyke and again lost in thought, he began, "When I was a child. . . [This in itself was a startling opening because so few in the audience could conceive of Adolph Meyer ever having been a child. But he continued—and here I must greatly condense his carefully qualified and richly involved delivery] . . . I had a profound belief in a Calvinist God . . . and when I wanted to do something different from what I had been taught I would look up at God and God would say 'no' [here Dr. Meyer emphasized the negative by solemnly shaking his beard] and so of course I wouldn't do it. . ." At this point Dr. Meyer had already taken about 10 minutes, during which time some in the audience had undoubtedly begun to wonder whether the aging dean of American psychiatry had perhaps gotten a little too tired to think clearly so late at night. But Dr. Meyer went on completely unperturbed: "But as I got a little older . . . gradually I lost my faith in this kind of God. I finally knew this because now, when I would want to do something different and would look up at God and God would go 'no'—I would go ahead and do it anyhow. . ." This took another 10 minutes and by now more of the audience were really a little sorry for the nice old man and wished he hadn't gotten off on such publicly senile rambling. Dr. Meyer went on: "Eventually I got to be a young man and I had to make a major decision. The decision was this: was I going to be a religionist or was I going to be a scientist? I thought and I thought and I decided that if I were going to be a religious man I would be a Catholic, and if I were going to be a Catholic I would be a Jesuit. . . But after thinking it over very carefully I decided I was not going to be a religious man—either Catholic or Jesuit. . . Instead, I was going to be a physician and a psychiatrist!"

Here Adolph Meyer sat down amid a predominantly strained, puzzled, or mistakenly commisserative silence. But those of us who had spent 3 years learning to interpret the old teacher's wisdom couldn't help chortling

quietly to ourselves. He had implied, of course, that what really characterized the psychoanalysts of the day was not their vaunted "integrity," but
the fact that many retained a childlike faith in unquestioned authority and
never deviated from the official dogma. But this was hardly all: not only
did analysts constitute a quasi-religious cult, but, like Jesuits, they felt it
their divine mission to spread their revelations to everybody, else the souls
of the heathen benighted would be lost. I did not altogether agree with
him then and do not now—but was there a better way open to self-revelatory
tact and incisive analogy?

But my last contact with Professor Emeritus Meyer was much sadder,
and occurred when I visited Baltimore some years after his retirement. As
was my custom, I had called up his home enroute through the city to give
him my greetings via the telephone. Unexpectedly, I got a request relayed
by Mrs. Meyer to please come to their home. I did so, and after talking
briefly with Mrs. Meyer, I sensed what the situation was. Dr. Meyer had
been the center of a quite influential circle in American psychiatry, but
after he left his professorship at Johns Hopkins he had lost a great part
of his administrative influence. Most of the people who had previously
congregated around him had since become self-important in positions he
had secured for them, and then somewhat forgetful of how much they
owed to him. There were, indeed, few of us left who, contrary to the new
fashion, still paid open respect to this retired dean, and he recognized that
I, though not among the major luminaries, was one of those few. He was
lonely, and he wanted to reconstitute associations that had once meant a
very great deal to him.

Another aspect of this appeared when I was admitted to his room. He
was lying in an upstairs bedroom by himself, surrounded by his books
and by various mementos of his previous influence—scientific awards,
academic honors, and so on. He had obviously suffered an occlusion of the
left middle temporal cerebral artery, and was partially aphasic and hemi-
plegic. He had also apparently had an adverse neurologic survey from
someone in whom he had, of course, chosen not to repose complete confidence. Since I had learned much of my neurology from him he greeted
me in his reserved, courtly fashion and finally asked, "Dr. Masserman, I
may hope to presume you have been fairly well trained in neurology, as
well as in psychobiology. May I ask you to please examine me to see
whether or not this leg of mine, which had become slightly paralyzed after
my mild stroke, is getting better fast enough?" It was obvious what he
was seeking: a friend to relieve his anxieties and welcome him back to
physical and social recovery. I did a careful examination and interpreted
my findings as euphemistically as I could. Or, to put it more bluntly, I

unashamedly lied a little. Thus reassured, he began talking more freely to me, and as he spoke, he himself showed the failing powers of a human mind—of which he had possessed a truly remarkable specimen. Among other examples of wishfully colored amnestic substitutions, he said, "I have just seen a review of your book in the American Journal of Insanity. . . It is an interesting book, but I don't believe it covered sufficiently all the subjects it should have. [Let me here interpolate that he was referring to my *Principles of Dynamic Psychiatry,* published in 1946, and that the American Journal of Insanity, which he had edited, had actually ceased publication decades before.] . . . I think you did not stress sufficiently the viewpoint of Psychobiology. . . In your future writings you will, of course, expand a little more on Individuation and the Ergasias? . . . It is my *Verdacht das heute. . . .*" And his voice trailed off into the soft, then unintelligible Schweitzer Deutsch of his happier days. . .

Here epitomized, then, were the pathetic efforts of all aged people to relive their time of strength and power and to perpetuate themselves vicariously through loyal offspring or disciples. The last memories I have of Dr. Meyer are likewise symbolic: his bed was placed against a west window through which could be seen the rapidly setting sun. As his voice drifted off into a restless sleep, only a dying glow was left in the sky. I paid what proved to be my last respects to him and Mrs. Meyer; he died just a few weeks later.

I shall, in Dr. Meyer's words, "hope to presume" that these anecdotes, like his own story of his youth, will be taken not as sentimental private reminiscences, but as vivid illustrations of the "dynamics of aging" as only poignant interpersonal (a term preferable to "clinical") experiences can be. For these are the reactions not only of the declining artist or the impaired intellectual, but of every person in every walk of life who becomes embittered by or attempts to compensate for his failing powers and threatened status. And they are often accompanied by other patterns that appear not only in aging but in any chronic debilitating process. For example, the paranoid grandiosity of the paretic, as Ferenczi and Hollos demonstrated, is not due to the disease itself, but is a function of the patient's reaction to the unconsciously sensed threat to his integrity. Ultimately, even in "normal" aging, there is an intensification of the basic Ur-defenses of the personality which I have described in detail elsewhere.* In the first of these, the presenile tries strenuously to renew his narcissistic prowess in various activities, from gynecophilia to golf. In the second, he avidly erects

---

See Progress in Psychotherapy, vol. I. New York, Grune & Stratton, 1956. Pp. 196 ff.

and ardently defends philosophic or mystical systems promising some form of immortal existence and power; in the third, he attempts, sometimes with frenzied futility, to retain or re-establish whatever human relationships he hopes he can still salvage here on earth.

Psychotherapy

Perhaps the first consideration, then, is to apply the Golden Rule and not try to deprive our elders of what we ourselves will eventually cherish. If dear old Uncle Harry thinks that yoga or yogurt will make him a centenarian, or if Aunt Harriet believes that she still looks enticing in low-cut dresses—why, then, such foibles up to the edge of practicality may do much less social harm than individual good for Harry and Harriet. As to the propensity of the aging for cants and cults, let us remember that even great men in their last years professed some fairly odd philosophies: the sociologist Comte began literally to worship the members of a deified Society presided over by his dead wife Clothilde; the aging cosmologist Eddington came to believe that God, too, was but a fellow-mathematician; Sir Oliver Lodge became an ardent Spiritualist; and Freud himself, facing his fatal cancer, symbolically mastered a putative "death instinct" by arbitrarily including dark Thanatos in his supposedly deathless metapsychology.

But wishful fantasies and self-aggrandizements are not enough; mundane social contacts and control are also necessary. If these are not furnished along constructive channels, the aged may retreat to querulous dependencies, and in a sense demand indulgent baby sitters for their second childhood. In contrast, if they are given continued opportunities to exercise their remaining occupational and social skills, the cycle of familial disruption and parasitism may be long postponed.

This also raises the question of mental hygiene for the later years. Obviously, one way to avert the empty isolation of old age is to develop, while still young, a versatility of interests, techniques and satisfactions that can be continued throughout life. Literature, music, art, philosophy—these are perennial joys, and almost independent of retained manipulative skills. Broad experience in itself may also become a commodity the marketability of which does not depreciate: the ancient mariner who loves the seas and still knows the proper trim and rig of a boat invites the respect and company of ship lovers of all ages. And without undue cynicism it may also be said that a certain rugged expectation of and tolerance for disappointment and even injustice is another asset to be acquired long before the senium in this, not quite best of all possible worlds.

As may now be inferred, then, the therapy of what was formerly called the senile patient is, whenever possible, best conducted where the oldster can at least in part retain his place as a senior citizen still valued by his community. Indeed, this attitude appears also in the unique filial trans-ference-counter-transference relationships (or, in Moreno's more concise term, the *tele*) necessary in individual psychotherapy, in that the aged like to picture the therapist or social worker not as a loved or feared parent-figure, but as a dutiful son or daughter properly devoted to their interests. But grown sons and daughters don't question, let alone imprison, their parents; instead, they visit them at home, bringing presents, and are rewarded by advice and benedictions. Hence the many advantages of tact-fully arranged family care plans, as opposed to even the cleanest Homes for the Incurable Aged—as balanced also, however, by a gentle but firm and seasoned supervision of bright young Case Workers eager to treat everyone—including poor doddering Mr. and Mrs. Methuselah—at a Deeper Level.

Nor need the prognosis be as guarded as this might imply; on the contrary, a quite satisfactory degree of rehabilitation is often possible. I remember a patient who, before his retirement at 65, had been very successful as the owner of a string of cigar factories. After half a decade of idleness or aimless travel, he had begun to drink, gamble and—perhaps with not altogether unconscious intent—"disgrace his children" with various escapades until they almost literally dumped him in my office. My therapy was simple: I abjured the role of parole officer or preacher, and told him that, though he was always welcome he need never visit my office unless he really wished to. However, I was interested in the social implications of his "pioneer contributions to American Industry"—particularly as to how he had eliminated marginal labor by substituting machines for cigar-rolling Puerto Ricans. This encouraged him to give me quite a number of instructive lectures on various topics, during which he evolved a plan for starting a string of little tobacco counters in downtown buildings which were to feature the products of the various factories that still bore his name. Once he started on this project he was, even at the age of 75 and almost until his death 8 years later, a sometimes forgetful and fretful, but mostly alert, active, reasonably self-restrained, certainly quite likeable, and undoubtedly happier old man.

INSTITUTIONAL CARE

But if institutional control does become necessary, let us change its rationale from total custody to hospital provisions for relieving the family and the community of the most burdensome aspects of caring for their aged while yet retaining their extra-mural contacts insofar as possible. Methods for this have been quite well worked out in England by Cosin, in Montreal by Cameron and in various other places along the following lines: The family is assured that in case of emergency they have somewhere to take Gramps or poor old Aunty, instead of having to nurse them the rest of their lives. Indeed, the family can be sure that during episodes of illness, or even if they simply want a holiday, they will have some place to leave the oldsters. This relief can range from 2 or 3 hours a day through a few days a week, to total in-patient care for several months when absolutely necessary—but never with the intent of "terminal commitment." By this means the community's conscience is neither overstrained nor lulled; and the family, under this covert surveillance, cheerfully resumes its lightened obligations.

But such an institution must be organized along special lines. There must be a diagnostic unit in which the physician, psychiatrist, psychologist and social worker collaborate in clarifying and modifying favorably the medical, psychodynamic and social factors in the patient's behavior. According to current statistics, 9 out of 10 of the aged so hospitalized, if given appropriate medical care, can be returned within 2 or 3 weeks to their families, free of the toxic delirious reactions that had been mistaken for senile deterioration. Patients who must remain longer are sent to a Continuous Treatment Unit, and then to a Rehabilitation Section or—in remarkably few cases—to a small ward where chronic bedfast patients are kept. But it is the Day Hospital that is the most important aspect of this new institution. Here are provisions for physiotherapy, occupational therapy and for transportation of the patient at optimal intervals both to the hospital and back to his family. The goal is, indeed, almost the minimum number of inactive hours: even if the patients are doing nothing better than whittling and sanding tongue depressors out of old orange crates, they are proudly accomplishing something they know is useful. Hours of idleness or unsupervised "group discussion" are avoided since they become no more than periods of boredom, spite and squabble. There is also a "night hospital" (without the necessity of a doctor or a nurse in residence) for those who can be maintained at outside work and simply come in in the evening and stay overnight. Finally, there are group day-and/or-night units of 8 or 9 rooms, where a kind of *esprit de corps* is built around one meal a day and various group activities. Here the old people generally run the organization and live as a little community with minimal protection and provisions by the state. All in all, such geriatric clinics and hospitals will differ markedly from the huge custodial institutions we are still erecting in this country. They will require fewer dollars, but greater medical skill, intelligent social work and a great deal of familial reorientation and community education—and, let us add, psychiatric competence of a higher order.

BIBLIOGRAPHY

BETTAG, O. L., SLIGHT, D., WENIG, P. W. AND SORENSEN, W. H.: Mental illness in the aged population. *Ill. Welfare Bulletin,* p. 15, March, 1956.

BOWMAN, K. M.: Mental adjustment to physical changes with aging. Geriatrics *11*: 139-145, 1956.

COMFORT, A.: The Biology of Senescence. New York, Rinehart, 1956.

ENGLE, E. T. AND PINCUS, G. (eds.): Hormones and the Aging Process. (Proceedings of a conference held at Arden House, Harriman, N.Y., 1955). New York, Academic Press, 1956.

FEDERAL COUNCIL ON AGING: J.A.M.A. *161*:16, 1956.

GITELSON, M.: The emotional problems of elderly people. Geriatrics *3*:135, 1948.

HOEBEL, E. A.: The Law of Primitive Man. Cambridge, Harvard University Press, 1954.

KAPLAN, O. J.: Mental Disorders in Later Life. (2nd ed.) London, Oxford University Press, 1956.

MASSERMAN, J. H.: Principles of Dynamic Psychiatry. Philadelphia, Saunders, 1946.

———: Practice of Dynamic Psychiatry. Philadelphia, Saunders, 1955.

SHINDELL, S. AND COMFIELD, E.: Aged in Connecticut state mental hospitals. J.A.M.A. *160*:1121, 1956.

SPARER, P. J. (ed.): Personality, Stress and Tuberculosis. New York, International Universities Press, 1956.

Part IV: SCHOOLS and TRENDS
in PSYCHOTHERAPY

Rankian Will or Dynamic Relationship Therapy*

OTTO RANK HAS BEEN for many years at once one of the most controversial and influential figures in modern psychotherapy. This is not only because of his special relation to Freud and the early psychoanalytic movement, but also because of the significance of his many contributions to and departures from orthodox psychoanalysis. An innovator and pioneer in various areas of theory and therapy, Rank was a forerunner in the development of what has recently come to be known as "short-term psychotherapy" and "client-centered therapy," as well as in the recent attempts to interrelate psychoanalysis and cultural studies, popularized at the present time in terms of the "culture-and-personality" approach to psychological and psychotherapeutic problems.

During his very active career, Rank was in close professional association not only with Freud himself for twenty years but also with some of the most prominent American as well as European analysts, educators, and social workers. He analyzed many of the modern leaders in these fields. Through them, as well as through his own many-sided professional activities, he influenced thought and practice markedly.

In this country Rank has had a special vogue, having early become interested in the application of his views in the field of social work, since this provided for a more socially-oriented type of therapy. A recent publication, "A Comparison of Diagnostic and Functional Case Work Concepts" (1950), published by the Family Service Association of America, highlights the importance of his position in this expanding field as the chief rival of the more orthodox Freudian position. Both directly and indirectly, his influence is also prominent in other fields close to analytic therapy: counseling,

*In the case of Rank, more so than in the case of most psychotherapists, it is necessary to present his views in historical perspective, for such was the course of their development and Rank's method of specifying them that their special significance is most easily reflected in this manner. For this reason, a brief historical sketch is included in this article.

132

psychotherapy, education, guidance, various areas of group and community work and other therapy-related areas of professional endeavor.

Background and Early Work

Rank joined the first Freudian circle when he was still a student and barely out of his teens. Freud himself documents the importance of the event when he notes that already at this time Rank presented him with a manuscript "which showed very unusual comprehension" and when he further states that "the little society acquired in him a zealous and dependable secretary and I gained in Otto Rank a faithful helper and co-worker."*

Under Freud's guidance and sponsorship, Rank became a prominent and favored figure in the psychoanalytic movement both locally in Vienna and on the international scene. In addition to producing a series of brilliant publications dealing with the wider aspects of psychoanalysis in the fields of literature, art, and mythology, he was secretary of the Vienna group; he edited two important psychoanalytic journals; he collaborated with other leaders in the field, notably Sachs and Ferenczi; he was director of the International Psychoanalytic Institute; he was a valued member of the Freudian inner circle, organized by Freud for the protection of psychoanalysis; and in general he was regarded as one of the most promising younger figures on the psychoanalytic horizon.

Commenting on Rank in this connection, Hanns Sachs said, "For many years Rank had been Freud's trusted assistant, collaborator, disciple, and friend, bound to him by the strongest ties of allegiance, gratitude, and communion of thought. Freud appreciated highly his restless energy and sharp intelligence; he had done everything in his power to make Rank's way through life smooth and to bestow on him a leading part in the psychoanalytic movement."†

However, around 1920, Rank was becoming increasingly restless. Psychoanalysis was hardening into a standardized procedure. Instead of the inventive and creative adventure it had been in the early years, it was increasingly taking form as a routine technique of constantly lengthening duration and consequently restricted clientele. It was a situation of general concern but, in the case of Rank, it also ran counter to his artistic temperament and his developing view of the central importance of creative flexibility in the therapeutic process. Seeking to remedy the situation, Rank began to search out lines of experimentation and innovation in therapy, connected

*Sigmund Freud: Collected Papers, Vol. I. London, Hogarth Press, 1927, p. 307.
†Hanns Sachs: Freud, Master and Friend. Cambridge, Harvard University Press, 1944. P. 149.

with the troubling time factor, the related therapeutic problems of activity and passivity, and other such technical issues.

As long as these experimental innovations remained on the level of technical consideration, they were more or less tolerated and even commended by some. But when Rank also began to develop the theoretical implications of his therapeutic innovations, controversy broke loose from the side of the defenders of orthodox doctrine and procedure. Rank nevertheless continued with the documentation and elaboration of his views in the spirit of all his previous work; they were intended to be part of the general body of developing psychoanalytic theory and practice. In 1924, he published his "Trauma of Birth," in which he finally elaborated his new insights in wide scope and applied them in a variety of connections in the areas of theory and therapy. Although the volume was dedicated to Freud and presented Rank's views within the framework of psychoanalytic doctrine, the book created a sensation in psychoanalytic circles, for it appeared to be in conflict with the established scheme of psychoanalytic thought and supposedly challenged its basic foundation.

As so frequently happens in such situations, Freud himself was less disturbed by Rank's deviation than some of his followers. For a time Freud even tried to mediate between Rank and his critics in order to preserve harmony in the movement. But so threatened did some in the group feel that even Freud could not control the situation, and eventually the drama of painful separation experienced earlier with Adler and Jung was repeated with Rank.

The result was a regretful parting of the ways between the two. Rank left Vienna and transferred his center of operations first to Paris and then to New York. Sad as this parting was for Rank, it set him free to pursue his further development unhampered. After a period of difficult readjustment, he set about in earnest to formulate his distinctive views in a series of works that represent one of the most instructive and thought-provoking chapters in the history of modern psychotherapy.

TRANSITION AND LATER WORK

What was the basis of opposition to Rank's "Trauma of Birth" and why was it supposed to threaten the scheme of established psychoanalytic doctrine? First and foremost, Rank introduced a mother-centered conception of fear and anxiety, insecurity and dependency (later also relationship) and gave it primacy over the Freudian masculine-centered doctrine. The birth trauma was primary, according to Rank, and the Oedipus complex was secondary. This difference seemed of such great moment at the time that it forced Rank to sever his official connection with the psychoanalytic movement. Then too, Rank argued for a more flexible, inventive and creative type of therapy which again seemed to threaten the hard-won established order. (It only goes to show how far we have traveled since those early troubled years, for both of these themes have since been incorporated into various systems of therapy without serious threat to any of them.)

At this time, furthermore, Rank did not directly attack psychoanalytic doctrine as such. He considered that his work would rather provide a firmer foundation for psychoanalysis itself. It was only in the course of later developments that his innovations and deviations gradually took on more general significance and eventually led to the formulation of a distinctive and characteristic therapeutic and theoretical position.*

Rank followed up his "Trauma of Birth" in quick succession with his "Technique of Psychoanalysis" (Vol. I, 1926; Vol. II, 1929; Vol. III, 1931) and his "Genetic Psychology" (Vol. I, 1927; Vol. II, 1928; Vol. III, 1929). These two works appeared simultaneously and were intended to supplement each other, the latter supposedly providing the theoretical foundation for the former. Also at this time (1931) appeared the strange-sounding "Psychology and Belief in the Soul." These publications all appeared in German and were later selectively translated into English because of developing confusion between Rank's classical psychoanalytic background and his new orientation which was gradually emerging in the course of these publications. Then followed directly in English translation "Modern Education" (1932), "Art and Artist" (1932), and, posthumously, because his life was suddenly cut short, "Beyond Psychology" (1941).

Our chief interest here, of course, lies in the "Technique of Psychoanalysis," which incidentally is also the most revealing of Rank's publications from the standpoint of his struggle to free himself from the restrictions of his old background and to supplant it with an orientation more in line with his new insights and interests. The rest of this discussion will therefore be confined to an analysis of this important psychotherapeutic work.

When the English translation of the "Technique of Psychoanalysis" was under consideration, Rank was no longer content to keep "psychoanalysis"

---

*Rank's position is both practically and historically important, for in many respects it happened to be in the line of later development. Besides the patient, for example, and the process of therapy, it brought the therapist and therapeutic situation into prominence as factors of importance for consideration and study. It also placed emphasis on ego psychology and on the integrative approach to the individual-society relationship. (Clara Thompson: Psychoanalysis, Evolution and Development. New York, Hermitage House, 1950. Pp. 15, 106, 171 ff. Cf. Fay B. Karpf: The Psychology and Psychotherapy of Otto Rank. New York, Philosophical Library, 1953. Pp. 51-52, 60-61, 68 ff., 101 ff.)

as a designation for his new viewpoint and position. He was also no longer interested in technique in the narrow sense, which he felt was developing in the orthodox psychoanalytic group. Instead, he wished to emphasize "A Philosophy of Helping." Accordingly, volumes II and III were translated under the title "Will Therapy," with the subtitle "An Analysis of the Therapeutic Process in Terms of Relationship." The first volume Rank refused to have translated at all, for he now considered it too much in the tradition of his psychoanalytic background to do justice to his new outlook and perspective.*

Psychotherapy—Distinctive Views and Innovations

As already suggested, Rank disapproved of attempts to characterize his therapeutic position in narrow technical terms taken out of context of his more general theoretical and therapeutic orientation. That is why he shifted his interest from a "technique" to a "philosophy of helping." It is possible, however, to epitomize his basic frame of reference—as he eventually did himself—in terms of the two central concepts featured in the English translation of his "Technique," namely, will and relationship.

Will is the theoretical concept which he adopted to offset Freud's increasingly atomistic, mechanistic, deterministic, and pessimistic outlook on human nature, personality, and conduct.† And relationship is his therapeutic translation of his earlier biologically-oriented trauma of birth theory, now presented on the psychological, social, and symbolic levels on the basis of his intensive analysis of the dynamics of the therapeutic process and the interaction of patient and therapist in the setting of the therapeutic situation.

It is clear from this basic frame of reference that Rank, even in his final formulations, never really intended to separate completely from Freud. Rather, he sought to translate psychoanalytic thought into more acceptable terms from the standpoint of his positive interest in culture and creativity and his basic orientation in the psychological and social sciences in contrast to the biologic and physical science orientation of Freud's thinking. The two "observed facts," the "starting points" which Freud made the criterion

---

*The same was true of his "Genetic Psychology," of which only the third volume appeared in book form in English translation as "Truth and Reality." Volume II appeared as an article in the *Psychoanalytic Review.*

†Rank termed Freud's one-sided libido theory of human nature a developing "philosophy of despair" ending in the concept of the "death instinct." He was the only one among the earlier deviants to challenge Freud's instinct conception. (Clara Thompson, *Ibid.,* pp. 15, 171-74 ff.) In this he has of course been followed by some of the more recent neo-Freudians.

of psychoanalysis remain:* will instead of resistance; relationship instead of transference. These translations of the foundation stones of psychoanalysis were his attempts to bring psychoanalytic doctrine into line with modern developments in the psychological and social sciences—his attempt to arrive at what he himself termed a *social* psychology, in contrast to Freud's *biological* psychology.

Both Freud and Rank started out in their formulation of basic theory from observation of "resistance" in the therapeutic situation. Freud arrived at the theory of repression and the associated instinct doctrine from these observations. Rank came to the theory of will. As used by Rank, will is an expression of unified personality in its creative, self-directive and individual-society interrelated aspects and as such is opposed to the reductive, departmentalized, libido-dominated and individual-society contrasted aspects of Freudian theory. This highlights the difference between the two viewpoints insofar as Rank's later position and deviation from Freudian theory are concerned. It is a difference which runs through the entire pattern of Rank's later thinking and is constantly reflected in both his theory and therapy.

With the foregoing as necessary background, we can now outline some of the more specific features of Rank's psychotherapy.

1. According to Rank's view, psychotherapy is to be understood primarily in terms of growth and development, rather than disease and cure. It is essentially a process of patient-therapist relationship in which the therapist in his role as helper is engaged in mobilizing the patient's "creative will impulse" for positive, constructive, and creative self-realization.

Within the framework of this conception, the following departures are notable:

2. His emphasis on emotional dynamics and, more specifically, on

---

*Freud stated in this connection, "Any line of investigation, no matter what its direction, which recognizes these two facts (the facts of transference and of resistance) and takes them as the starting-point of its work may call itself psychoanalysis, though it arrive at results other than my own." (Collected Papers [London, Hogarth Press, 1927] Vol. I, p. 298.) In this formal sense, at least, but also because of his method of presentation, Rank's views remained close to the issues of psychoanalysis and his therapeutic innovations were consequently a more direct challenge to its procedure than those of other deviants. For example, they have continued to agitate the field more directly than those of Adler and Jung. For this reason, Rank remained for years the most popular target for orthodox psychoanalytic defensive criticism, until the rise into prominence of the more recent neo-Freudian positions, particularly the critical psychoanalytic views of Karen Horney, as outlined in her new "Ways in Psychoanalysis" (New York, W. W. Norton & Co., 1939).

"experiencing" in the therapeutic situation, in contrast to instruction, recall, making conscious, giving insight by interpretation, and the like.*

3. His orientation of the therapeutic process in the "present," especially in reference to the therapeutic situation, in contrast to the Freudian concentration on the "past," especially the infantile past.

4. His concern with what is "new" in the therapeutic situation, in contrast to the Freudian interest in infantile reproductions and behavior repetitions.

5. His shift of attention from specific content, that is, from reliving experiences in detail, to the forms or patterns of reaction, in his terms, to the "algebra" in contrast to the "arithmetic" of the situation.

6. His use of the special devices of the "time limit" and "end-setting" as steps toward securing control of the separation problem and the termination phase of therapy. Experimentation with these devices and the associated problems of activity and passivity were the original source of his deviation from orthodox procedure. In due course these devices led to a shortened form of analytic therapy which then became one of the identifying features and most controversial aspects of his procedure.

7. Most of all, Rank stressed the positive, constructive, and creative handling of the patient-therapist relationship in the therapeutic situation.

Constantly, in this connection, he stressed the importance of adapting the therapeutic situation to the unique and individual needs of each patient. The process, according to him, must be patient-centered, not therapist-centered; it must be flexible, adaptable, alert to the new and unexpected— a genuinely creative experience for both patient and therapist. Eventually, if the task is successfully carried out, the patient will reach a point when he will be ready to dispense with the artificial assistance of the therapeutic situation. Thus, he will determine the natural ending of the process, not in terms of preconceived content as in orthodox psychoanalysis, but in terms of the dynamics of the situation and the developing need of the patient for self-determining independence and self-directive creative expression.

It has been argued that this is a highly idealized view of therapy. This Rank readily admitted. It is a goal toward which to strive and is realizable in greater or less degree depending on the particulars of the situation and personalities involved. In essence, however, it is a view which has a special appeal to non-authoritarian therapists who respect patients as self-reliant and self-responsible persons, as one is supposed to in a free and democratic society. And, interestingly enough, Rank also observed that his viewpoint was much influenced by contact with American patients, American thought, and American life. He considered that Freud's views were in this respect highly restricted by intimate acquaintance with only a single cultural situ-

---

*(Cf. F. Alexander's later "corrective emotional experience."—Ed.)

ation, and that chiefly in its pathologic aspects, which he nevertheless constantly sought to generalize and universalize.

This point touches on the complicated problems of cultural and psychological relativism, which it is impossible to discuss in this brief article. Also, and for the same reason, Rank's personality theory, which essentially corresponds to the distinctive features of his psychotherapy, along with his view of neurosis as frustrated or inhibited creativity, have been omitted from specific consideration. Again, Rank's socio-culturally integrative view has barely been touched upon, even though this aspect of therapy has become increasingly prominent in the light of the present inter-disciplinary approach in the behavioral sciences, including particularly the field of psychotherapy.*

---

*These points are considered in various connections in Fay B. Karpf, *Ibid.,* pp. 64 ff., 90 ff., 110-111.

BIBLIOGRAPHY AND NOTES

RANK, O.: Will Therapy, An Analysis of the Therapeutic Process in Terms of Relationship. Trans. Jessie Taft. New York, Knopf, 1936.

——: Truth and Reality, A Life History of the Human Will. Trans. Jessie Taft. New York, Knopf, 1936.

(Rank's own presentation of the essentials of his psychotherapeutic position. These two volumes also appear together as a single volume under the title Will Therapy and Truth and Reality: New York, Knopf, 1947.)

KARPF, F. B.: The Psychology and Psychotherapy of Otto Rank. New York, Philosophical Library, 1953.

(The authorized historical and comparative introduction (based on two previous publications) to Rankian theory and therapy, together with a biographical sketch and a discussion of the philosophical framework of Rank's views.)

ALLEN, F. H.: Psychotherapy With Children. New York, Norton, 1942.

ROBINSON, V. A.: A Changing Psychology in Social Case Work. Chapel Hill, University of North Carolina Press, 1930.

——: The Dynamics of Supervision Under Functional Control. Philadelphia, University of Pennsylvania Press, 1949.

TAFT, J.: The Dynamics of Therapy in a Controlled Relationship. New York, Macmillan, 1933.

——: (ed.): Family Case Work and Counseling: A Functional Approach. Philadelphia, University of Pennsylvania Press, 1948.

A series of publications by these authors and, under their influence and guidance, by associates is available which seek to interpret and apply Rank's views in various areas of therapy, counseling, education, and social work. The above are representative and illustrative.

Pavlovian Principles and Psychiatry

W. HORSLEY GANTT

MY THIRTY YEARS' WORK in the field of experimental psycho-physiology has been oriented toward the discovery of scientific laws: the principles at the basis of normal and abnormal higher nervous activity. The methods of investigation used by my collaborators and me have been chiefly, though not exclusively, those which I learned from Pavlov, generally referred to as the *conditioned reflex methodology.*

Although my major interest has been in the discovery of laws governing higher nervous activity rather than the application of these laws—the scientific rather than the practical—it is now possible to indicate some applications of what has been discovered.

When, at the turn of the century, Pavlov translated the desire for food, the subjective feeling accompanying the watering of the mouth, into a physiologically measurable phenomenon, he initiated a new epoch in medicine.

Most new discoveries do not find an immediate applicability, e.g., the law of gravity, calculus, electricity, magnetism, structure of the atom. Even in our own era of rapid spread of new knowledge, a decade or more may elapse between the discovery of the fact and its use, as was true with the sulfonamides and the observation leading to antibiotic therapy: that molds inhibit the growth of bacteria.

Because Pavlov began his research on the salivary gland, an organ whose physiologic function is of no importance clinically, an appreciation of the value of the discovery to medicine has long been delayed.

A new field should not have to justify itself by practicality: neither should the freedom from this obligation serve as an excuse for sloppy or unsystematic work. When, as often happens, I am asked what of use has come out of fifty years' research in this area, I am tempted to quote Alan Gregg, one of my early medical friends: "What is the use of a new-born baby?" Knowledge based on facts, i.e., real knowledge and not fantasy, will sooner or later find an application.

But now, with a confidence based on many facts that I did not have a decade ago, that there are applications which we can make today from these researches, I accept the challenge to indicate how a few laws of this new science may be of help in our mid-twentieth-century psychiatry.

One of the earliest facts that Pavlov demonstrated is one of the most

140

important to psychiatry, viz., the law of generalization. After forming a conditioned reflex to any auditory stimulus, e.g., a metronome, the subject reacts to a wide range of related auditory stimuli given in the same milieu. It is imperative to emphasize here the importance of the milieu in which the stimulation is given, for the environment is part of the complex stimulus. Unless special training is carried out (differentiation) to form the response to only one specific stimulus, generalization occurs—the subject reacts to all similar stimuli. In a normal subject the generalization is less extensive and fixed than in the psychopathic; the latter may give the same pathologic response to diverse stimuli, e.g., almost all auditory stimuli presented in the original environment. Furthermore, the pathologic response is not disturbed by those things that would normally be inhibitory, such as the presence of strangers in the laboratory. The pathologic dogs can be counted on to behave in the stereotyped pathologic way![5]

Generalization may occur even before conditioning has been established. When a certain mood or emotion or tension has been created, any[*] other sensory stimulus coming within a short period will evoke the same reaction as the unconditioned stimulus did. It seems that excitation has the property of drawing to itself any other unrelated, not too intense, sensory stimulus. Consider the following illustration from the laboratory experiment: when a hungry dog is fed, there is a rise of heart rate and a secretion of saliva during eating; if a tone, metronome or other auditory stimulus is given within a few minutes after the dog has eaten, but after the heart rate and the secretion have returned to normal, the auditory stimulus evokes a rise in heart rate and secretion which may equal in amplitude the response to the food. However, if the auditory stimulus is repeated several times in the intervals between feedings it loses its ability to evoke the food response until the dog has been fed again. This experiment differs from conditioning in that the auditory stimulus does not precede and overlap the feeding but comes in the intervals.[17]

Generalization of conditioning is universal in human beings, normal and abnormal. Every psychiatrist knows the importance of milieu, including people, in evoking responses in patients. A precise mechanism of generalization may be the basis of many responses. I shall cite some examples.[†] A patient suffering from depression complains of certain episodes in which she assumes she has been mistreated, and slighted. During the course of

---

[*]We have tried only auditory stimuli—I allow myself the privilege of "generalizing" to say *any*.

[†]Although I am well aware of the fallacy inherent in drawing deductions from a few instances, I submit that such deductions furnish a plausible basis for future more exhaustive and critical evaluation of the method.

the conference irrelevant and neutral matters are discussed. The patient, however, takes many of these stimuli as being directed against her in a specific way. When it is explained that these remarks are in no way personal, that they do not apply to her, she accepts this explanation, and is able for the time to see them for what they are. More complete therapy by the conditional reflex method would involve going back into the past of the patient to ascertain the first time the extreme hurt occurred, with its emotional upheaval, resulting in the paranoid attitude, this oversensitiveness, where, by the generalizaton, stimuli, irrelevant and without previous association, touch off the old emotion. Such examples are too familiar in psychiatry to require mention except to point out they are often explained by the law of generalization. Shakespeare expresses this law when he says, "It never rains but it pours."

Emotion—not only of violence (fear, anger) but also the state of the organism (hunger)—play an enormous role in determining behavior. The emotional state ("motivation") at the time of origin of the conditioning should be scrupulously examined. This factor is usually carefully controlled in conditional reflex experiments; emotional states are avoided as much as possible, or at least kept constant, except where we want to study the effect of emotion on behavior. If we satiate an animal we reduce the food conditional reflexes to almost zero, the cardiac component as well as the salivary.[5] In any application of laboratory-found facts and everyday life, we should bear in mind the state of the organism as well as the conditions of the experimental milieu.

There are many instances of a serious neurotic symptom being successfully traced, on investigation, to its origin and development according to laws which were worked out in the laboratory by the conditional reflex methodology. A homosexual patient I had several years ago experienced erection with orgasm and ejaculation when he was tied with ropes in a chair by his homosexual partner. This neurosis originated when, at about eight years of age, punished by his aunt by being tied in a chair, he had an erection and ejaculation.

Erotic fetishism was cured in a patient using the principle of conditional reflex extinction by Dr. N. J. Raymond in the Clinic of Dr. Desmond Curran at St. George's Hospital, London.[3,16] The patient, a 33-year-old married man, was referred because of his attack on baby carriages, and subsequent arrest by the police. He had slashed and set on fire two perambulators, scratched and cut or squirted oil on a woman's skirt and damaged another during the years 1948-1954. He spent some time in a mental hospital and with the police. The patient stated that he had had impulses to steal or injure perambulators and handbags since the age of 10, that the number of assaults was "legend," an average of two or three a week. He traced his sexual arousal to an original incident in childhood when he had disturbed a woman by striking the keel of his toy yacht against a passing perambulator, and at another time "he became sexually aroused in the presence of his sister's handbag." "Perambulators and handbags were for him symbolic sexual containers." Previous psychiatric treatment was unavailing. "A collection of handbags and perambulators were shown to the patient after an injection of apomorphine, given every two hours day and night, with amphetamine at night, food being withheld." The treatment was suspended after a week, when he was allowed to go home. On his return eight days later the treatment was continued. "He reported jubilantly that he had for the first time been able to have intercourse with his wife without the old fantasies." The patient has remained well for the last two years. In spite of Freud's view that overhomosexuality might result if the fetish objects were removed, this has not happened in this patient.

When we reveal the mechanism to the patient, giving him insight into himself, we implant a focus of excitation that continues to work therapeutically. The elaboration of this focus, its establishment from within, is what I refer to as *autokinesis*.

Obviously, not all neuroses and psychoses can be so easily and effectively treated by the application of simple conditional reflex principles. In numerous patients the situation has become very complicated and diffusely elaborated. Many of the symptoms involve relations with people, predominantly those in the family, occurring at an early age, as has been voluminously documented and delved into by Freud and his followers. Psychoanalysis has emphasized the subjective feelings of the patient, his associations coupled with those of the analyst and the elaboration of early childhood experiences. The parallel development applying the laws which have been revealed in the laboratory through conditional reflex studies could be of tremendous value in many of our psychiatric patients. But very little of this has been done.

Animal experiments have revealed some of the basic laws operative in psychopathology, such as those carried on by Masserman, Liddell and collaborators (Sutherland), Dworkin, Skinner, as well as a host of workers following Pavlov in Russia.[1,12,14] Disturbances in behavior similar to what we see in the clinic have been produced in a variety of animals, from the chimpanzee to the rat.

My studies of the "experimental neurosis" has confirmed Pavlov's classic experiments in this field, and adduced evidence that (1) stress in one physiologic system may spread to involve many other systems, especially the sexual; (2) the *person* may be a major factor and one of the potent conditional stimuli in the production of the neurosis as well as in the therapy; (3) there is a gradual development of symptoms and pathology—and, on the other hand, a positive development, an improvement—occurring from forces *within* the organism in the absence of the external stimuli (*autokinesis*). These principles will not be elaborated here because they have been reviewed elsewhere.[7,18] Several psychiatrists in both England and in the United States have noted the parallel between the symptoms in certain patients and those phenomena described by Pavlov under the term paradoxical phases (Leo Alexander, Howard Fabing, Wm. Sergent). A few, like Leslie Hohman, Edward Kempf and Joseph Wortis have successfully employed Pavlovian concepts in psychotherapy.

The human being is capable of vastly more elaboration through his enhanced capability for symbolization, especially through the means of language, than is the dog. Pavlov hypothecated that language constitutes a second signaling system erected on the basis of the primary conditional stimuli. Here, of course, is a tremendous field for investigation. Without doubt, words can act as powerful conditional stimuli. Grievous errors leading to both personal and international misunderstandings and misconceptions with their tragedies, arise from the false notion that the same word means the same thing for different people; each word is a conditional stimulus acquired under different circumstances.* Both the wealth of intercommunication and its errors rest upon this prodigious capability for symbolization in the human.

The principles which have been worked out in the laboratory from animal studies of the physiology of the higher nervous activity are applicable not only to the explanation of mental nervous symptoms of the psychiatric patient but to the explanation of organ neurosis as well, generally referred to in this country as "psychosomatic." The advantage of the laboratory approach is one of precise laws and relationships. The knowledge of the conformity of salivary secretion to the accidental experiences of the individual has been extended to cover a number of other viscera under autonomic control. Bykov and collaborators have shown that the kidney, the spleen, the thyroid, and many metabolic functions can be conditioned just as can the salivary gland or the muscular movements.[1] The reader is referred to his current book for details.

My own research in this field has been focused chiefly on the cardio-vascular system. My collaborators and I have demonstrated that the heart

---

*The situation has been aptly described by a famous character: "When *I* use a word it means just what I choose it to mean—neither more nor less" (Humpty Dumpty), to which Alice, with childish naivete, replies, "The question is, whether you can make words mean so many different things."[2]

adapts as quickly as does a muscular movement; the cardiac rate is specific for not only acquired excitation and inhibition[5,18] but to the *quantitative* meaning of the signal, i.e., the cardiac rate is larger to a tone representing 10 Gm. of food than it is to a tone representing 5 Gm. We have also recently shown that hypertension, like tachycardia, can be conditioned.[4]

Although there is a close parallel between the formation of cardiac conditional reflexes (the general supporting, perhaps emotional, basis for conditioning) and the more specific conditional response, there are also important differences. The cardiac rate conditions even more easily than the movement of a muscle or a secretion of a gland, but, once conditioned, the acquired cardiac habit is removed with more difficulty; it may persist for weeks, months or even years after the more superficial conditioned movements and secretion have dropped out (*schizokinesis*). Paul McLean, at Yale, using electrical stimuli in the gyrus cingulus, has confirmed our findings. We have a basis for the psychopathologic development of cardio-vascular disease, expressed in hypertension.[8,13]

An important chapter of the experimental study of behavior has been the recognition of characteristic patterns of reactivity depending upon the type of individual. These types have been divided by Pavlov into the four Hippocratic temperaments, and are generally referrable to an excitatory and inhibitory with a stable and unstable subdivision of each.[15]

My laboratory studies have indicated that by appropriate conditional reflex experiments we may determine to which group a given dog belongs, and having done this may predict which ones are susceptible to stress.[6,9]

My collaborators and I have applied the conditional reflex methods to the study of the human patient.[16] This method has been successfully utilized in the differential diagnosis between organic and psychogenic psychoses.[10,16] Another study currently being made by Gliedman has revealed the importance of the orienting reflex in anxiety and also the role of tranquilizing drugs in protecting the heart through the damping out of the cardiac component of this reflex.[11]

Thus, we have a basis for predicting organ susceptibilities, e.g., which individuals will tend to become hypertensive, and which ones will be susceptible to the development of neurotic and psychiatric symptoms. In such way may be laid the basis for a rational *prophylactic psychiatry*.[6,9]

REFERENCES

1. BYKOV, K. M.: Cerebral Cortex and the Internal Organs. (Trans. W. H. Gantt). New York, Chemical, 1957.
2. CARROLL, LEWIS: Through the Looking Glass. London, 1897.
3. CURRAN, DESMOND: Personal communication.

4. DYKMAN, R. A. AND GANTT, W. H.: Relation of experimental tachycardia to amplitude of motor activity and intensity of the motivating stimulus. Am. J. Physiol. *185*:495-498, 1956.
5. GANTT, W. H.: Experimental Basis for Neurotic Behavior. New York, Hoeber, 1944.
6. ———: Measures of susceptibility to nervous breakdown. Am. J. Psychiat. *99*: 1943.
7. ———: Principles of nervous breakdown—schizokinesis and autokinesis. Ann. New York Acad Sc. *56*:143-163, 1953.
8. ——— (ed.): Proceedings of the Pavlovian Sociaty, vol. I. Springfield, Thomas, 1957.
9. ———: What the Laboratory Can Teach us About Psychiatry. New York Acad. Med., 1957.
10. ——— AND MUNCIE, W.: Analysis of the mental defect in chronic Korsakov's psychosis by means of the conditioned reflex method. Bull. Johns Hopkins Hosp. *70*:467-487, 1942.
11. GLIEDMAN, L. H. AND GANTT, W. H.: The effects of reserpine and chlorpromazine on orienting behavior and retention of conditioned reflexes. South. M. J. *49*:880-889, 1956.
12. LIDDELL, H. S.: Emotional Hazards in Man and Animals. Springfield, Thomas, 1956.
13. MacLEAN, PAUL: Personal communication.
14. MASSERMAN, J. H.: Behavior and Neurosis. Chicago, University of Chicago Press, 1943.
15. PAVLOV, IVAN: Lectures on Conditioned Reflexes. (Trans. and ed. by W. H. Gantt). New York, International, 1928.
16. RAYMOND, M. J.: Case of fetishism treated by aversion therapy. Brit. M. J. *7*: 854, 1956.
17. REESE, W. G., DOSS, R. AND GANTT, W. H.: Autonomic responses in differential diagnosis of organic and psychogenic psychoses. Arch. Neurol. & Psychiat. *70*:778-793, 1953.
18. ROBINSON, J. AND GANTT, W. H.: The orienting reflex (questioning reaction): cardiac, respiratory, salivary and motor components. Bull. Johns Hopkins Hosp. *80*:231-253, 1947.
19. STEPHENS, J. H. AND GANTT, W. H.: The differential effect of morphine on cardiac and motor conditional reflexes—Schizokinesis. Bull. Johns Hopkins Hosp. *98*:245-254, 1956.

Trigant Burrow's Thesis in Relation to Psychotherapy

_____HANS SYZ

RATIONALE

BURROW'S CONCEPTS postulate an adaptive defect, which is socially patterned to permit a unified understanding of a large range of phenomena and dynamics involved in behavior disorders. The therapeutic principles he developed are closely interwoven with his main concepts and with the processes involved in his phylobiologic researches. Therefore, I shall first present briefly the essential features of his investigations.

1. As early as 1914 Burrow called attention to the social aspect of neurotic disorders—unrecognized disintegrative forces existing quite generally in socially accepted behavior.[1] He later suggested that these destructive undercurrents be investigated in their bearing upon neurotic disorder. Coincidentally, he developed the *principle of primary identification,* which postulates a preconscious feeling-mode concomitant to the organic rapport (prenatal and postnatal) between infant and mother (1917).[2] This preconscious phase, first psychoanalytically conceived in relation to narcissism, homosexuality and neurotic developments, was subsequently considered as the biologic matrix of societal continuity and spontaneous personality integration. Henceforth, phylo-organismic integration or *species solidarity* formed the background of Burrow's studies.[3] He suggested that with the growth of the cognitive function man came to apply image and symbol in an inappropriate manner to his total feeling experience. The resulting internal interference, rather than the introjected conflict between instinct and social prohibition, was considered by him the essential source of behavior disorder.

These early formulations, based on clinical and other behavioral material, were further developed in the course of the group- or phylo-analytic studies introduced by Burrow in 1918. In laboratory meetings composed of normal and neurotic individuals, as well as in the setting of everyday activities, socially disguised and corroborated hostilities, sentimentalities, self-contradictions, deceptions and defenses were submitted to analytic scrutiny, as they occurred in the immediate moment. Discounting distinctions of professional status and social roles, each observer included his own affects and their projections as part of the material examined. In this social self-

147

inquiry the effort was made to establish a basis of "consensual observation" (1925)[4] which, through mutual challenge of the personal affect-bias, made possible an increasingly objective approach to a socially constellated behavior defect (*the social neurosis,* 1926)[5] in which each student participated.* In this way it became possible to get in closer touch with the complex of preferential self-identifications within the group and within oneself.[6]

With continued analysis in the group-setting there were, among the participants, improved communication, less dependence upon parental images, and other constructive personality changes. However, interested as Burrow was in the rehabilitation of the individual, his dominant concern was the analysis of the normal reaction structure with a view to liberating constructive processes on a community scale from the imposition of disintegrative involvements.

Burrow's group analysis, vigorously opposed in many quarters, was one of the forerunners of the group therapeutic methods. However, it differs from them in that it emphasizes the investigative aspect, the observer is more consistently included as an active component of the adaptive deflection studied, and the goal, as indicated, is not adaptation to a social norm.

2. In connection with these studies Burrow suggested that an evolutionary miscarriage provided important roots for neurotic disorder and antisocial behavior in individual and community. He proposed that, coincident with the development of language, total feeling and organismic forces became attached to symbolic part-features of the environment, and word and gesture were endowed with artificial power. More important, a separatively conceived image of the self arose, and the isolated self-symbol came to assume an authoritarian position. A world of self-centered individuals was thus created in which each insists on his esoteric "right," and each child is trained to respond to right-wrong signals, which are used for personal advantage and distinction. The early omnipotent trend, reenforced by universal affect-projection, became socially systematized and is enacted in our daily interchanges, in language-usage and customs, and in the prevailing forms of socialization. This *affecto-symbolic* systematization, dominating the individual (Burrow's *"I"-persona*), embodies an organismic decentering which, with its bent toward hostility and threat of isolation, calls for constant compensatory adjustments. The obsessively defensive cycles thus set in motion in the individual and in social interaction further consolidate the image-dependent trend. A certain equilibration and lessen-

---

*In spite of the growing emphasis on "participant observation" and "consensual validation" in more recent psychiatric and sociological studies, it seems that the autistic bias of the observer as a participant in a socially systematized, self-referent situation has not yet been adequately considered.

ing of anxiety may be effected by these superficial adjustments, but the autistically biased, unstable structuring of the self and of "social reality," with its pathogenic implications, remains unaltered.

To present the situation in terms of basic human characteristics, man's ability to objectivate his environment and himself was partly diverted into hostile oppositeness or detachment, into an "I"-versus-"you" dichotomy. Constructive self-awareness changed into autistic self-preoccupation, creative self-determination into competitive self-assertion. The urge toward symbolic transformation of experience and its cultural transmission was deflected by the defensive use of the symbolic process. The capacity for responsible relatedness with the world and with others was impeded by image-dependent interaction. That is, man's evolutional innovations of objectivation and symbol-usage were not adequately integrated with his basic organismic forces and with his fundamental need for phylic cohesion.

From the background of field or gestalt concepts, individual and socio-cultural processes involved in the adaptive defect are seen as interlinked components within a total configuration which embodies a common denominator. Undue emphasis and dependence upon an autistically distorted self-image and its social projections are expressed in authoritarian and submissive enactments, hostility and guilt, and associated self-defensive maneuvers. We find in this image-fixation a root of disturbed empathy and communication, of inadequate identifications and sexual distortions, of self-affirmative social cluster-formations with their inter-group antagonisms. Thus, important aspects of neurotic phenomena, both individual and social, may be regarded as variations or secondary elaborations of a basic theme. The outcome in any specific situation may become complicated by accidental stresses and conditioning factors. But in spite of the resulting complexity and the tremendous variety of behavior expressions, Burrow emphasized the significance of an underlying dysfunction which is consistent in its structure.

3. Unremitting observation and sensing of the self-referent affect in the group analytic setting resulted in an impasse which could not be resolved through further analysis on the behavioral level. In this situation observation turned to physiologic sensations concomitant to the affect-blocking. Tensional strains became perceptible in the forepart of the head, the facial and ocular regions which make contact with the world through verbal and nonverbal functions. The internal differentiation of these local-ized sensations against the background of tensional patterns relating to the organism as a whole, involved an attentional shift. This shift was accom-panied by a marked decrease or elimination of self-referent affects and image-preoccupations and by an enhanced capacity for objective assessment of the socially structured affect-bias. Thus, the adaptive defect, previously

approached on the behavior level, was dealt with directly by the internal proprioceptive procedure and began to lose its stress and urgency. Henceforth, priority was given to the endorganismic discrimination of tensional patterns. Burrow distinguished between *cotention*,[7] with its direct contact with the environment, and *ditention,* in which attention is habitually deflected upon the preferential self-image and behavior is dominated by personal bias.* While the cotentive mode was first established in a relaxed experimental setting, it was found that with continued practice it could be carried into everyday activities and that it affected behavior and interrelational contact constructively. In Burrow's view the neurodynamic adjustments concomitant to the reintegration of the localized tensions within the total pattern form the physiologic substrate of the behavioral change. We deal here apparently with a withdrawal of emotive emphasis from symbolic self-constructs, which coincides with a more organismically oriented motivation.

4. The differentiation of the two attentional patterns with their behavioral concomitants cuts across the distinction between normal and neurotic reaction types and establishes an altered frame of reference with regard to behavioral health. Burrow's concept of an interference with man's bionomic or phylo-organismic development by a generic misuse of the symbolic function provides a consistent formulation applicable to the neurotogenic process in the various forms of human existence. The behavioral defect thus understood does not consist merely of general human characteristics which, under adverse conditions, lead to behavior disorder. There is evidence rather of a dynamic, self-corroborative configuration which in itself tends to generate antisocial and morbid action formations. This concept does not necessarily imply that we are confronted with unalterably set dynamic patterns. Rather, we may be dealing with an evolutional alternative or a developmental impediment that, although socially structured and reenforced, is accessible to scientific investigation and reintegrative measures.

From the basis of his observation of a generic maladaptive process, present even in "mature" and analyzed persons, Burrow concluded that "the psychopathologist must awaken to his wider function of clinical sociologist and recognize his obligation to challenge the neurosis in its social as well as in its individual intrenchments."[9] He felt that, without including a consideration of the social neurosis, understanding and treatment of the

---

*Instrumental recordings of various physiologic functions showed valid differences in respiration, eye-movements and electrical brain potentials in the two attentional modes.[8]

It may be evident that the attentional shift is not identical with E. Jacobson's Progressive Relaxation or with the Autogenic Training of I. H. Schultz.

individual's disorder must remain inadequate. The further development and utilization of the proprioceptive technique, in the setting of a vital awareness of the adaptive defect, was for him the basic task confronting behavior students and physicians. He hoped that other investigators and therapists would test the method he had found effective by applying it to themselves. This he saw as the first step in the extension of the therapeutic process. As the investigator in this field is necessarily impeded by his participation in the social neurosis, Burrow realized that group interaction is essential for developing the insight and effecting the attentional readjustment needed to activate an organismically motivated adaptation. He therefore looked forward to concerted research by groups of scientists and behavior students as a means of bringing about the reconstructive process.[10]

THERAPY

5. It is perhaps in terms of psychodynamics that Burrow's approach makes closest contact with contemporary psychotherapy. Having had the privilege of participating in the group analytic studies, I applied my interpretation of Burrow's concepts to the treatment of individual patients (neurotic and mildly psychotic). There resulted interesting modifications in my procedure which proved therapeutically effective. Of course, I realize that from the point of view of phylopathology treatment of the individual can lead only to incomplete adjustments; nevertheless, it may be of interest to indicate those features of Burrow's approach which I made an effort to include in the psychotherapeutic procedure.[11]

From the phyloanalytic background the patient is placed in a social field in which, as a responsible student, he explores a common human problem with the therapist. His difficulty is considered in relation to an adaptive dysfunction observable also in significant persons, in social interaction generally, and familiar to the therapist in his own behavior. Thus, various aspects of the patient's interrelational experience, for instance, resentment against authoritarian imposition and its sequels, are viewed as interdependent expressions of a general behavior defect in which a moralistically over-accentuated self-image plays an important role. Incongruities are brought to awareness, especially the discrepancy between a socially cooperative *appearance* and a self-centered undercurrent, a discrepancy interlinked with identical self-contradictions in commonly accepted behavior. But these destructive and dissociative aspects are always viewed as deviations from the organism's basic integrity.

In the course of this reinterpretation the therapist may refer incidentally to or imply his revaluation of his own self-referent trend. *This self-inclusion —if it is an experiential reality and not mere verbalization—removes important incentives for resistance on the part of the patient.* His fundamental value and capacity are endorsed not by verbal encouragement but by the operations inherent in the therapeutic situation. Although positive transference is not encouraged, a vital relationship with the therapist is maintained which makes it possible to consider from the start authoritarian-submissive involvements as they come up in the patient's history or in his immediate reactions. Their depersonalizing revaluation in the wider social frame assists the patient to sense his actual interconnectedness—both on an image-dependent and on a biologically symbiotic level—of which he had previously been unaware, not only because of his neurotic incrustation, but also because the general social prejudice favors self-isolating interpretations. In this way identification with the therapist's revaluating trend is facilitated and a beginning is made of a reorientation which at times leads rather readily to a decrease of hostility and guilt and to a reduction of associated defenses.

On this inclusive basis, then, it is often possible to enter quite directly, at times in the first interview, upon material that is close to important roots of the neurotic disorder. No elaborate explanations are necessary and there is no tendency to urge insight or to impose theories of behavior. Nor does the therapist follow a specific intellectually planned technique. Guided by the material presented and taking into account the patient's educational and cultural level, he calls attention to pertinent connections as well as to erroneous egocentric perceptions of self and world. It is left to the patient to decide how far the interpretation offered gives a more realistic picture of the factors involved. While the therapist acquaints himself with the patient's developmental and situational setting, there is no emphasis on biographical details. Rather, emotional reactions are taken up which are relatively accessible to conscious consideration but which reflect or are continuous with early unsolved issues. Early and current experiences are seen in their relation to a defective mode of adaptation which is observable in its social extension everywhere, including the therapist's own responses.

This socio-individual revaluation, with its far-going reassessment of accustomed self-appraisals, may arouse in the patient a reaction of startle or wonderment, but in my experience it has not caused anxiety, resentment or increase of guilt. The socially integrative, nonmoralistic understanding of what appeared to be disparate and incompatible tendencies is rather welcome and helps remove much confusion and anxiety. It assists the individual to make contact with the world also on the conceptual level. The increasing awareness or insight embodies a reconstellating experience in which the relation to the therapist is significantly involved. But the procedure does not necessitate the recall and analysis of early interrelational frustrations in terms of a transference neurosis. Rather, transference and countertransference phenomena, together with symptoms and defenses, are regarded as part manifestations of a more general internal and interindividual dysfunction. That is, they are consistently revaluated by therapist and patient as expressions of a pervasive self-referent deflection of attention which, with its internal decentering, is in my interpretation an essential cause of anxiety and protective measures. The inclusive reconsideration and reduction of habitual image-dependent attitudes apparently liberates organismically rooted connectedness which is expressed in the therapeutic interchange as well as in the patient's everyday activities.

In this setting, which facilitates spontaneity on the basis of a predominantly nondependent interrelationship, the patient may volunteer observations on past and current experiences and may bring up rather readily conflict material that previously had not been accessible to him. He often applies a revaluating attitude in his daily life during the time he is under treatment as well as later, when regular interviews are no longer necessary and the patient returns only occasionally for a checkup.

Obviously, great caution is needed in the approach to basic conflicts and causes of anxiety. Nothing could be more unwise than an attempt to apply the procedure here outlined as a mere intellectually learned technique. But if the therapist has been thoroughly trained to include his own tendency toward attentional deflection, no untoward effects should occur.

While the emphasis is on this socio-inclusive approach, other stresses and accidental or especially noxious conditioning are, of course, also taken into account. Dependency needs are not disregarded, but even in markedly disorganized or dependent conditions I have found the inclusive, revaluating approach of assistance.

On the basis of this procedure, I have often seen marked and lasting improvements in symptomatology and personality attitudes which at times occurred more rapidly than I had dared to expect. Not infrequently patients are surprised at their ready increase of security, objectivity, and better feeling-contact in their daily lives. This reorientation may be regarded as a withdrawal of emotional emphasis from parent-child dependencies and identifications, with a concomitant release or activation of inherent biologic capacities for integration and relatedness. But such improvements in personality function, while important for the patient and gratifying to the therapist, constitute of course only limited adjustments. There still remains the socially structured inadequacy within the normal reaction-average, the social neurosis, whose recognition and elimination was Burrow's main concern.

Burrow's thesis defines a reorientation toward which various forms of psychotherapy seem to be tending, though they do not include the full social implications of the therapeutic process. Whatever procedures are applied in working toward behavior reconstruction, the individual's rehabilitation involves a larger biosocial problem which awaits intensive research and application of appropriate remedial measures.

REFERENCES AND NOTES

1. BURROW, TRIGANT: The psychoanalyst and the community. J.A.M.A. *62*:1876-78, 1914.

2. ——: The genesis and meaning of "homosexuality" and its relation to the problem of introverted mental states. Psychoanalyt. Rev. *4*:272-84, 1917. First presentation of Burrow's *principle of primary identification,* which was more fully discussed in his Biology of Human Conflict (New York, Macmillan, 1937), Chapter IV, 66-103. *See also* J. T. Mac-Curdy's chapter, The Primary Subjective Phase of Burrow, in his Problems in Dynamic Psychology (New York, Macmillan, 1922), 188-205.

3. ——: The Social Basis of Consciousness—A Study in Organic Psychology. New York, International Library of Psychology, Philosophy and Scientific Method; London, Kegan Paul, Trench, Trubner, 1927. An early comprehensive presentation of Burrow's thesis.

4. ——: Psychiatry as an objective science. Brit. J. M. Psychol. *5*:298-309, 1925. In this and many other early papers Burrow discussed the need of a consensual basis of observation that would eliminate the distorting effect of personal and social prejudice.

5. ——: Psychoanalytic improvisations and the personal equation. Psychoanalyt. Rev. *13*:173-186, 1926. The term *the social neurosis* used by Burrow to designate the socially structured behavior defect which was discussed throughout his writings was also referred to by him as *mass neurosis.*

6. ——: The laboratory method in psychoanalysis, its inception and development. Am. J. Psychiat. *5*:345-355, 1926. Address as president of the American Psychoanalytic Association before the Ninth Congress of the International Psychoanalytical Association, 1925. Contains the first detailed statement regarding group analysis, first mentioned in 1924 (see ref. 9). *See also* Syz, H.: Socio-individual principles in psychopathology. Brit. J. M. Psychol. *10*:329-343, 1930.

7. ——: The Structure of Insanity—A Study in Phylopathology. London, Kegan Paul, Trench, Trubner, 1932. Introduces the term *cotention.*

8. ——: The Neurosis of Man—An Introduction to a Science of Human Behavior. London, Routledge & Kegan Paul; New York, Harcourt, Brace, 1949. See Appendix, pp. 353-392 for report on instrumental recordings of differences in respiratory, oculomotor and electroencephalographic changes in cotention and ditention. The full text of The Neurosis of Man is included in Science and Man's Behavior, The Contribution of Phylobiology (William E. Galt, ed. New York, Philosophical Library, 1953). The latter volume contains excerpts from a correspondence

Burrow carried on with men of science concerning various aspects of his thesis.

9. ——: Social images versus reality. J. Abnorm. & Social Psychol. *19*:230-235, 1924.

10. ——: Emotion and the social crisis—a problem in phylobiology. *In*: Feelings and Emotions. New York, McGraw-Hill, 1950. Pp. 465-486.

11. Syz, H.: An experiment in inclusive psychotherapy. To be published in the Proceedings of the American Psychopathological Association, 1955. This article contains many references to behavior studies in animals and humans corroborating the biologic basis of interrelatedness and personality integration. For an earlier report on the psychotherapeutic application of Burrow's concepts see Syz: The concept of the organism-as-a-whole and its application to clinical situations. Human Biol. *8*: 489-507, 1936.

"Daseinsanalysis" and Psychotherapy

MEDARD BOSS

Modern Psychotherapy in Need of a Basis

ALL PROBLEMS, ANSWERS AND RESULTING ACTIONS are invariably guided by the prescientific notions about the general nature and goal of man which each investigator carries within himself. No matter whether he is explicitly aware of his "philosophical" assumptions or whether he rejects all "philosophy" and attempts to be a "pure empiricist," the fact remains that such more or less hidden philosophical presuppositions, which are at the root of all science, are of fundamental importance. Up to now modern psychologists believed that their therapeutic approaches had found a sound basis in terms of their various psychodynamic theories about the human psyche. Freud thought of the human being as a telescope-like psychic apparatus; Reich, Alexander and Horney on the other hand attempt to explain all instinctual reactions in terms of a Total I or a Total Personality; for Jung the "Psyche" is a self-regulating libidinal system controlled by the archetypes of the "Collective Unconscious"; Sullivan conceives of man as the product of interactions between him and his fellowmen; Fromm and others speak of man as a Self molded by society. Yet all these modern anthropologic theories can't possibly warrant an adequate understanding of the psychotherapeutic processes. For none of them answers what ought to be the first and foremost questions: what would have to be the nature of such a "Psyche," such a psychic apparatus, such a human I or Self or total personality in order that something like a mere perception of an object and of a human being, or even something like object relations and interpersonal and social relations, be at all possible? How should a telescope-like psychic apparatus or a self-regulating libidinal system be able to perceive or understand the meaning of anything, or to love or to hate somebody? Even less can such anonymous psychic structures or forces develop a transference or a resistance in the course of psychotherapy. Yet all these phenomena are central factors for a true healing.

Martin Heidegger's "Daseinsanalysis" Revealing Man's Basic Nature

The eminent importance of the "Daseinsanalysis" in the sense of Martin Heidegger's fundamental ontology for psychology and psychotherapy lies in the fact that it helps overcome just these shortcomings of the basic anthropologic concepts of our psychological thinking, shortcomings which

156

until now actually kept us groping in the dark. The "Daseinsanalysis" is able to do so because its concept of man's basic nature is nothing more or less than an explicit articulation of that understanding of man which has always guided our therapeutic actions, independent of all secondary theories, although secretly only and without our awareness. Therefore, the dasein-sanalytic understanding of man helps us comprehend directly and funda-mentally why therapists *can* demand of their patients what they have in fact been asking all along, and why they even *must* demand it if they want to cure at all. In all their endeavors psychotherapists rely on the peculiar ability of man to exist in a variety of instinctual, feeling, thinking and acting relationships to the things and in social and interpersonal patterns of behavior towards the fellowmen of his world. The therapist tacitly counts on this human ability when he asks of his patient—and tries to help him achieve it by this or that psychotherapeutic method—that he knowingly and responsibly seize and adopt all his potentialities of relationships so that they no longer remain frozen in unconscious neurotic mental or physical symptoms because of early childhood inhibitions and repressions.

In order to gain real insight into these preconditions and this goal of all practical psychotherapeutic approaches, the daseinsanalytic thinking had to guard against approaching man dogmatically with preconceived notions about his reality, no matter how self-evident they might seem. It also had to avoid forcing man blindly, by means of such preconceived ideas, into categories whereby he would be nothing but a "Psyche," a "Person" or "Consciousness." On the contrary, the daseinsanalysis had to learn again to see man unbiased, in the manner in which he directly reveals himself, and, in so doing, it made a very simple but all the more significant discovery about the fundamental nature of man. It found that man exists only *in* his relations and *as* his relations to the objects and fellowmen of his world. In order to exist in such manner, however, man must intrinsically possess a fundamental understanding of the fact that something *is* and can *be* at all. Man's special manner of being-in-the-world can therefore only be compared to the shining of a light, in the brightness of which the presence of all that is can occur, in which all things can appear and reveal themselves in their own, proper nature. Man is fundamentally an essentially spiritual brightness and as such he genuinely exists in the world. As this world-revealing brightness he is claimed by the ultimate be-ness. If a primordial understanding of be-ness were not the very essence of man, where would he suddenly find the ability to acquire any special knowledge and insight? In fact each single comprehension of the meaning of all the different encountering objects and all actual dealing with them is possible only because man is intrinsically "brightness" in the sense of being a primordial understanding of be-ness. This holds true in an all-embracing way: it is the prerequisite for the possibility to be concretely touched and affected by something as well as for all emotional experience and all conscious or unconscious instinctual behavior toward something: without it there can be no handling and grasping of mechanical tools, nor can there be conceptual grasping of scientific matters. This also refutes the widely heard objection that the daseinsanalysis is relevant only for the psychology of the conscious mind. The intrinsic ability of the human "dasein" to be open to the world in this way does not just discover things which can be located somewhere in space and time. It also opens up ways for the direct and immediate understanding of beings, who, as human beings, not only are altogether different from the things, but who, according to their manner of being as "dasein," are in this world in the same way as I am. These other human beings are likewise there and together with me. Humanity, as a whole, therefore, is best comparable to the full brightness of the day which also consists of the shining-together of all individual sun rays. Because of this being-together-in-the-world the world is always that which I share with others, the world of "dasein" is world-of-togetherness ("Mitwelt").*

Just as the objects cannot reveal themselves without such brightness of man, man cannot exist as that which he is without the presence of all he encounters. For if he did not find his proper place in the encounter with the objects, plants, animals and fellowmen, in his ability to be with them, in his relationship to them, how else could man be in this world as such brightening understanding of be-ness? Even physical light cannot appear as light unless it encounters an object and can make it shine.

THE DASEINSANALYTICALLY ORIENTED PSYCHOTHERAPIST

This, then, is the anthropological essence of Martin Heidegger's Existential Analysis (Daseinsanalysis). Meanwhile, the term "existential analysis" has come to include a variety of philosophical, scientific, psychopathologic and psychotherapeutic schools of thought. Although they differ in their methods and goals, they are all derivatives of Heidegger's Daseinsanalysis. At least they received from it their initial impetus even if, as in the case of J. P. Sartre's philosophy, they have turned the real substance of the "Daseinsanalysis" into its complete opposite, namely, an extreme, subjectivistic Cartesianism.

The psychotherapist who lets himself be thoroughly pervaded by Heidegger's ontologic insight will not be able to derive new words or phrases from the daseinsanalyis for his psychopathologic descriptions. But he will win by it a tacit, but all the more reliable and all-embracing attitude

---

*M. Heidegger: Sein und Zeit. Halle, 1927. P. 118.

toward his patient and the therapeutic process. If the therapist really under-
stands that man is intrinsically a world-unfolding and world-opening being
in the sense that in him, as the bright sphere of be-ness, comparable to a
glade in a forest, all things, plants, animals and fellowmen can show and
reveal themselves directly and immediately in all their significance and
correlations, then he will have an unceasing reverence for the proper value
of each phenomenon he encounters. At the same time he will have become
aware that this way of being is the prerequisite that our destiny could
claim man as a being who should care for the things and his fellowmen
in the manner that all that is and may be, can best unfold and develop.
To exist in this sense is man's intrinsic task in life. How else could it be
that his conscience tells him so relentlessly whenever he falls short of fulfilling it? This call from the conscience and this guilt feeling will not abate
until man has taken over and responsibly accepted all those possibilities
which constitute him, and has born and carried them out in taking care
of the things and fellowmen of his world. Thus, he has completed his full
dasein and hence can consummate his individual, intrinsic temporality in
a good death. The daseinsanalytic understanding of man makes the analyst
gain so deep a respect for all phenomena he encounters that it bids him
to abide even more fully and more firmly by the chief rule of psychoanalysis
than Freud himself could, handicapped as he still was by theoretical
prejudices. The therapist will now, according to Freud's technical prescrip-
tions, really be able to accept as equally genuine all the new possibilities
for communication which grow "on the playground of transference," without mutilating them through his own intellectual and theoretical prejudices
and his personal affective censure. The daseinsanalytically oriented psychoanalyst will have a clear conscience if he remains unpartial to all unproved
scientific theories and abstractions and therefore refrains from attributing
sole and only reality to one kind of behavior—the instinctual reactions, for
instance—and does not consider them more "real" than all other potentialities. Thus, the danger of a so-called unresolved transference can often be
avoided. This therapeutic difficulty usually develops only because the
analyst has attempted to interpret and thereby reduce a new possibility
of communication which unfolded for the first time in the therapeutic
situation to a mere repetition of a relationship which existed earlier in life,
considering this one primary and causal. Therefore, this new possibility
can never properly unfold and mature and thus must inevitably remain in
its embryonic state, i.e., the "transference fixation." How different, though,
if one respects for instance the divine, which also reveals itself during psychoanalysis, in its divineness, just as one is ready to concede to the earthly its
earthliness, and does not degrade the divine to a mere product of sublima-

tion of an infantile-libidinal fixation, nor to a mere subjectivistic "psychic reality" produced by some supposed archetypal structure in the psyche of a human subject.

Of equally decisive influence on the attitude of the analyst is a thorough daseinsanalytic understanding of the fact that man is intrinsically and essentially always together with others. Heidegger's fundamental ontology helps us understand this in terms of a primary participation of all men in being the same open sphere of the be-ness. This insight teaches us that there is a being-together which is of such intrinsic and essential nature that no man can in fact perceive another even in the distance, without being already— through the mere act of perceiving—involved in the other's particular world-relatedness in some specific way. Thus, from the very first encounter between the therapist and patient the therapist is already together with his patient in the patient's way of existing, just as the patient already partakes in the therapist's manner of living, no matter whether, either on the part of the therapist or the patient, their being-together manifests itself for some time only in aloof observation, indifference or even intense resistance.

Already the knowledge of just this one essential trait of man provides an enormous impetus and a firm basis even for psychotherapeutic endeavors which formerly were a venture requiring an almost blind courage. For, only in the primordial being-together as it was brought to light by Heidegger's "Daseinsanalysis" we are able now to recognize the very foundation of all psychotherapeutic possibilities. Owing to this basic structure of man's existence, the most seriously ill schizophrenic patient, for instance, partakes in some way or other as human being in the wholesome mode of living of his psychotherapist; hence, such a patient's fundamental possibility of being cured by the adequate being-together of a psychotherapeutic situation through which he may recollect his true self again.*

Apart from the confidence which we derive from the daseinsanalytic insights for our practical dealings with such difficult patients, the daseinsanalytic way of thinking affords us also some important "theoretical" gain. For example, it helps us understand such central phenomena as "psychic projection" and "transference." Until now modern psychology could conceive of them only in terms of a tossing-out and carrying-over of psychic contents from within a "psyche" into something in the external world. Those concepts, however, are entirely unexplainable and can only be maintained on the basis of abstract intellectual constructions. The daseinsanalytic thinking allows us to understand these phenomena simply and with full justice to reality out of the primary, intrinsic being-together of all men in the same world.*

*M. Boss: Psychoanalyse und Daseinsanalytik. Bern, Hans Huber, 1957.
*M. Boss: The Dream and its Interpretation. London, 1957.

BIBLIOGRAPHY

1. BINSWANGER, L.: Freud's Auffassung vom Menschen im Lichte der Anthropologie. Bern, A. Francke, 1947.
2. BOSS, M.: The Dream and its Interpretation. London, Rider, 1957.
3. ——: Einfuhrung in die psychosomatische Medizin. Bern, Huber, 1957.
4. ——: Psychoanalyse und Daseinsanalytik. Bern, Huber, 1957.
5. HEIDEGGER, M.: Sein und Zeit. Tubingen, Niemeyer, 1927.
6. ——: Ueber den Humanismus. Frankfurt a.M, Klostermann, 1953.
7. ——: Einfuhrung in die Metaphysik. Tubingen, Niemeyer, 1933.
8. —: Was heisst Denken? Tubingen, Niemeyer, 1947.

Sociometric Milieu Therapy

ROBERT W. HYDE

TODAY, THE CONCEPT of looking upon the ward as a living community and studying how the relationships among people in the community can in themselves come to be of therapeutic benefit to the patient has been quite generally accepted.[1-3]

Methods are needed for describing the web of connections between patients and personnel in the ward and the more extended connections between ward members and the outside community through relatives, volunteers and friends. Methods are needed also for changing the interpersonal network in a way that permits the patient fullest utilization of his recovery potential.

A clear statement of how sociometrics applies to milieu therapy was made by Moreno in 1934[4]: "When the organization of a group is uncovered through the sociometric test, the contribution is revealed also which each of its members makes toward the mental or social disorder by which a particular individual is especially caught. This recognition of the community structure and the position of each individual within it can be used for the therapeutic ends through a form of individual treatment, through group therapy or through assignment therapy."

Lindzey and Borgatta present a short section on the application of sociometrics to mental hospitals and psychotherapy in the "Handbook of Social Psychology."[5] They state, "While still in an exploratory stage, the application of sociometric procedures in mental hospital settings and in conjunction with the therapeutic process has already led to some suggestive findings. The importance of interpersonal relations in personal adjustment, in addition to their crucial status in the treatment process, makes it understandable that sociometric measures have some function in these problem areas."

This presentation will focus upon sociometric and related methods applied to the mental hospital and upon sociometrically oriented milieu therapy.

THE HUDSON SCHOOL EXPERIMENT[4]

The background, method and exemplification of the application of sociometrics to milieu therapy was presented by Moreno in 1934 in "Who Shall Survive?", in his description of the sociometry of the New York

State Training School for Girls, Hudson, New York. Here, in 16 cottages, were housed 505 girls sent in from the courts from every part of New York State.

The study is directly applicable to the mental hospital. The needs and problems of these adolescent girls sent by the courts resemble closely those of the patients in a mental hospital.

Here was presented the therapeutic value of assignment by sociometric choice methods in the subsection Assignment Therapy. This is a form of sociometric milieu therapy which would be advantageous in mental hospitals. Some of the areas of application are mentioned here in brief:

"A housemother can embrace with her given emotional energy only a certain number of girls. . . . The limit of expansiveness has, thus, an effect upon the organization of the group through producing a number of girls isolated from the housemother either because there are too many in the cottage or because of 'faulty' assignments."

This problem of isolation of the patient is particularly pertinent and damaging when we consider the mental hospital ward. Like the housemother, the ward nurse has limited expansiveness as to the number of patients she can include, and problems tend to occur with the remainder.

Describing the familiar crush situations which developed between the adolescent girls, Moreno says: "Instead of driving one partner from the other, it is possible to use one girl as the therapeutic agent of the other, to utilize the relationship existing."

Immaturity similar to that of the adolescent is present in many psychotic patients leading to similar crush situations, not only between patients but also between patients and personnel. The same attitude usually tends to hold, that the existing relationship can be utilized to the end of developing the socializing capacity of both parties, while a rupture of the relationship would give further proof to the schizophrenic patient of his unsuitability for relating to anyone. The practice of breaking up these relationships seems to lead to progressive isolation of the patient.

Moreno mentions the ways in which home groups and work groups differed: "But when we applied the sociometric test to work groups in the community an additional factor had to be considered: materials, tools, machines."

This distinction between the home group and the work group is carried over in the mental hospital as a distinction between the ward (home group) and the groups for occupation and industry (work groups). The recreational group may add even a third constellation. The introduction of materials, tools and machines alters the situation to such an extent that many patients can find acceptance in work groups who otherwise were not able to.

There is a short section in the 1932 edition of "Who Shall Survive?" which illustrates how one can apply assignment therapy to the treatment of mental disorders. Although this specific consideration has many useful implications, I feel that the rest of the Hudson School Experiment is equally pertinent to the needs of the mentally ill.

SUBSEQUENT STUDIES

In 1940 Jenkins and Curran[6] made a study of "evaluation of the persistence of groups in a psychiatric observation ward" of 40 adolescents. They used a sociometric questionnaire and discussed a number of illustrative sociograms in relation to the known attributes of some of the patients.

In 1945 Shauer[7] studied "patients as therapeutic agents." The test results reflected the social hierarchy of the community, with the majority of the choices going to the few individuals in key positions. "In evaluating the contribution made by patients. . . sociometric testing showed this to be approximately 20 per cent of the total 'therapeutic energy' determined by this method."

He followed this in 1946 with a study of "social adjustment in a mental hospital community"[8] where he described briefly the method of sociometric study of a small mental hospital community.

In 1948 Hyde and York,[9] after exploring the application of conventional sociometric tests to an acute ward of psychotic patients and finding that a large number of patients would not respond to the questions of a sociometric test, developed an observational method to determine the social configurations and presented the data in the form of a sociogram. Analysis of the data from 43 of these observations gave important information on the "effectiveness of games in a mental hospital"[10] and later upon the variety of "factors in ward motivation in a mental hospital."[11]

In 1951 Maas, Varon and Rosenthal[12] developed a simple observation method designed to correct the limitations of the Hyde and York method so that it could be applied to more patients in larger wards; it had the shortcoming, however, inherent in both methods: it did not provide for sociometric choice.

In 1951 French, in an evaluation of "sociometric status and individual adjustment among naval recruits"[13] found 23 cases for whom neuropsychiatric data were available. For the 23 cases the median number of total choices received was five, in contrast with the median value of 9.4 for the entire sample. Six of these 23 were finally either discharged or hospitalized. These 6 showed a median of one choice received.

Studies at Boston Psychopathic Hospital*

Kandler made a sociometric study of three of the four wards of Boston Psychopathic Hospital.[14] Her early sociometric findings, which identified the usual patterns of attraction and repulsions in the wards, led to the development of an informal system of classification of patients in terms of the nature of the bonds that developed between them and personnel. The classification consisted of the following:

1. "Petted" patient—Chosen by five or more personnel. No negative choices.

2. "Liked" patient—Chosen by two, three or four personnel. No negative choices.

3. "Usual" patient—Intermediate patterns of choice not included in other categories.

4. "Ambivalent" patient—Highly chosen both positively and negatively to about equal degree (3 positive, 3 negative).

5. "Not liked" patient—Two or more negative choices, no positive choices.

6. "Forgotten" patient—No choice, either positive or negative.

Patients of each of these classifications were focused upon for special studies to determine the implications of their positions in the ward to their welfare. Methods were developed to alter favorably the position of the patient in the ward system.

Rapid informal and continuously applied methods of determination of the ward sociometric design are spontaneously adopted for everyday use. For example, patients forgotten by the nurse or attendant in a report are usually found to be the ones who are neither accepted nor rejected. The number of ward personnel reporting unfavorably to the head nurse about a patient is an indicator of how many regard the patient adversely. The ambivalently liked patient is one whom some personnel criticize and others defend. Patients likewise report their rejection of each other. *Utilizing this spontaneous flow of natural choices, the head nurse can make assignments to create a therapeutic milieu.*

Conventional sociometrics and the improvement of the unfavorable ward position of patients are combined as topics for group discussions in which the members of the group—for example, student nurses, attendants or the ward team of head nurses, students and attendants—state their attractions and repulsions for a patient and discuss the reasons for these feelings to the point that many are altered favorably. Where discussion is

---

*Renamed Massachusetts Mental Health Center in May, 1956.

difficult or ineffectual, psychodrama brings about a telling change of attitude.[15]

Several examples of this are given in "Experiencing the Patient's Day."[16] One consists of a series of meetings with attendants with the discussions focused entirely upon comparing which patients irritated which personnel. It became clear that they were not irritated by the same persons or even by the same characteristics of the same patient.

An important point came out: where personnel feel that the patient's disturbing behavior is entirely outside the patient's control, they tend to be tolerant and understanding. This suggested that the more personnel learn about the difficulties patients have in controlling their behavior, the more tolerant they will become.

Another discussion (page 184) showed the manner in which interpersonal attitudes become justified and reinforced when they are shared by others, particularly those in more authority. "Everyone feels that way about her. Even her doctor can't stand her." This reinforcement has been pointed out by Stanton and Schwartz.[2]

The disturbing patient (page 203) after discussion was often seen to be the one who was shut out of the ward community and trying to force an entrance. An epidemic of suicidal attempts (page 204) is discussed and the clique and leadership relations between the patients seen.

With most problem patients the personnel could see the extent to which the problem rested more in their own fears, hostilities and resentment than in the patient's behavior and the degree to which the patient's behavior was a response to those about him. Here also, where discussion failed to portray the situation, psychodrama was effective.[15]

Methods of resolving the negative choices for patients made by affiliate nurses were described in the paper "Altruism in Psychiatric Nursing."[17] "Careful scrutiny of common factors in the entire series of cases suggests that the factor of a more personal, interested and sincere expression of feeling between nurses and patients accounted not only for the resolution of 16 (of 33 negative choices) but was significant in the remainder."

Another study[18] stemming from sociometric findings was an exploration of the determinants of the empathy of student nurses for patients and how it altered in the course of their three months of affiliation. The reciprocity of friendly and unfriendly interchanges between patients and personnel was also scrutinized.[19]

Discussions of the reasons for choices of personnel for patients brought out the fact that one common reason given for positive choices was that the patient was "cooperative," "helps with the ward work." Common reasons given for negative choices were "doesn't get along with other patients," "breaks ward rules," "does not help with the ward work."

So much of the satisfaction of personnel rested on their ability to enlist the patients' cooperation in the ongoing life and work of the ward that difficulty in doing so became a cause for rejection of the patient. This led to an attempt to determine what was involved in the relationship of the attendant and patient in the area of authority and compliance.[20]

A study of an "outbreak of gang destructive behavior on a psychiatric ward"[21] showed the necessity of earlier identification of patient cliques, of the effect of fear or resentment of personnel upon any patient group against which it is directed; of the necessity for the physician to take the attendant's reports more seriously.

Kandler[14,22] found other common reasons for the positive choices of student nurses for patients, namely, that they were "friendly," "quiet," "easy to get along with," "does things for others," "patient is improving," "feels sorry for the patient," "has something in common with the patient." Several patients fell into the "petted" category of being the first choices of several personnel. This led Morimoto to her study,[23] in which she showed that "favored patients" showed the most frequent ward interactions.

However, experience has shown that the favored patient may also be injured by the favoritism through the hostile jealousy of other patients, through perpetuating his dependency and through falling out of favor. Perhaps we are just beginning to understand the special advantages and disadvantages of the favored patient. Morimoto made a similar sociometric study to determine how common interests and hobbies influenced choice or rejection of patients.[24]

In 1951 Kandler et al.[25] made a study of the acute female ward at Boston Psychopathic Hospital using (1) sociometric test; (2) intensive observation of interactions; and (3) spot check (interactions observed at one time) of a total of 316 such observations. These three methods yielded the following findings:

a. Patient interaction with personnel increased directly as the number of personnel increased up to 4 (on a 30-patient ward). Above that, personnel interacted more with each other, less with patients.

b. The affectivity of student nurses was more neutral than that of graduate nurses and attendants.

c. Nurses tended to interact more with single patients, the ward occupational therapist with groups.

d. Students' contacts with patients were usually of short duration; they interacted longest with each other. They often failed to enter patient groups even when it would have been more beneficial to patients if they had.

e. Ward social life was usually organized around one or more central figures who were connected as clique and had a tremendous effect on the ward society. The interaction rates of these central figures were highly correlated with the interaction rate of the ward as a whole and may actually have determined it.

The value of these findings to nursing education, supervision and ward management is apparent.

The influence of the central figures was such that when they were discharged from the ward, it left a tremendous gap in the ward society. The study of one such "ward leader," called Ruth Center,[26] is summarized as follows:

"The ward social life was highly organized about one central figure. The patient was a young, attractive female with a diagnosis of psychopathic personality, interested in other patients and ready to listen to their complaints uncritically. She and four other patients constituted a clique toward whom the great majority of 'choices for companionship' of the other ward members was directed. . . . After the discharge of Ruth and two clique members from the acute ward, a profound change occurred in the ward social organization. Although the number of isolates remained constant, the central figures were much less dominant in terms of 'choices for companionship' and a significant number of choices were directed either towards personnel or outside the ward population."

Patients who have lost the central (patient) figure who was their choice may select instead a responsive member of the psychiatric personnel who aids the patient by relinquishing this relationship when no longer needed.

In 1950 the morale of patients waiting for electric shock was studied by a sociometrically oriented observation method, and the tension of the situation was alleviated.[27] The situation was also explored repeatedly in sociodrama where personnel achieved insight into how patients felt about the staff's attitudes toward shock.[15]

The effects of nurses using craft and recreational materials on the wards was studied by Kandler and Moon.[28] Morimoto made extensive studies of the hobby, sport, art and activity interests of patients and personnel and how the pre-illness interests of patients influenced their hospitalization and whether they were responded to by personnel.[29-32]

An observational time sampling was used by Bockoven to compare the social behavior of patients before and after lobotomy,[33] while the occupational therapist also studied task application.[34] Ward occupational therapy was studied by a time scan method.[35] This was later refined to present a group of six patients with an opportunity to work together or separately at a stable number of tasks. Here the type of direction was graded from laissez-faire to ordering.[36] Technically, this was much in the nature of sociodrama. Although this was used primarily for the study of changes of patients from before to after lobotomy, it yielded information applicable to all task engagement of patients. Bales Interaction Process Analysis, a sociometrically oriented observation, and the evaluation of the occupational therapist were all used to evaluate the social behavior and performance of patients in this test.*

TOTAL TREATMENT (MILIEU THERAPY)

There are many barriers between patients and patients, patients and personnel, and between different classes and groups of personnel which limit their acceptance of each other. These barriers are not only those of locked doors separating the patients from each other and from the outside community, but of institutionalized attitudes that have become a part of the hospital culture which fosters non-interaction of personnel with patients and between patients. Sociometric milieu therapy at this time is largely concerned with the reduction of barriers to acceptance and with providing opportunity for patients to interact with and form mutually accepting relations with other patients and personnel.

When closed wards become unlocked the patient is given an opportunity to leave the ward[1]; the chance of meeting people who accept him is increased. When patients come together in occupational and activity areas more hours of the day, they have more opportunity to work together in a way that fosters their mutual acceptance. When male and female patients are together in these activity areas, the attraction of sex difference is a further leverage towards socialization.

Psychotic patients constantly encounter rebuff because of the inept ways in which they attempt to win acceptance. These unusual types of behavior are often those which were so unacceptable to the outside community that the patients were segregated in the hospital.

By providing special stages for expressive contact in the form of social events, occupational groups, psychodrama and group psychotherapy, as well as the constant stage of ward life, the patient can learn how others feel about his inept attempts to win acceptance and develop more effective means.

After Hotchkiss[37] studied the interactions of visitors with personnel and patients and saw there were many unnecessary barriers separating them, visiting hours were extended from 1 to 7:30 p.m. daily and the opportunity for association increased. This brought about improved contact between patients' relatives and hospital personnel, as well as with patients.

The ruptures of the patients' connections with the outside community are not only with his relatives but with all other people. By permitting young students, volunteers[38] and hospital auxiliary members[39] to work

*Chapters 5, 19, 20, 21 of Frontal Lobes and Schizophrenia, Greenblatt, M. and Solomon, H. C., Eds. New York, Springer, 1953.

throughout the hospital, the patient has an opportunity to come in contact with people who represent the outside community to him.

Just as contact with the outside community is increased by volunteers, students and auxiliary members coming to the hospital, so is it increased by patients leaving the hospital and making visits outside to stores, movies, museums, ball games, picnics, parks, etc. All this provides contact with the community outside the hospital that can be a substantial encouragement to recovery.

Patients were interviewed in groups where they were encouraged to express fully their feelings about the hospital. They grouped in collusion in anticipation of these discussions and formed a committee to write their grievances to the Superintendent. From this, Patient Government[40] emerged with weekly meetings in which the interested patients came together to plan activities for themselves, to determine how they could be of mutual help, and to collectively work with the hospital.

In summary, the combination of sociometric and other related social research, when applied directly to study and improve patient relationships, can bring about a therapeutic milieu. Such action and applied research affects all elements in the hospital, all classes of patients and personnel; it is equally useful in research, education, in patient care and treatment, and in bringing about a functional association of the hospital with the "outside" community, thereby becoming important in the preventive and rehabilitative areas.

REFERENCES

1. GREENBLATT, M., YORK, R. H. AND BROWN, E. L.: From Custodial to Therapeutic Care in Mental Hospitals. New York, Russell Sage Foundation, 1955.
2. STANTON, A. H. AND SCHWARTZ, M. D.: The Mental Hospital: A Study of Institutional Participation in Mental Illness and Treatment. New York, Basic Books, 1954.
3. JONES, M.: The Therapeutic Community: A New Treatment Method in Psychiatry. New York, Basic Books, 1953.
4. MORENO, J. L.: Who Shall Survive? New York, Beacon House, 1934.
5. Handbook of Social Psychology, ed. Gardner Lindzey. Cambridge, Addison-Wesley, 1954.
6. JENKINS, R. L. AND CURRAN, F. J.: The evaluation of and persistence of groups in a psychiatric observation ward. J. Social Psychol. 12:279-289, 1940.
7. SHAUER, G.: Patients as therapeutic agents in a mental hospital. Group psychotherapy, a symposium. Sociometry 8:394-395, 1945.
8. ——: Social adjustment in a mental hospital community. Sociometry 99:144, 1946.
9. HYDE, R. W. AND YORK, R. H.: A technique for investigating interpersonal relations in a mental hospital. J. Abnorm. & Social Psychol. 43:287-299, 1948.

10. HYDE, R. W., YORK, R. H. AND WOOD, A. C.: Effectiveness of games in a mental hospital. Occup. Therapy and Rehab. *27*: 1948.

11. HYDE, R. W.: Factors in group motivation in a mental hospital. J. Nerv. & Ment. Dis. *117*: 1953.

12. MAAS, H. S., VARON, E. AND ROSENTHAL, D.: A technique for studying the social behavior of schizophrenics. J. Abnorm. & Social Psychology *46*: 1951.

13. FRENCH, R. L.: Sociometric status and individual adjustment among naval recruits. J. Abnorm. & Social Psychology *46*: 1951.

14. KANDLER, H. M.: A Study in the Elements of Rapport. Thesis submitted to B. U. School of Nursing for degree of Master of Science, Aug. 1950.

15. GOLDBERG, N. AND HYDE, R. W.: Role-playing in psychiatric training. J. Social Psychol. *39*:63-75, 1954.

16. HYDE, R. W.: Experiencing the Patient's Day. A Manual for Psychiatric Hospital Personnel. New York, Putnam's, 1955.

17. HYDE, R. W. AND KANDLER, H. M.: Altruism in Psychiatric Nursing. *In:* Forms and Techniques of Altruistic and Spiritual Growth: A Symposium (P. A. Sorokin, ed.). Boston, Beacon Press, 1954.

18. KANDLER, H. M. AND HYDE, R. W.: Changes in empathy in student nurses during the psychiatric affiliation. Nursing Research *2*: 1953.

19. EICHORN, H. AND HYDE, R. W.: Friendly and unfriendly interactions in a mental hospital. *In:* Altruistic Love and Behavior, (P. A. Sorokin, ed.). Boston, Beacon Press, 1950.

20. HYDE, R. W., GREENBLATT, M. AND WELLS, F. L.: The role of the attendant in authority and compliance: notes on ten cases. J. Gen. Psychol. *54*:107-126, 1956.

21. BOYD, R. W., KEGELES, S. S. AND GREENBLATT, M.: Outbreak of gang destructive behavior on a psychiatric ward. J. Nerv. & Ment. Dis. *20*: 338-342, 1954.

22. KANDLER, H. M.: Problem-solving techniques and methods. Nursing Research *2*:79-84, 1953.

23. MORIMOTO, F.: Favoritism in personnel-patient interaction. Nursing Research *3*:109-112, 1955.

24. MORIMOTO, F., BAKER, T. AND GREENBLATT, M.: Similarity of socializing interests as a factor in selection and rejection of psychiatric patients. J. Nerv. & Ment. Dis. *1*:56-61, 1954.

25. KANDLER, H. M., BEHYMER, A. F., KEGELES, S. S. AND BOYD, R. W.: A study of nurse-patient interaction in a mental hospital. Am. J. Nursing *52*:1100-1103, 1952.

26. KEGELES, S. S., HYDE, R. W. AND GREENBLATT, M.: Sociometric network on an acute psychiatric ward. Group Psychotherapy *5*: 1952.

27. KANDLER, H. M.: Studying a problem in psychiatric nursing. Am. J. Nursing *51*: 1951.

28. ———: AND MOON, J. R.: Patient-participation in socializing activities. Nursing World *128*: 1954.

29. MORIMOTO, F. AND GREENBLATT, M.: Personnel awareness of patients' socializing capacity. Am. J. Psychiat. *110*:443-447, 1953.

30. MORIMOTO, F.: Socializing role of psychiatric ward personnel. Am. J. Nursing *54*:53-55, 1954.

31. KANDLER, H. M. AND MORIMOTO, F.: New clues to mental health: A comparison of skills and interest of patients and nursing personnel in a psychiatric hospital. Nursing World *1*:21-22, 1955.

32. ———: Nurse patient interaction as related to patients' pre-illness interests. Nursing World.

33. BOCKOVEN, J. S. AND HYDE, R. W.: Application of a sociometric technic to the study of lobotomized patients. J. Nerv. & Ment. Dis. *114*:95-105, 1951.

34. HYDE, R. W. AND WOOD, A. C.: Occupational therapy for lobotomy cases. Occup. Therapy and Rehab. *28*: 1949.

35. ———: Studies of technique and effectiveness of ward occupational therapy. Am. J. Occup. Therapy *2*: 1948.

36. HYDE, R. W. AND SCOTT, B.: The occupational therapy research laboratory. Occup. Therapy and Rehab. *30*: 1951.

37. HOTCHKISS, G.: The psychiatric patient's visitors. Nursing Outlook *4*: 1956.

38. HYDE, R. W. AND HURLEY, C. F.: Volunteers in mental hospitals. Psychiatric Quarterly Supplement *24*:233-249, 1950.

39. STETSON, E. R.: The role played by volunteers in a mental hospital. Am. J. Occup. Therapy *5*:203, 1951.

40. HYDE, R. W. AND SOLOMON, H. C.: Patient government: A new form of group therapy. Digest Neurol. & Psychiat., Inst. of Living xviii, 1950.

Autogenous Training[1]

I. H. SCHULTZ

THIS PAPER WILL ATTEMPT to elucidate the nature of autogenous training. In 1920, psychologically trained test subjects made auto-observations in hypnosis to determine whether normal subjects are capable of hallucination. The test was designed to ensure that the subjects were capable of giving information about every detail of their experiences. In all cases, the onset and the actual condition of hypnosis were featured by characteristic physical sensations which were described with great accuracy.

The first sensation to impress the auto-observer was a peculiar *heaviness,* particularly in the extremities, and a strange feeling of flowing *heat* which was compared, depending on previous experiences of the test subject, with the warmth felt under diathermy following an injection of Pantopon, etc. This heaviness physiologically corresponds to relaxation of muscles, while the warmth corresponds to relaxation of blood vessels.

The actual process of autogenous training consists of systematic and skilled instruction of test subjects in the independent performance of suitable training—in other words, autohypnosis.

The test persons are not submitted to hypnotic treatment in the usual sense. Instead, after brief instructions regarding the aim of the work, they are stimulated to train themselves. It has been found, in agreement with the experiences of critical investigators of hypnosis, that positive results are usually obtained with normal subjects, less readily with neurotics and never with excited mental patients. The test subjects are placed in a sitting or a recumbent position, free of mechanical tension, and are asked to close their eyes; they then concentrate on their inner self as intensively as possible. (Whether this is effected with the aid of optical, acoustical, kinetic or symbolic lines of thought is entirely dependent on the type of individual.) The patients concentrate on the thought that "the arm is very heavy" (the right arm for right-handed and the left for left-handed subjects). The concentrative formula "the right (left) arm is very heavy" (concentrative autorelaxation is the password in autogenous training; there is no question of autosuggestion) is repeated five or six times at a rate of speed suited to the individual personality. The aim is then interpolated ("I am quite quiet"), whereafter the subject concentrates again on relaxation of the extremity. The average subject reacts to the very first attempt, in that hypotonia of the training arm occurs. This can be demonstrated without difficulty by cautious elevation and dropping of the arm and by feeling the muscles; it can objectively be determined by assessing the motor chronaxia. The test subject should perform this training for a few minutes, and conclude with energetic, rapid flexion and extension of the training arm, deep breathing and subsequent opening of the eyes.

This first training is done by the test subject twice daily or, at the most, three times a day; it can be continued as long as it does not feel unpleasant. The subject invariably concentrates on the training arm. In accordance with the well-known phenomenon of psychological transfer, it is then found that, without any volition on the part of the test subject, the feeling of heaviness occurs more immediately and is more intense and also becomes noticeable in other extremities (generalization). In this manner the process develops, and the average subject is capable of attaining immediate heaviness in the arms and legs within two weeks. The subjects can perform this training alone at home and merely report by telephone if they notice something out of the ordinary.

It is not until after two or three weeks that they report again to the instructing physician, who then controls the result and gives directions as to the second phase of training. The first exercise must be repeated, with this addition to formula: "the right (left) arm is very warm." Like the heaviness, the warmth gradually becomes apparent in the training arm of the average test subject. It is not merely a purely subjective phenomenon but can be objectively measured. The radiating heat shows an increase of more than 1° C. (H. Binswanger, 1928), while the skin temperature rises 5-7° C., as demonstrated by Polzien in 1955. With continuing training the test subjects are increasingly enabled to control their vasomotor mechanisms. A good example is found in the case of a sportsman who was buried with his party under an avalanche of snow; his autogenous training enabled him to restore the circulation in fingers, toes, nose and ears, and he was the only one to be rescued without frostbite. The temperature training also requires an average of two or three weeks. The feeling of rest and aloofness associated with the heaviness is considerably enhanced by the temperature training. After autoregulation of the blood vessels is attained the activity of the heart is subordinated to relaxation and autoregulation. In a test subject with a normal pulse (76), immediate adjustment of the pulse to 44 or 144 was measurable without any associated change in respiration, emotion or other factors. This subject was capable of immediate regulation of the activity of the heart as such. This capability is demonstrable to some (lesser) extent in every trainee; in the above mentioned test subject it was objectively measured because it was unusually marked.

The heart training likewise requires two or three weeks, after which the respiration is included. In autogenous training this requires two or three weeks but it should be left to self-development. Via interesting by-roads this often leads to marked, lasting changes in respiratory posture which, in turn, intensify the results of previous training. Some singers, for instance, have increased their vocal volume by autogenous training.

A few particularly striking clinical applications should be briefly mentioned here. It has been found that autogenous training, among other adequate forms of systematic clinical treatment, has yielded remarkable results in the treatment of bronchial asthma. In these cases autogenous training may be used for a variety of purposes. In the first place—and this holds true for all patients suffering from these attacks—concentrative auto-relaxation and induced composure enable the patient to control the ever present anxiety with regard to possible recurrence of an attack. The deep organismic experience expressed in "I am quite quiet," which pervades all the regions of physical and neuro-emotional existence, affords a very real protection in these cases.

Autogenous training is equally valuable in patients in whom true infarction is followed by recurrent attacks of angina pectoris. It was found that patients with well established severe organic changes of the heart, but without marked neurotic alteration, could be freed from attacks by means of careful and consecutive autogenous training. As a result of training the physician was often confronted with another, new task. The patients confused the absence of attacks with organic physical recovery and had to be constantly warned against unwise actions and overstrain.

The technique of painless delivery with the aid of autogenous training was adopted at the Wurzburg Gynaecological Clinic (Prill in *Psychotherapie*, 1956.) It was found that judicious autogenous training yielded effects comparable to those previously obtained by alien hypnotic support.

Special mention should be made of a few among the many other possible applications. The autogenous trainee is capable of exerting considerable influence on otherwise involuntary reactions, and is able to control to some extent affects which flow out too violently; this performance can be described as a typical "muffling of the resonance of affects." On the other hand, the concentrative trainee is capable of intensive inner experiences at will; in this manner autogenous training can be used to stimulate, for example, artistic production. The trainee can also impress upon himself "formulae of intention" which automatically become active, e.g., effortless giving up of smoking, the taking up of disagreeable activities, the control of disturbing habits, etc. In the case of severe neuroses, autogenous training, while capable of alleviating separate symptoms, naturally does not penetrate to the heart of the matter, which can only be analytically approached.

Correct formulation is of extremely great importance in the use of formulae of intention.

Like all methods using exercises, autogenous training is also more fruitful and stimulating when done in *groups* rather than when practiced individually. In this respect it touches on the problem of group therapy so successfully elaborated by Moreno, preferably involving 12-30 participants and with careful selection, even larger numbers. The aloof individual is capable of greater impartiality and objectivity not only when he has to face external experiences and dispensations of fate but also in confrontation with other individuals.

However, it must be emphasized that autogenous training should be applied by physicians only and practiced only under their continuous supervision.[2]

REFERENCES

1. SCHULTZ, I. H.: Das autogene Training. Stuttgart, Thieme, 1956.
2. *See* Psychotherapie, Vierteljahrschrift fur aktiv-klinische Psychotherapie, ed. I. H. Schultz (Huber, Berne).

Hypnosis in Psychoanalytic Psychotherapy

LEWIS R. WOLBERG

HYPNOSIS MAY SOMETIMES SERVE as a valuable adjunct in psychoanalytically oriented psychotherapy. It is especially useful for the resolution of certain obdurate resistances that do not yield to the traditional techniques. For the past fifteen years I have employed hypnosis selectively in psychoanalytic practice, and it has contributed to the successful outcome of cases which, in my opinion, would otherwise have terminated in failure. Enumerated below are some of the situations in which hypnosis has proven effective.

1. *Where the patient lacks motivation for therapy.* Hypnotic techniques may be helpful in convincing a nonmotivated patient that he can derive something meaningful from treatment. Resentment toward the referring agencies, fear of revealing secret or disgusting aspects of one's life, distrust of the therapist, refusal to recognize an emotional basis for one's complaints, and other obstructions that contribute to the lack of incentive for therapy can usually be handled by a skilled therapist in the initial interviews without recourse to hypnosis.[7] But, occasionally, even adroit management does not resolve the patient's resistance to the acceptance of help. Here hypnosis, if the patient permits induction, may provide him with a positive experience that significantly alters his attitudes.

For example, a patient was referred to me by an internist with the symptom of urinary frequency which had defied all medical intervention and which had become so urgent that it threatened the patient's livelihood. He resented being sent to a psychiatrist, and he announced that he could see no sense in starting what might prove to be a long and costly process when he was not fully convinced that he needed it. I accepted the patient's negative feelings, but I speculated that his tension might be responsible for at least some of his symptoms. I then offered to show him how to relax himself so that he might derive something beneficial out of the present session. He agreed and I induced a light trance, in the course of which he achieved a generalized state of relaxation. After the trance was terminated, the patient spontaneously announced that he had never felt more relaxed in his life, and he asked if he could have several more sessions of hypnosis. In the course of hypno-relaxation, I casually suggested to him that there might be emotional reasons why his bladder had become tense and upset, and I asked him if he would be interested in finding out whether this was so. He agreed. I gave him a posthypnotic suggestion to remember any dreams that might occur in the next few days. He responded with a series of dreams in which he saw himself as a mutilated and a frightened person escaping from situations of danger and being blocked in his efforts toward freedom. His associations concerned themselves with the democratic rights of oppressed people throughout the world and with the futility of expressing these rights in the face of cruel and uncompromising dictatorship, which seemed to be the order of the day. When asked how this affected him personally, living as he was in a democratic regime, he sarcastically replied that one could be a prisoner even in a democracy. Since his father had died, he had been obliged to take over the responsibility of looking after his mother. Not only did she insist on his staying in her home, but she demanded an account of all his movements. He realized that she was a sick and frightened woman, and, therefore, he believed duty demanded that he devote himself to her comfort for the few of her remaining years. It was possible to utilize these revelations as a fulcrum to convert our sessions from palliative relaxation to active exploration of his needs and conflicts. As he recognized his repressed hostility and his powerful demands for personal freedom, he realized that he was largely responsible for the trap which was virtually mutilating him. It was possible then for him to help his mother find new friends and make plans for an independent life. With resolution of his dependency and his deep resentments, his bladder symptoms disappeared completely. Even more significant was a growth in assertiveness and self-esteem that promoted a much more constructive life adaptation.

2. *Where the patient refuses to begin therapy unless he is assured of immediate symptomatic relief.* Symptoms may be so upsetting to the patient that he refuses to engage in a therapeutic exploratory process unless there is first a reduction or removal of his symptoms. Where the patient's complaints are of a conversion nature and actually constitute an emergency, e.g., severe vomiting, hiccoughing, aphonia, or paralysis, the therapist may be able to restore function through hypno-suggestion, following which he may proceed with the usual analytic techniques. In less severe cases, the patient's insistence on relief is often a cover for demands that the therapist demonstrate himself as a sympathetic person concerned with the suffering of the patient. The latter resistance is sometimes resolvable by simple interpretation. Where interpretation fails, hypnosis with suggestions aimed at relaxation, control of tension and symptom reduction may create an atmosphere conducive to a therapeutic working relationship.

A patient with an obsessional neurosis complained of uncontrollable belching and hiccoughing that caused her great embarrassment and that frequently forced her to skip meals. She was so preoccupied with whether or not her symptoms would overwhelm her that she could scarcely enjoy food when she did dine. Inanition forced her to seek medical help, in the course of which she was referred to me. At the initial interview, she testily protested starting psychiatric treatments in view of a past unsuccessful psychotherapeutic experience. What she wanted, she insisted, was sufficient relief from physical distress to enable her to function at work and in her relationship with her family. Recognizing her disappointment with her former therapist, I suggested hypnosis as a possible way of helping her stabilize herself. She agreed to give it a trial. The next five sessions were spent in teaching her how to relax and how to control her symptoms. Her response was dramatic, and her attitude toward me changed from suspicion and hostility to friendly cooperativeness. She readily entered into a therapeutic relationship, and, once therapy had started, recourse to further hypnosis was unnecessary.

3. *Where the patient has a negative transference or a defensive characterologic detachment which obstructs the development of a working relationship.* Mandatory for any kind of psychotherapy is a good working relationship between patient and therapist. This is particularly essential in reconstructive therapy where considerable anxiety may be released in the course of probing for conflicts, challenging habitual defenses, mobilizing transference, resolving resistance and laboriously completing the working-through process. In some sick patients, like borderline cases, the proper working relationship may never develop or may take many months to appear due to such factors as fear of closeness or intense hostility toward authority. Hypno-relaxation may resolve fears, reduce hostility and cut down the time period required for the development of rapport. The patient often feels, even after only one or two hypnotic sessions, an extraordinary warmth and closeness toward the therapist. His dreams may indicate that he projects into the hypnotic relationship wishes for an idealistic experience with another human being. A therapeutic relationship may crystallize under these circumstances so that it is possible thereafter to procede with psychotherapy without hypnosis.

One of the most difficult patients I have ever treated was a paranoid individual who upbraided me severely during the first session for my delay in arranging a consultation with him. He was upset, he said, because he was involved in litigious proceedings against his business partners for presumably deceiving him about the prospects of their business when they first induced him to buy a share. Another legal case was pending against a neighbor who had built a garage which the patient considered an eyesore. But what he most desired from the consultation with me was to determine the feasibility of hypnotizing his wife to extract from her the truth of her exact whereabouts during an evening when he was out of town on business. He had carefully examined her tube of contraceptive jelly prior to his departure, and again upon his return. At first he could see no difference, but he compulsively returned to it, ruminating about whether he had not made a mistake in his original estimate of his wife's innocence. For weeks he had been subjecting his wife to a cross-examination, carefully tabulating contradictory remarks until he had convinced himself she was concealing the truth about a rendezvous with her lover. The poor woman, protesting her innocence from the start, had become so confused by his confrontations that she desperately tried to make up stories to cover tiny discrepancies in her minute-by-minute account of activities on the fatal evening. With acuity, the patient had seized on her flounderings to trap her into an admission of lying, which then convinced him all the more of her infidelity. A firm believer in the powers of hypnosis, he challenged her to submit herself to a hypnotic reliving of the evening in question.

Upon presenting this complaint and request, the patient inquired about the methods I employed of trance induction. I volunteered to demonstrate the hand levitation technique to him, and he cautiously agreed to be a subject. In not too long a time he entered into a deep trance, during which I suggested that he would soon begin to feel more relaxed, secure and self-confident. If he visualized a happy scene or had a dream about the most wonderful thing that could happen to a person, he would probably feel freedom from tension as well as a general state of pleasure that would make him happier than he had ever been in his life. After an interval of ten minutes, he was brought out of the trance. Upon opening his eyes, he revealed with humor having had a dream of lying on a hammock while lovely slave girls circled around him with baskets of fruit. I suggested that he return in two days and bring his wife if she desired to accompany him.

During the second session, his wife tearfully proclaimed her innocence, whereupon the patient petulantly asked her to leave my office if she was going to "act like a baby." When she promised to control herself, he requested that she wait for him in the reception room. He then confided having felt so well since his first visit that he had decided that several more sessions of hypnosis would be valuable for his insomnia. His wife's problem could wait, he claimed, until he had "healed his own nerves." After this initiation into therapy, he received 90 sessions of psychotherapy with and without hypnosis, during which he worked out several important aspects of his personality problem. He terminated therapy when he had achieved a marked reduction of his symptoms, an easing of his tensions with his partners, and the reestablishing of a satisfactory relationship with his wife.

Another patient spent the first three months of his treatment with me in empty associational explorations. He protested that "nothing was happening" in regard to his symptoms or "anything else." He felt neither good nor bad about me; indeed, he avowed, I was "neither his friend nor his enemy." He resented my continued questioning about his feelings about me, insisting that I was being paid to do a job and that it was not necessary for him to get personally involved. There was a constant negation of my interpretations. When induced to try hypnosis, he was able to achieve a medium trance. From the very first session, his enthusiasm and energy increased, resulting in a cessation of broken appointments. His activity and productivity improved remarkably and we were able to achieve a good therapeutic result. Without hypnosis, I am convinced, his detachment could not have been penetrated.

4. *Where the patient is unable to verbalize freely.* Where communication is blocked, there can be no therapy; however, the usual unblocking techniques may fail to restore verbalization. Hypnosis may sometimes function effectively here. The manner of its employment will depend on the causes of the difficulty. The mere induction of a trance may uncork explosive emotions against which the patient has defended himself by not talking in the waking state. Cathartic release in the trance may restore normal verbalization. If the patient's silence is due to some resistance, it may be possible to explore and resolve this by encouraging the patient to talk during hypnosis. In hysterical aphonia these techniques may not suffice and direct suggestion may be indicated toward reduction or removal of the symptom. Speech disorders may respond to the lessening of tension in the trance, and there may then be a carry-over into the waking state. Where the speech difficulty is caused by needs to prevent oneself from expressing painful sounds or ideas, an explosive outburst during hypnosis may not only release the capacity to talk freely, but also will open up pockets of conflict which may be beneficially explored.

A young woman, a severe stammerer, came to therapy because of incapacitating phobias. Once she had established contact with me, she verbalized satisfactorily, but as we began to examine her phantasies and dreams, she experienced so pronounced a relapse in her speech disturbance that she was practically inarticulate. She complained that while she could verbalize better with her friends than ever before, she could scarcely talk with me. Since progress had come to a halt, I suggested hypnosis as a way of helping her relax. She responded with anxiety, but agreed to try nevertheless. During the process of deepening the trance, she suddenly broke down and cried fitfully. Encouraged to discuss what she felt, she clenched her fists and shrieked, "No, no." She then exploded with a coughing spell and could hardly catch her breath as she gasped over and over that she was choking. To my suggestion that she "bring it up," she broke into a torrent of foul language, pronouncing the word "shit" repeatedly, spitting with angry excitement. A few minutes of this frenzied behavior were followed by complaints of exhaustion. A restoration of normal speech followed which persisted for the remainder of the session even after she had been aroused. This performance was repeated in subsequent sessions, but she responded with diminished fury. The analytic process gained great momentum, being concerned with a working through of the anal material which she was resisting by her speech symptom.

5. *Where the patient is unable to engage in free association.* Fears of penetrating conflictual areas may force the patient to maintain rigid control over his verbalizations. He is thus unable to permit his ideas to bounce around in an unrestrained way while exploring unguarded aspects of his psyche. Where free association is the preferred kind of communication and the patient is unable to engage in it due to resistance, hypnosis may not only cut through resistance immediately to bring the patient into contact with the repudiated material, but it may also help the patient to analyze his blocks.

A patient relapsed from free association to highly structured and rigidly directed content. Attempts made to analyze his loss of spontaneity brought little response. After a week of floundering, with repetition of insignificant items, hypnosis was induced and the patient was encouraged to talk in the trance about what really was bothering him. He responded by revealing how guilty he felt in the past weeks for having masturbated after one of our sessions in my office bathroom. He had not wanted to tell me about this incident because he knew it was not an adult act. He then associated having been caught as a child masturbating in his aunt's bathroom. Not only had he been reprimanded and warned by his aunt, but his parents had promptly been notified. The physician who had referred the patient to me had also frowned on his masturbatory practices, classifying masturbation as "idiot's delight which was never indulged in by a mature person." Reassured by my handling of these revelations, the patient was able to continue with his free associations in the waking state.

6. *Where the patient is unable to dream or to remember his dreams.* In cases where there is a dearth of dream material, it may be possible to train the patient to dream in the trance or to stimulate spontaneous dreaming by posthypnotic suggestions. Once this process is started, it may be possible for the patient to continue dreaming without hypnosis. Hypnosis can also be used to restore forgotten elements of dreams, to clarify secondary elaborations, and to help the patient explore by means of dreams his attitudes toward selected suggested topics. Hypnotic dreams resemble in

their symbolism and structure daydreams when the trance is light and spontaneous dreams when the trance is deep.

It is usually advisable to suggest to the patient after a hypnotic dream that he may remember or forget the dream after he awakens, depending on how he feels. In this way he feels protected and will not elaborate further resistance. For example, a patient with severe rectal itching came to psychotherapy after experiencing no relief with medicinal and injection treatments. Although a good working relationship was soon established, his productions were minimal; there were no dreams. In the trance it was suggested that he would have a dream that would explain his rectal itching. He responded with an anxiety dream of a man with a huge penis approaching him from the rear. He was told to forget the dream or recall any part of it that he wished to remember after he had awakened. Upon opening his eyes, he complained of tension, but he recalled no dream. He admitted some relief in his rectal itching. The same evening he had a dream of riding a roller coaster with a male friend. In later dreams, he was able to countenance homosexual impulses and to discuss them during the session. Hypnosis here served to open up a repressed and repudiated pocket of guilt and conflict.

7. *Where the patient seems blocked in bringing up transference material.* In cases in which the development and exploration of transference is believed essential and where the patient cannot seem to enter into transference, hypnosis may facilitate its appearance.

A female patient, who suffered from periodic attacks of nausea, vomiting and gastro-intestinal crises, was referred to me for hypnoanalysis after two years of traditional psychoanalysis had failed to relieve her symptoms. Because of the hysterical nature of her complaints and the intense repression, I felt that transference, which had not developed significantly during her previous therapy, might be important in activating processes of insight. After she had been trained to enter a medium trance, I suggested that she would dream of her feelings about me. She failed to produce a dream, but instead she developed a gustatory hallucination, a peculiar taste in her mouth that she described as "bitter sweet." This taste persisted for several hours after her session. That evening she had a nightmarish dream in which a woman with initials on her handbag of "B.S." took a small boy into the bathroom to help him to urinate and to wash up. She was unable to associate to the dream. A trance was induced in which she recalled forgotten elements of the dream, namely, that the sexes of the two participants had changed as they had entered the bathroom; the adult had been a man, the child a girl. The next few sessions were spent discussing a "reaction" to me that the patient had developed that made her want to stop treatment. She was positive that I resented her, and she recounted several minor incidents that indicated to her that I had not had her best interests at heart. She was positive that I preferred a young man whose sessions had preceded hers because I once had kept him late overlapping her time.

In the trance that followed, she broke into hysterical crying, identifying me as her father, whose nickname was Bing Steward (initials B.S. in the dream), who had both fathered and mothered her (changed from male to female in the dream), had preferred her brother to her (her reaction to the male patient whose hour preceded hers), and had always reminded her that he regretted that she had not been born a boy (her being brought into the bathroom as a boy in the dream possibly indicated that she had finally succeeded in achieving a masculine status). Thereafter, she experienced strong sexual feelings toward me and demanded that I express a preference for her among all my other patients. It was possible then to analyze the origins of these feelings in her relations with her father and to see that her gastric symptoms were associated with phantasies of incorporation of a penis. Hypnosis here succeeded rapidly in accentuating and clarifying transference relationships.

8. *Where the patient has repressed certain traumatic memories, elucidation of which may help the therapeutic process.* In certain conditions, particularly hysteria and traumatic neurosis, painful past experiences and memories may be repressed, initiating, by their constantly threatening exposure, anxiety and defensive symptoms to bolster repression. Sometimes the exposure in the trance of the repressed experience and the working-through of the associated emotions helps to eliminate offensive symptoms.

A patient with periodic attacks of dyspnea resembling asthma was given a suggestion in hypnosis that he would regress to the first attack of shortness of breath. He described a scene in which he saw himself as a child of three standing in a snowsuit on a back porch, slipping and falling into a huge snow drift and gasping for breath as the snow filled his nose and throat. With great panic, choking as he talked, he described his rescue by his mother and father. It was possible to validate this phantasy as a true experience by checking with his parents, who were amazed by the patient's having remembered the details of the accident as it had occurred. They recalled that "asthmatic" attacks had followed the accident. It was established in therapy that interpersonal situations where the patient felt trapped caused him to respond with the symptom of choking for breath, which had developed originally under circumstances when he actually had been physically trapped. A complete eradication of the symptom was soon accomplished.

9. *Where the patient seems to "dry up," being unable to produce any more significant material.* Periods of resistance may develop during the course of therapy characterized by an almost complete cessation of activity.

The patient here will spend many sessions in fruitless attempts at free association; he seems up against a barrier which he cannot surmount. Attitudes of disappointment and hopelessness contribute to his inertia until he resigns himself to making no further efforts. He may even decide to abandon therapy. Where such circumstances threaten, hypnosis may be tried to stimulate productivity. A variety of techniques may be utilized, including free association in the trance, dream and phantasy stimulation, mirror gazing, automatic writing, play therapy, dramatic acting, regression and revivification, and the production of experimental conflicts. The specific method employed is usually determined by the therapist's experience and preference as well as by the patient's aptitudes in working with one or another technique. The therapist may advantageously acquaint himself with different hypnoanalytic procedures to coordinate these with the specific needs and aptitudes of his patients.[5]

10. *Where the patient is unable to deal with forces which block a translation of insight into action.* The mere development of insight is not enough to insure correction of neurotic attitudes and patterns; it is essential that insight be employed toward constructive action. Unfortunately, many anxieties and resistances obstruct this aim and may interrupt therapy. Hypnosis is sometimes useful here, and it may achieve this goal in a number of ways. First, one may attempt by various hypnoanalytic techniques to explore resistances to change, the patient associating in his phantasies, dreams or dramatic acting out certain healthy courses of action. Second, posthypnotic suggestions may be made to the effect that the patient will want more and more to expose himself to the actions that are necessary and that are being resisted. Third, role-playing may be used, the patient projecting himself into various situations in the present or future and play-acting his insights or fears. Fourth, in somnambulistic subjects, experimental conflicts may be set up to test the patient's readiness to execute necessary acts and to investigate his reactions to their positive completion.

A patient with a passive personality makeup had gained insight during therapy into the roots of his character problem and into the destructive consequences of his failures in self-assertion. He expressed a wish to change, but he was paralyzed in initiating change. The most he could do was to phantasize himself walking into his employer's office, boldly asking for a promotion and being rewarded with a higher post and a handsome raise in salary. But he could not muster the courage actually to face his employer. In the trance, he voiced fears of being turned down. In hypnotic role-playing, he took the part of himself and his employer and discussed with vehemence pros and cons of his position. However, he still could not get himself to act. Since he was able to develop posthypnotic amnesia, I decided to try to set up an experimental conflict. I suggested that he phantasize asking for a promotion, forget having been given the suggestion, yet feel, upon emerging from the trance, as if he had actually gone through with the act. The first two attempts were followed by tension, headaches and discouragement that indicated that the patient was not yet prepared to take the necessary step forward. With continued discussion and role-playing, a third experimental situation resulted in a feeling of elation and accomplishment. The next day the patient spontaneously approached the employer and his effort fortunately was rewarded with success. This was the beginning of a series of positive actions which were coordinated with continued therapeutic improvement.

11. *Where the patient has problems in terminating therapy.* Difficulties in termination are sometimes encountered in patients who, having found freedom from symptoms in therapy, are fearful of giving up their gains and suffering a relapse. Patients with weak ego structures, especially borderline cases and extreme characterologic dependencies, may stubbornly resist ending treatment. Contrary to what may be anticipated, the adroit application of hypnosis may help some of these patients toward self-reliance by relaxing their tensions at points where they are obliged to exercise independent actions. The patient may also be taught to induce self-hypnosis for purposes of relaxation, and to investigate problems spontaneously, through dreams, phantasies and associations, as they arise in his daily adjustment demands. In this way responsibility is transferred to the patient, and he may become more and more capable of depending on himself. Intervals between visits with the therapist are gradually prolonged. At the start, the patient may, because of anxiety, resort to daily sessions of self-hypnosis; but as he develops more and more confidence in his ability to survive, he usually forgets to invoke regular self-hypnosis, finally employing it only when his tensions cause him to seek relief. Eventually, as his thrusts into the world are rewarded, he becomes capable of functioning without the need for any props. In very sick patients, however, regular relaxation exercises constitute an important adjustment measure and may be indulged indefinitely with beneficial effect.

The indications for hypnosis in psychoanalytic therapy outlined above are merely suggestions of how the trance may be employed as an adjunctive procedure. Individual therapists may creatively utilize hypnosis under other conditions after experimenting with the effects of the trance on their own ways of functioning. Since all psychotherapy is a blend of the personality structure of the therapist and his techniques, no two therapists will be able to operate identically. There are a number of books which may teach the induction of hypnosis and the implementation of various hypno-analytic procedures.[1-6] However, it is essential that each therapist do original research on how hypnosis influences, positively or negatively, his specific modes of working. There are some therapists who, for personality reasons or because of unresolvable prejudices, will be unable to use hypnosis with any measure of success. This does not invalidate hypnosis as a procedure; it merely proves that a particular therapist is unable to amalgamate hypnosis with his personality and technical training.

Even though a therapist may become skilled in executing hypnotic procedures, it does not necessarily follow that he will be able positively to influence all patients with hypnosis. Hypnosis will give him one more tool in dealing with resistance. However, resistance may be so strong in some patients that it may negate all of his hypnotherapeutic attempts as it has in these cases frustrated all of his conventional psychoanalytic efforts. Nor will hypnosis compensate for technical inefficiency or destructive countertransference. Didactic courses, personal psychoanalysis and intensive supervision are mandatory for the fullest development of the therapist's potential.

A word about the presumed dangers of hypnosis: Any psychiatrist who employs hypnosis will be convinced that such dangers have been greatly exaggerated. Indeed, they are nonexistent if the therapist is well-trained and has a good idea of what he is doing. Hypnotic rape fantasies, sexual acting-out, and unfortunate dependencies resulting from hypnosis are no more common than in psychotherapy without hypnosis. In a recent survey among therapists who utilize hypnosis in their practise, not a single therapist could testify that dangers exist that discourage its employment by trained professional persons.[8] The concensus was that hypnosis is valuable in all types of psychotherapy, palliative and reconstructive.

It goes without saying that hypnosis must be intelligently used within the context of a comprehensive treatment plan and with due regard for its indications and limitations. Applied indiscriminately, hypnosis not only serves no therapeutic purpose, but its failures tend to discredit it as a scientific procedure and to relegate it to a position of undeserved oblivion.

REFERENCES

1. BRENMAN, M. AND GILL, M. M.: Hypnotherapy. New York, International, 1947.
2. LINDNER, R. M.: Rebel Without a Cause. The Hypnoanalysis of a Criminal Psychopath. New York, Grune & Stratton, 1944.
3. ROSEN, H.: Hypnotherapy in Clinical Psychiatry. New York, Julian Press, 1953.
4. WATKINS, J. G.: Hypnotherapy of War Neuroses. New York, Ronald Press, 1949.
5. WOLBERG, L. R.: Hypnoanalysis. New York, Grune & Stratton, 1945.
6. ———: Medical Hypnosis. New York, Grune & Stratton, 1948.
7. ———: The Technique of Psychotherapy. New York, Grune & Stratton, 1954.
8. ———: Current Practices in Hypnosis. In: Progress in Psychotherapy (Fromm-Reichmann, F. and Moreno, J. L., eds.). New York, Grune & Stratton, 1956. Pp. 217-233.

Special Problems of Psychotherapy

JAMES G. MILLER

FACTORS IN PSYCHOTHERAPY

THAT MANY DIFFERENT THINGS are done to patients in the name of psychotherapy is apparent to all who are conversant with the field. One reason for this, of course, is that psychotherapists operate in terms of many diverse theories of personality, mental disease, or emotional disturbance. Probably, the general assumption is that eventually, after a slow process of testing alternatives and gradually arriving at common agreement, and after generations of men committed to a single school or point of view have died and new generations not so indoctrinated have arisen, a single theory underlying psychotherapy will gain broad acceptance, just as other fields have coalesced around unitary theories.

There are other more legitimate reasons than schoolism, however, for divergent psychotherapeutic practices. It is obvious, for instance, that individual patients differ in diagnosis, in family and social situations, and in duration of illness. The financial resources of one patient are greater than those of another and, in our present economy, this affects what we can do for them. Therapies differ because some patients have complicating physical ailments and others do not, and, as the present symposium indicates, age is also an important consideration. A five-year-old child requires different treatment from an adult of 35, and he from an aging person of 75.

If there were a precise basic science of human development and of the alterations of normal and abnormal behavior with age, we would begin to have a rationale for selecting therapeutic techniques in consideration of the patient's age. How can theory help in this, and in the evaluation of the effectiveness of the method chosen?

A single theory of personality psychodynamics and psychopathology can engender a number of criteria in terms of which one may select a method of psychotherapy, evaluate the changes it produces, and determine when it should be terminated. Elsewhere[1] I have suggested a number of such criteria which can be derived from the psychoanalytic orientation. They are as follows:

1. Important memories, attitudes, and feelings which, unavailable to awareness and unreportable before therapy, become conscious and can be verbalized after therapy.

2. The resolution of conflicts. Before therapy the patient may state

that he is in conflict or is ambivalent about certain situations, and that consequently his behavior is irrationally variable. Psychoanalysts commonly recognize that these conflicts are usually between super ego and id factors, and that they are often of long duration and repetitive. The absence of such unresolved problems at the end of therapy would be evidence of favorable change.

3. Flexibility of adjustive mechanisms. Psychoanalytic theory has dealt at length with various defenses of the personality and methods for handling traumata and reestablishing adjustment. An index of the physical health of an organism is the rapidity and completeness with which it can recover from injury; an arteriosclerotic leg does not do this as well as a normal one. Similarly, measures of rigidity and flexibility, perhaps by projective techniques or other methods, which indicate the rapidity of recovery from an emotional trauma and the seriousness of its after-effects, can be used as criteria of therapeutic change.

4. Suitability of the mechanisms of ego defense. The mass of clinical experience that has engendered psychoanalytic theory has led to the general conclusion that there is a sort of hierarchy of desirability of mechanisms of ego defense, somewhat like the chemists' displacement series of metals. Sublimation is usually thought to be a more adequate handling of a problem than flight from reality, and certainly symptom formation and repression are usually considered undesirable. Techniques which can demonstrate the typical, most frequent, or most readily chosen mechanism of defense before and after therapy may be useful as criteria.

5. The effectiveness in handling anxiety is another possible criterion— *the ability to handle* anxiety and not the actual amount of anxiety reported at any moment. This distinction is important because many hysterics, for example, feel little anxiety because of strong repression, and effective therapy for them often involves release of anxiety so that free anxiety is greater before it finally becomes less and the patient can deal adequately with it.

6. Working through of the Oedipus situation. The psychoanalytic doctrine of the universality of the Oedipus problem suggests that one criterion of therapeutic change might be development of recognition of this situation and of ways to handle it. It is difficult to suggest what operations available to the scientific public might indicate that this had happened, except evidence from recordings and other protocols of the therapeutic course.

7. The resolution of transference. Psychoanalytic theory does not imply that the development of transference in itself necessarily has therapeutic effect. However, if the transference can make the patient aware of his repetitive patterns of emotional relationships and if these insights enable

him to deal more effectively and realistically with similar problems in the future, one of the goals of psychoanalytic therapy has been attained. Comparisons of the patient's ability to handle transference situations productively before and after therapy might constitute significant criteria of effectiveness of therapy.

Other theoretical points of view, of course, emphasize other criteria for successful therapy. Often even the various criteria suggested by a single theory can give conflicting indications as to the success of therapy in a given case, because when one thinks of the adjustment of the individual, one can think of so many different dimensions of the adjustment, not only within himself but also in his various relations between himself and others.

A good many of these criteria could be listed:[2]

(1) The satisfaction of the patient with himself as a human being.

(2) Effective "intrapsychic adjustment of the patient" according to some specific theory of personality.

(3) Adjustment to the society at large, keeping within the bounds of accepted social behavior.

(4) Work adjustment, which is one subclass of the over-all social adjustment.

(5) Adjustment to the home environment, another particular aspect of the social adjustment, commonly emphasized as a criterion in child psychiatry.

(6) Alleviation or disappearance of the presenting symptoms which brought the patient into therapy. Although this is often derogated as a partial and naive evidence of success, the fact often is that frequently it is the only one obtainable.

(7) Behavioral changes which are desired by some member of society or some group as, for example, a prison warden.

(8) Behavioral or social adjustment on the part of the patient which fits in with the therapist's ideal in such matters.

The criteria derived from psychoanalytic theory included flexibility of mechanisms of adjustment. This appears to be a criterion that is acceptable to therapists of several orientations. Two or three psychiatrists in this symposium, of differing theoretical viewpoints, have referred to this or similar notions, and it appears likely that this concept would not be rejected by any of them. Increasingly, we seem to find agreement that not only biologic phenomena must be maintained in some sort of equilibrium but also many psychological adjustments. More and more discussion in scientific literature is devoted to physiologic and psychological stresses from the environment which impinge upon the individual, altering his adjustment. Among those mentioned have been the general incapacity of children to protect themselves against physical threats in the environment; lack of an adequate input of affection from parents and others in the environment from whom a child would ordinarily receive love; separation from the family which has met many previous needs and provided satisfactions; isolation from companions, especially in the case of the aged, whose older friends die and whose children and grandchildren desert them; decrease in erotic sensations which previously gave gratification; sensory and motor restrictions which come to the aged. On the other hand, there was also emphasis on various individual, group, and societal mechanisms of defense available to the individual to help him in withstanding these stresses. Not only were intrapsychic defenses considered, of the sort which have been classic in psychodynamics, but also interpersonal supports, like advice and affection that can be received from other individuals to aid the patient in solving his problems; compensatory gratifications provided by others; various means of financial assistance; aids to sensory acuity and motor acuity; community support through companionship and recognition; and so forth. One of the really promising orientations toward unification of biologic and social sciences is the concept of the stress—either physiologic, psychological, or social—which impinges upon the individual, and the concept of mechanisms available to maintain his equilibrium or steady state against onslaughts from his environment.

PSYCHOTHERAPY AND SYSTEMS THEORY

The group of scientists with whom I have worked since 1949 has been reviewing the different biologic and social sciences of man in order to find out whether a sufficient body of facts exists to point toward a general theory of behavior which can be evaluated in the clinic, in the laboratory, by social surveys, or by other methods. We would hope that such a theory could eventually be developed for direct application to diagnostic and therapeutic work in neuropsychiatry, as well as other fields of applied psychodynamics and psychopathology.

This group has included representatives from the fields of history, anthropology, economics, political science, sociology, psychology, psychiatry, medicine, physiology, and mathematical biology, as well as consultants from mathematics, physics, theology, and other fields of interest. At first we all expressed a good deal of skepticism about our project, tending to feel that the time was not ripe to unify schools or disciplines which had not yet sufficiently refined their own views to make integration feasible. We also soon learned of the linguistic Tower of Babel that prevented the various sects of behavioral scientists from understanding each other. Gradually, however, we began to discover certain common issues which we could agree upon, even though our words were quite different. Eventually, after various shifts in personnel, we have reached a measure of agreement on a point of view which we call general behavior systems theory.

Systems are bounded regions in space-time, involving energy interchange among their parts (which are associated in functional relationships) and with their environments. General systems theory is a series of related definitions, assumptions, and postulates about all levels of systems, from atomic particles through atoms, molecules, crystals, viruses, cells, organs, individuals, small groups, institutions, societies, planets, solar systems, and galaxies. General behavior systems theory is a subcategory of such theory, dealing with living systems, extending roughly from viruses through societies. Perhaps the most significant fact about living things is that they are open systems, with important inputs and outputs. Laws which apply to them differ from those applying to relatively closed systems.

All behavior can be conceived of as energy exchange within an open system or from one such system to another. Any exchange of energy across a boundary results in some alteration or distortion of the energy form. Those specific functions of systems which we can stipulate and whose magnitude we can measure in relative scale we will call "variables" if they are within the system and "parameters" if they are in its environment. Each system except the largest of all—the universe—has its environment. The system and its environment together constitute a suprasystem. Each system except the smallest has subsystems, which are any components of an organism that can affect a variable.

Inputs and outputs may be either coded or uncoded. Coding is a linkage within subsystems whereby process A_1 is coupled with A_2 so that either will elicit the other in the future. Coding involves conditioning, learning, or pairing of two processes in a system and the memory or retention of this union over a period of time. Any action is uncoded unless—like speech or gesture—it has some added significance as a result of such a bond. It then conveys information.

All living systems tend to maintain steady states of many variables by negative feedback mechanisms which distribute information to subsystems to keep them in orderly balance. Not only are subsystems usually kept in equilibrium, but systems are also commonly in balance with their environments, which have outputs into systems and inputs from them. This prevents variations in the environment from destroying systems, either by collapse or by explosion. There is a range of stability for any parameter or variable in any system. It is that range within which the rate of correction is minimal or zero and beyond which correction does occur. Inputs (or loads), either coded or uncoded, which, by lack or excess, force the variables beyond the range of stability, constitute stresses and produce strains within the system. These strains may or may not be capable of being reduced, depending upon the equilibratory resources of the system.

The above general statement can be translated into terminology of several behavioral sciences. In individual psychology or psychiatry, for instance, the system has generally been known as the organism, the input as the stimulus, and the output as the response. Uncoded inputs, we have recognized, can result in strains or disequilibria within the organism which are known as primary or somagenic drives. Coded inputs result in secondary, learned, acquired, or psychogenic drives. Reduction of strains is called drive satisfaction. When inputs or loads create strains great enough to call into play complex subsystems to restore equilibrium, we sometimes refer to such processes as "defense mechanisms." When these mechanisms fail, severe disruption of the steady state of the organism, known as mental or physical illness, or ultimately death, occurs. The total of the strains within the individual resulting from his genetic input and variations of the input from his environment is often referred to as his values. The relative urgency of reducing these individual strains determines his hierarchy of values.

We have attempted to employ where possible objective terminology comparable to that which is used in natural science. We have discovered that many aspects of systems at various levels can be measured in natural science units—centimeters, grams, seconds, and those recently developed in the field of information theory. We hope that perhaps classical dimensions of the psychiatric-psychological sciences can be translated into such terms so that more effective quantification can be possible in the evaluation, for example, of process and outcome in psychotherapy.

We are often asked whether an effort to find similarities or formal identities between different levels of behaving systems isn't essentially poetic metaphor rather than scientific generalization. We recognize the issue but believe that empirical measurement of similar functions of systems at different levels is the best way to settle the matter, for that will enable us to find out with some degree of precision whether or not formal identities actually do exist and are helpful in making predictions about behavior.

We have developed several dozen specific theorems or propositions, each of which can apply to or is potentially capable of being tested at, various levels of systems—cell, organ, individual, small group, and society. We recognize that even if the general statement of a proposition is shown to be accurate, there are obvious differences in size of systems involved, in their constituents, in the duration of their existence, and in a number of other important aspects. These differences are as important to us as the similarities. In other words, we do not overemphasize the formal identities, but are equally concerned with systematic and quantitative dissimilarities.

In a brief paper it is possible only to suggest a few of these propositions. One deals with the comparability of the rates of growth of systems. In some ways growth rates are mathematically similar, whether they concern the number of amebas in a culture or the size of the human populations considered by Malthus. Another of the propositions states that there is always a constant systematic distortion—or, better, alteration—between input of energy into a system and output from that system. We know, for example, that the input of glucose into some cells is altered to an output of carbon dioxide and water. When the stimulus from a Rorschach card enters the eye of a patient, he responds, and this response is characteristically different—or distorted—for each patient. We view this distortion as a sign of the internal state of the individual. In like manner, distortion occurs in the passage of information through groups, as, for example, when the same piece of political news is interpreted by the Democratic or the Republican party during a campaign. Distortion also appears in the crossing of boundaries between societies, as in the propaganda flow which goes on in a cold war. Another related proposition is that the nature of the distortion is determined by the strains within the system or its equilibratory needs.

Other propositions deal with the rate of return of a system to equilibrium after it is moved away from the equilibrium point by stresses, the character of the restorative or defense mechanism which restores the equilibrium, and the strength of these forces.

CLINICAL APPLICATIONS

Various experimental and clinical researches with patients are now going on at our institute in order to evaluate these interrelated propositions and discover their promise in psychodiagnosis and psychotherapy. We fully recognize that our primitive effort is only one of many potentially valuable ways of organizing our understanding of the nature of man, though we hope that ultimately it can be productive. It is difficult to give any brief description of general behavior systems theory that is also clear.[3] However, it may be possible to give some impressionistic picture of how this framework is helpful in understanding such clinical problems as some of those that have been discussed in this symposium.

Let us consider the case of a child whose mother, divorced when he was three, has the responsibility of trying to raise him while at the same time she carries on a part-time night job. She is involved in her own emotional problems as a woman without a man. She is busier than most mothers and becomes so restless and overwrought that she takes a tranquilizing drug to aid in relaxation and to permit sleep. This total situation means that her son receives less affection than most and grows up as an affectionless child who in adolescence resorts to delinquency to gain compensatory gratification, and then enters psychotherapy.

It is difficult for us to picture the sociologic or small-group aspects of the mother's job situation and the family life in the same framework as the intimate relationship between the therapist and the boy, or the effects of the tranquilizing drug on the mother's nervous system. What sort of conceptual system can unite these dissimilar aspects of this case?

Any final answer in the framework of systems theory must wait, of course, for extension of basic research. However, it is helpful to look at the son and mother as subsystems of various larger social systems—such as family, working group, or hospital ward, if either is hospitalized. There are other subsystems in each of these groups which interact characteristically, and the patient's involvement with these other individuals may be mechanisms of support for him or sources of stress, or both. The mother provides her son with certain inputs of energy and information which help maintain his equilibrium and adjustment, but her lack of demonstrated affection or irregular affection can constitute a severe stress. A child's relationship with his therapist is an information exchange between two individuals in which the therapist is trying to help him learn new mechanisms of defense against the severe stress of his mother's attitude. At the same time a social worker may be working with the mother to alter her attitudes and so help reduce this stress upon the child. And where would a tranquilizing drug fit into this picture? Suppose we view the mother as a system including a complex net of many neural and glandular subsystems which organize stimuli and other inputs, transmit information, make decisions, and emit responses. Just as a telephone dial central office can break down, so this particular network can break down. Abnormal chemical states in the transmission systems can increase certain types of systematic distortion. We can assume that effective tranquilizing drugs help compensate for such distortion, and consequently the mother's normal information-processing system can be more normal. So it is possible to unite into a single framework social and group factors, interpersonal interactions, biochemical and physiologic processes in the cells of the nervous system.

Some of the discussion in this symposium has concerned aids to the aging in reinforcing their defenses against stresses from the environment. Hearing aids and glasses diminish the distortion of input subsystems, just as crutches and wheelchairs augment the motor abilities of the output subsystems.

Improvement of the general physiologic state of the aged will increase the accuracy of central decision-making functions. If the elderly person is given supportive affection by a therapist or participates actively in the work of a group, he can be protected from the stress of loneliness which comes to an isolate. Moreover, he can receive aid in his infirmities from others in his group who do not have the same difficulties. The role of the large social system in providing social security and consequently alleviating economic and financial stresses on the individual also clearly fits into such a framework.

The effectiveness of psychotherapy in alleviating various physiologic and social problems of patients of all ages will increase as our basic understanding of the sciences of man advance. We will clarify our criteria in these matters as we test alternate influences on behavior by laboratory, clinical, and field studies, and by follow-up of experimental and control groups treated in different ways. Massive efforts in integrated fundamental research are required—in which psychiatrists can take a major role—but ultimately the art of psychotherapy will be abetted by a rigorous behavioral science.

REFERENCES

1. MILLER, J. G.: The implications of psychoanalytic theory for the evaluation of psychotherapy. Psychol. Serv. Center Journal 2:123-129, 1950.
2. ———: Criteria and measurement of change during psychiatric treatment. Bull. Menninger Clin. 18:130-137, 1954.
3. ———: Toward a general theory for the behavioral sciences. Am. Psychol. 10: 513-531, 1955.

Part V: DEVELOPMENTS ABROAD

Psychotherapy in the Indian Cultural Setting

K. V. RAJAN

IN EVALUATING THE REACTION of Indian people to modern methods of psychotherapy, it is important to bear in mind certain cultural patterns by which Indian personality is being shaped. In particular, one has to consider the way in which people relate to one another, and in which social institutions like the home, village and caste system function.

One dominant feature of Indian life is the system of the joint family. A child usually grows up in a home where he is surrounded by his father's parents, brothers or other relatives. The parents, having been married by their families without having had any active part in the choice themselves, may be very young and inexperienced. In spite of their emotional immaturity and possibly their lack of economic independence, they are expected by an unwritten law to have their first child during the year following marriage. If they fail to produce children, they become the object of much talk in the village or family circle. The barren wife is blamed by the in-laws for not giving them a child; she may be unkindly treated or cast aside. She may even be rejected in favor of another wife. At any rate, she is not fully accepted into the society of married women until she has borne a child. In other situations, the husband may be blamed and teased about his sterility, which creates in him the embarrassing feeling that he is not quite a man. Both husband and wife have to face the prospect of an insecure old age without children to care for them, to inherit their property and to perform the last rites at their death. Thus the child is desired for cultural and religious reasons instead of being welcomed for his own sake as a token of the growing love between husband and wife.

The ambition of the young couple is not only to have a child as soon as possible, but to have a boy, since girls are considered a burden. Because India is extremely color-conscious, the color of the child is also very important. While boys may simply be teased if their skin is a few shades too dark, lack of fairness in a girl may ruin her chances in the marriage market. The only saving factor is that the girl need not feel guilty herself about not attracting a husband, since getting her married is the family's responsibility.

197

What applies to color is true of any physical or mental infirmity; the handicapped child will find derision rather than helpful sympathy, even within his own family. Upon the birth of the child, most parents arrange for a horoscope to be cast. Any unfortunate prediction of the astrologer, or any ominous dream of a member of the family, may deeply affect the family's attitude toward the child, who will not be accepted with the necessary warmth and love. Any calamity that may befall the family will be blamed on the ill-fated child. If by some chance the child himself learns about the ominous prediction, he develops a sense of guilt and frustration. The psychic implications of astrological prediction present a field for further study.

The newborn baby is cared for by the whole household and treated like a god up to a certain age. It is not uncommon for a child to be picked up so often that he fails to get the necessary rest. Many a child is put to sleep on someone's shoulder before he is taken to bed. Constant attention is paid to the child until he reaches what may be called the age of accountability, which is determined by the caste, locality, social status of the family, etc. From then on, the child not only gets much less attention, but he also has to learn to play a social role in his relationship with others. The child experiences this sudden loss of attention as a shock. At about the same time many parents of the opposite sex begin to avoid any physical contact with the child, even to the point of not touching him. If by then a new baby arrives in the family, the older child may be required to take care of the little brother or sister.

In Indian married couples the phase of procreation is spread over a much longer period than in the West. It is not unusual to find the births of children in a family scattered over twenty to thirty years. Therefore, brothers and sisters may be old enough to play the role of parents; nephews and nieces may be older than their uncles and aunts. This prevents siblings from relating to one another as comrades and playmates. Old parents are unable to meet the emotional demands of their youngest children, born to them in their old age. Most of these late offspring live like orphans as far as their emotional needs are concerned, and experience an acute sense of loneliness. Some of the seekers of God who vanish into the forests of India come from this group. Their image of God is that of a mother, and they often refer to themselves in their prayers as orphans in quest of a mother's care and love. This, however, does not mean that all those who seek God are merely looking for a mother-figure.

The mother in this culture does not have a very high status. There is usually the mother-in-law or some other senior female relative who rules the home, as far as internal household matters are concerned. Instead of respecting the authority of the mother, the child sees her as a weak person in every respect. The girls, who identify with their mothers, see the same fate before them. Often the mother is just looked upon as a glorified wet-nurse who is very useful.

The child is expected to relate to different people in terms of the family hierarchy. Since any hierarchical setup breeds intrigue, the child becomes aware of tension within the family. He learns to adjust to this situation by compartmentalizing his existence and by skillfully grading his approach to people of different age and social standing. An example of this was provided in a letter written by one of our patients to his family: "Give my respects to elders, salaams to equals and love to young ones."

Small boys do not get close to female members of the family, and as the men in the home work during the day, the boys have little chance of enjoying physical closeness either with men or women. A consequence of this situation seems to be that adult men in this culture crave physical closeness, which takes the form of holding hands, hugging each other, etc., often quite openly. In this respect girls are more fortunate; most mothers stay at home and take care of them. This rigid separation of sex, while a breeding ground for incest on the one hand, may, on the other, determine the Indian attitude toward sex life in general. It is a recognized practice for men of a mature age to strive to overcome their sexual urge by spiritual exercise, including yoga. This tendency to try to get at one's emotions through control of the body seems to dominate Indian thinking. Mastery of all sexual feeling is the highest goal many people seek; therefore, any physical sensation is experienced as something not quite nice and decent, or merely as the craving of the flesh. The concept of love varies considerably. It is generally conceived and carried out as an obligation. Love as an experience of a sense of we-ness is strange to people in this country. Everything connected with the body is considered evil. Menses and childbirth are full of taboos and, as are many other spheres of Indian life, the object of strict purifying rituals. It is interesting to observe how naturally many psychotic patterns of behavior—catatonic withdrawal and refusal of food, but particularly, obsessive-compulsive syndromes—fit in with generally accepted, religiously determined practices. Syndromes of this kind may develop to a very severe degree before they are recognized as pathologic.

Superstition and learning seem to coexist. The modern ambition for a good education, preferably an academic degree, often produces nothing more than a kind of superficial whitewash that does not penetrate the personality of its wearer in a deep and lasting manner. This is possible because people arrange their lives in compartments. One is often reminded of a ship which continues to float, even though some of its compartments are filled with water.

In most places people live in groups, in terms of caste or social status. At times, a whole village consists of members of the same caste, who are interrelated. The tradition of the mores forms the basis of the code of behavior. A social setup of this kind creates a sense of security as long as the individual follows the mores and stays with the group. This close-knit community can survive to the extent to which it can maintain its particularity, which means that others who are different have to be rejected. Rapid modern means of communication tend to break up this isolation and thus put quite a strain on the emotional resources of the people.

Most of the patients who have sought help at the Psychiatric Center are the victims of this inter-group penetration. Persons of the first generation to be educated, who had to leave their group to seek a new way of life in the cities, are increasingly becoming victims of emotional stress. Women who no longer feel quite comfortable in their traditional role are beginning to escape into mental illness. When these patients come for psychotherapy, most of them have the idea that the therapist can perform some kind of magic.

Many of the patients are able to maintain an astonishing outward serenity. One of the main tasks of psychotherapy is to break through this compartmentalized existence which the patient has built up in order to survive in his joint family environment. Patients find it difficult to blame their parents or to say anything unkind about them. It is almost equally hard to make them talk about spheres of life that are regulated by superstitions and taboos. They are apt to accept most of their trouble as fate. This idea of fate, particularly in depressed patients, works as a most difficult hurdle to get over. It takes repeated effort to communicate to the patient that he can be helped to change himself.

On the other hand, patients are comparatively free in talking about their sex life, and many of them imply that their illness has to do with their masturbation or some sexual deviation. As already mentioned, it is not uncommon for patients to suggest a solution to their problems by spiritual exercise and mastery of the body.

Most patients relate to the therapist as though he were their local guardian who should take care of them. The patient has no compunction in asking the therapist to give him tenderness and affection. The author has had hardly any male patient who did not, in the course of therapy, express a desire to hug him. Since most patients come from authoritarian homes, they are very suggestible, and they seduce the therapist into playing the authoritarian role by telling them what to do. The passive attitude of the analyst is a tremendous threat to the patients. They are not quite pleased to have the analyst only listen. They relate to the therapist in terms of his age and social status in a given community. If the therapist is young and the patient is an older person, he relates to the therapist in terms of teasing. The patient will then find it difficult to accept any suggestion. If the patient is of social equality, he becomes very competitive and makes demands on the therapist. If the patient is a younger person, he plays a very subservient, obedient role. The patient will have a hard time expressing his hostility in such instances. Some patients, particularly the hospitalized ones, find it easier to go into a psychotic episode than to express hostility to the therapist.

Female patients may feel insecure with a male therapist. In the beginning they make it clear that they want to be a sister to the therapist. It is very, very hard for them to admit any sensual feeling they may have toward the therapist. Some time ago we had a hospitalized schizophrenic female patient who had been ill for four years and had been brought here from one of the state mental institutions. When first seen, she was very violent and did not talk to the therapist for a period of three months. But one day she met the therapist on the ward and tied a string on his wrist. This is a custom in this part of the country: on a certain day each year sisters tie a piece of string on the wrist of their brothers or of any other men they consider as adopted brothers. In a way this is an age-old custom to avoid incest. The patient's accepting the therapist as a brother was the beginning of a therapeutic relationship. She made a social recovery and is now profitably employed in a job of her choosing.

For group therapy the selection of patients should be done in terms of their social status and sex. When they are in a group, patients find it easier to express their negative feelings towards the therapist; they even unite in creating a protective front against him. The group immediately becomes a family setup, and members react to one another in the same way as in a family. Usually the oldest one or the most educated one takes the role of the head of the family. He is very careful to see that his prestige is maintained and becomes very anxious when the least disrespect is shown. If discussion in a group discloses to patients that others have the same problems as they themselves, they usually react with great surprise. This again may be due to the compartmentalization of existence.

One of the major differences in psychotherapy with Western and with Indian patients lies in the goal. In the West, through psychotherapy, a patient is supposed to become free from all infantile ties. He should be able to marry the person of his own choice, live apart from his parents, have his own opinion and not be upset when others disagree with him, but be able to maintain a sense of respect for someone who does not share his opinion. In India, he should be able to feel a part of his group, should gladly contribute his share to the joint family and should follow the social mores without violent reaction.

Taking into account all these cultural differences between India and the West and again within India itself, where customs vary from province to province and even from village to village, it is evident that not all Western methods of psychotherapy can be applied equally well in this country. In so complex a cultural setting, existential analysis is particularly suited to the patients' needs. In "Daseinsanalysis" the therapist attempts to accept things and human behaviour as they themselves appear, thus avoiding the mistake of projecting any preconceived theory of the human psyche onto the phenomena presented by the patient. At the same time the unprejudiced, direct understanding of man practiced in existential analysis prevents unnecessary resistance in patients of this culture, who are very sensitive to any artificial distortion of their motives. Thus the patient is helped to work out his problems in his own way, while the student of depth psychology gets an excellent chance of unearthing fascinating phenomena hitherto inaccessible or unnoticed.

Report on Psychotherapy in Holland

E. A. D. E. CARP

PSYCHOTHERAPY IN HOLLAND found its first special practitioners through the influence of Prof. Jelgersma, the first Professor of Psychiatry at the University of Leiden. With his rectoral address "The Unconscious Life of the Psyche" (1913) he established the official recognition of depth psychology at the Dutch universities. A branch of the International Psychoanalytic Association has existed in Holland for almost 40 years. From this, in the course of the years, a psychoanalytic association which bases itself on a less dogmatic viewpoint has split off. Further, there exists in Holland a society of followers of the individual-psychology school (Adler), while also the analytic psychology of Jung counts a good number of adherents, especially among the psychologists. A Dutch association for pschotherapy with a membership numbering more than 150 was established approximately 20 years ago.

Psychotherapy is practiced in increasing measure in the state universities at Leiden, Utrecht, Nijmegen, Groningen and in the municipal university at Amsterdam. In Amsterdam, an institute for medical psychology has also been organized, where psychotherapy in its various forms can be applied. The members of the Dutch Working Committee of the International Psychoanalytic Association publish an annual report dealing with the cases treated by this group. An institute for medical psychology (psychotherapy) was also opened recently in Utrecht.

In several sanatoriums for the nervously ill (among others Apeldoorn and Veluwerand), psychotherapy is systematically applied. In the majority of psychiatric institutions for the critically mentally ill, group psychotherapy, creative-expressive and sociotherapy are being practiced, e.g., Heiloo, Wolfheeze, Roosenburg, Leidschendam, and others.

Psychotherapy has been taught at the majority of universities for many years; it is the conviction that the basic beginnings of psychotherapy and the more simple methods rightly belong in the armamentarium of every physician. Furthermore, the resurgence of the psychosomatic viewpoint has acted as a stimulus upon the practice of psychotherapy.

The Jelgersma-Cliniek (The Psychiatric Clinic of Leiden University) at Oegstgeest remains the oldest psychotherapeutic clinic in Holland. Originally organized under the leadership of Prof. Jelgersma, it was further extended by his successor, Prof. Carp, and contains at present more than 100 beds, the majority of which are occupied by neurotic patients who are all in psychotherapeutic treatment. In order to stimulate a critical awareness of the meaning of the various psychotherapeutic methods at Leiden University, a series of monographs on psychotherapy was begun. In this series, the following appeared in the course of years: Carp, "Grondslagen der psycho-therapie" (Foundations of psychotherapy); Stokvis, "Hypnose" (Hypnosis); Carp, "De individual psychologische behandelingsmethode" (The treatment method of individual psychology); Carp, "De suggestieve behandelingsmethode en het suggestieve element in de therapie" (The treatment method of suggestion and the suggestive element in therapy); Hugenholtz, "De psychagogiek of re-educatieve methode" (The psychagogic or re-educative methods); Stokvis, "Auto-suggestieve therapie" (Auto-suggestive therapy); Carp (in cooperation with Stokvis and J. de Groot), "Problemen der groepspsycho-therapie" (Problems of group psychotherapy); Carp, "Socio-therapie" (Socio-therapy); Carp, "Psycho-drama" (Psychodrama); Carp, "Analytisch psychologische methodes volgens Jung" (Analytic Psychological Methods according to Jung). The appearance of this series was also meant to serve the goal of establishing the purest possible methodology. A research report appears annually in order that the consolidation of the results obtained may be assessed. The greatest value is attached to the cathartic element of all methodology.

As far as child psychiatry is concerned, the various Child Guidance Clinics in Holland have given this field an important boost. A medico-psychological clinic was formed in 1935 in connection with the University at Leiden. A general reorganization after the war was made possible, partly through the appointment of a lecturer in child psychiatry at the Leiden University. At the universities of Utrecht and Amsterdam too, psychotherapy is practiced at the clinics for child psychiatry organized there, while the University at Groningen even appointed a professor of child psychiatry several years ago.

There are in Holland at the moment two pedagogic Institutes (Amsterdam and Nijmegen) where mentally disturbed children are observed. Educational institutions are connected with them.

Group psychotherapy also is being practiced in several university centers. The Psychiatric Clinic in Leiden produced a detailed investigation by Dr. A. C. Barentsen about group psychotherapy (1952) with a report on the various techniques, especially the analytic-cathartic one.

In the socio-therapeutic field there is a growing interest in the different psychiatric institutions, continuing the well-known insights of Simon, which had been propagated in Holland as far back as 1933, especially by W. M. van der Scheer. More and more the conviction is growing that the individual treatment of those suffering from neuroses also requires completion by sociotherapy. The insights of the French sociotherapeutic schools (Savadon, Daumezon, among others) have had a fertilizing influence in Holland. Through the construction of communities the beginning of the idea of "doing for the other" has been put into practice.

The structure of the Leiden University Psychiatric Clinic has been changed entirely under the influence of sociotherapy. All the patients carry a certain responsibility for one another and various patients have a special responsibility for a certain patient who has been assigned to them. By means of improvisation with the discussions which follow them, taking walks, and of completion of work assignments inside and outside the clinic, the consciousness of the community is strongly encouraged. The patients themselves put out a monthly chronicle of the clinic (approximately 20 pages). A council consisting entirely of patients has a far-reaching effect.

With reference to the psychotherapy of psychosomatic patients, these treatment methods are partly of suggestive, partly of analytic-cathartic nature. Particular attention is paid to group psychotherapy, especially in the case of these patients (suffering from various somato-neurotic disturbances). So-called brief psychotherapeutic treatment following the methods of Alexander and French is frequently applied.

Among the various cathartic methods the following are worthy of being mentioned: Hypno-catharsis according to Breuer/Freud; the sodium pentothal method; the method of rêve éveillé (Desoille); non-directive counseling (Rogers); logotherapy (Frankl/Caruso). Each of these may be the method of preference under certain circumstances; however, it is difficult to state this preference in such a brief presentation.

The limits of psychotherapy are determined by the structure of the patient, the structure of the psychotherapist, the developmental level of the patient, sex, management of the transference situation, and the goals of therapy. It is worthwhile to obtain an insight into the life curve of the patient (stamped by Rümke as the declining lifeline).

The physician engaged in psychotherapy requires a broad knowledge of humanity as background for his work of healing. Thus, more and more the problem of man's view of the world is brought into the foreground.

Progress of Psychotherapy in Norway

NIC WAAL

IN THIS FIELD the development has been favorable as regards both professional qualifications and organization. In the thirties there were only two small child guidance clinics in Norway, one headed by the author (who was the only child psychoanalyst in Norway who had trained at the Berlin Institute before Hitler came to power, the other, the out-patient clinic of the Mental Hygiene Association, accepting children for examination but giving no psychotherapy. Child psychiatry as a profession was not developed or organized. Since the war, many clinical psychologists have been trained partly in Norway and partly abroad. Since 1948 the mental hygiene movement has conducted a separate child guidance clinic, which is open, however, only two days a week. The consequent long waiting list made psychotherapy available only for a few patients. The Oslo Education Authority opened a child guidance clinic, which carried out group psychotherapy, usually with three groups. Later, several education authorities opened child guidance clinics. Until two years ago these were more concerned with educational psychology and guidance than with psychotherapy, since the training of psychotherapists had lagged behind and the lack of personnel made further development impossible.

In 1949 the Norwegian Association of Child Psychiatrists was organized as a genuine team organization. It was subdivided into sections: child psychiatrists, clinical psychologists, social workers, special teachers, treatment-home staff and nurses with special child psychiatric experience, and specialists in pediatrics from public health institutions. In 1950 child psychiatry became a separate specialized profession with its own board of certification.

The first child psychiatric clinic was opened by the University of Oslo in 1950. The author's institute started as a pioneer institution in 1951 and became a public foundation in 1953.

The individual treatment is of several kinds, i.e., child psychoanalysis, character analysis, vegeto-therapeutic, short psychotherapy, and supportive psychotherapy.

Group psychotherapy was introduced in different forms according to age groups. In the case of children of less than 8 years these were usually (1) psychoanalytical or (2) role playing; in the case of children from 8 to 16 (1) activity group psychotherapy, (2) musical group psychotherapy,

(3) role-playing, (4) art, (5) interview group psychotherapy, and (6) hobby groups and clubs of various types. All were supervised each week by two staff members. No children were accepted for psychotherapy if the parents did not cooperate by undergoing some form of psychotherapy themselves. Less neurotic parents received support of the case work type—sometimes child-centered—whereas severely disturbed parents were sent for deep psychotherapy.

Parents altered their attitude more quickly when the treatment was combined with group psychotherapy. Apart from this, all parents visiting the Institute were organized in an association for parents and friends to increase the parents' interest in and understanding of the problems of mental hygiene, and to help them accept their mentally disturbed children. The Mental Hygiene Association carried out well organized publicity in the form of a series of lectures which succeeded in raising considerable interest.

In the last few years, the group treatment has been broadened by the foundation of treatment homes with hospital status. The Child Psychiatric Clinic of the University in Oslo and the author's institute have opened four such treatment homes. The idea behind this was the creation of a permanent group-climate for the more disturbed children wherein individual group psychotherapy could be integrated. For the treatment of delinquent children and adolescents this was the most important development; with the inclusion of climate-therapy the treatment was successful in the majority of cases.

ADULT PSYCHOTHERAPY

Before the war psychiatrists did not feel the necessity of training in psychotherapy. They were in sharp conflict with the clinical psychologists. The growth of psychotherapy in Norway, however, was influenced to a great extent by psychology. This was mainly due to the Professor of Psychology in the University in Oslo, Harald Schjelderup, one of the first psychoanalysts in this country. Since the war, the younger psychiatrist has trained by personal analysis and by taking part in seminars in psychotherapy, the latter often in England and the United States. The conflict between the two professions was settled by means of an agreement, to the effect that clinical psychologists could be authorized as therapists if they worked in connection with psychiatric institutions or institutions for mental hygiene. The tendency seems to be to have all psychotherapy carried out in connection with a clinic.

It is significant to note that the legal profession in Norway is becoming more and more interested in using group psychotherapy in correctional institutions and prisons. In an open vocational school "without bars" for criminal youth, two psychologists have started group psychotherapy under senior supervision.

Public support for psychotherapy has been shown in two ways: All psychiatric examinations of children are fully paid by national insurance—the psychiatric, the clinical-psychological and the casework personnel are paid in this way. All forms of psychotherapy, both for children and parents, are subsidized in like manner, whether the therapy is conducted by a physician, clinical psychologist or caseworker. Although the payment is limited to 20 hours of treatment, this public recognition of the fact that mental disturbances are the responsibility of society is an important development.

Progress in Psychotherapy in South America

_____ARNALDO RASCOVSKY*

THERE IS A STEADILY growing concern about psychotherapeutic problems in Argentina. The celebrations of the centenary of the birth of Sigmund Freud were widely echoed in the principal scientific centers of the country. The year 1956 also witnessed the renewal of many activities that were suppressed under the previous dictatorial government; there were strong movements for reform in the university programs and for scientific orientation in general. In the Medical Faculty, for instance, a course of lectures was delivered as an introduction to psychosomatic medicine, and, for the first time, the Argentine Medical Association, which constitutes the leading medical organization in the country, solicited the preparation of a course on psychoanalysis for postgraduates. These facts point to the growing interest in the development of new techniques in the therapeutic armanentarium of the physician. Those responsible for psychotherapeutic training in Argentina consider indispensable the inclusion of either a didactic psychoanalysis or personal experience with psychoanalytic group therapy.

Formal psychoanalytic training in the Buenos Aires Institute is thorough and prolonged. The greatest stress is laid on the depth of the candidates' analysis, which takes on the average some 1000 hours. After 3 years of courses and seminars various study and research groups are organized. There has likewise been some attempt on the part of psychotherapists with analytic training to organize psychodrama along the lines described by Moreno.

The most significant progress in analytic-therapeutic research has been achieved by Angel Garma in his study of gastric ulcer and by Arnaldo Rascovsky and co-workers in their investigation of prenatal psychism. Garma has pointed out the significance of the internalized bad mother acting, through oral-digestive regression, in the production of gastric ulcer; therapy in such cases consists of making this destructive introjection conscious. Rascovsky believes that prior to the stage of postnatal relationship with the external object there exists an intense relationship of the ego with the inherited protophantasies lying in the id. At the earliest stages, perception, identification and delimitation of the ego constitute one single phenomenon. Phylogenetic inheritance is fulfilled in ontogenic development in that the ego

*With the collaboration of Durval Marcondes, Cyro Martins, Ignacio Matte Blanco, Carlos Alberto Seguin, and Juan Pereira Anavitarte.

perceives and identifies itself with the images originating from the id, which constitutes the ego's primitive environment before the advent of the real outer world.

The medical schools have not yet adopted measures to provide official psychotherapeutic training, but in the Philosophy Faculties of Rosario and Cordoba, the professional training of psychologists has recently been introduced. In Rosario the curriculum since 1955 is made up of 28 subjects, of which 23 are specifically psychological-scientific and 5 philosophical and pedagogical. The psychology course, based on practical research work which the students must complete in various districts and social institutions, includes psychometry, history of psychology, social psychology, characterology and typology, psychoanalysis, clinical psychology, parapsychology, etc. At the end of the year the student receives the degree of Assistant in Psychology; at the end of the fourth, that of Psychologist; and on acceptance of his thesis, that of Doctor in Psychology. The initial registration was 400 students. A corresponding modification of the medical curriculum is to be expected.

Besides the Argentine Psychoanalytic Association there is the Argentine Society for Psychology and Psychotherapy in Groups, which aims at promoting a type of collective psychotherapeutic training of a less exacting nature. There are also a number of psychoanalysts who are collaborating in group analysis and experimenting with the system of offering the patient both individual and collective sessions, following the general principles set forth by Bion, Foulkes, Ezfiel and Kraupl Taylor. The main premise is that in the individual psychoanalytic situation the patient acts with inner phantasied objects having a two-dimensional character, whereas in the group situation he can project these phantasies onto real outer objects of a four-dimensional character, which permits him a more intense cathexis. The Argentine Society of Medical Psychology, Psychoanalysis and Psychosomatic Medicine constitutes another important center of activity; it is of an exclusively medical character, being formed by members of the Argentine Medical Association, with which it is affiliated.

Four major congresses were held in Buenos Aires in 1956: the First National Psychiatric, the Latin American Psychoanalytic, the Second Ibero-American Medico-Psychologic, and the Second Latin American Mental Health. Over 1500 participants in the Medico-Psychologic Congress were addressed on its central theme of "Emotional Stress in Adaptation" by invited speakers from many countries, including Drs. Hans Selye and Erik Wittkower (Canada), Ramon Sarro (Spain), Heinrich Winnik (Israel) and Sidney Margolin and Jules Masserman (U.S.A.).

In Porto Alegre a psychoanalytic group, with facilities at the San Pedro

Hospital, has been formed with some members who have had their training in Buenos Aires. The most noteworthy effort is the development of analytic psychotherapy of groups, of which 13 have already been started with an average of 7 to 11 patients each. Both the Faculty of Medicine and the Medical Centers show warm interest in the training of psychotherapists, which is carried out mainly along analytic lines.

BRAZIL

Among the most important events in the field of psychotherapy in São Paulo during the year 1956 was the installation of the Department of Medical Psychology in the Riberao Preto Medical School, attached to São Paulo University. The aim of this department, which is under the direction of Prof. Sergio Rodriguez, is to impart instruction in psychology—including psychotherapy—to medical students in general, as part of their graduation course. A new medical school now being organized in the Santa Casa de Misericordia Hospital, also in São Paulo, is setting up an autonomous chair of Medical Psychology for the same purpose. The First Congress of the Brazilian Medical Association held in Riberao Preto, which had as part of its agenda the laying down of norms for medical training, resolved to promote the creation of chairs of this type in all the medical schools of Brazil, leaving it to the discretion of each school whether to set up an autonomous department.

Scientific reports presented during the year in São Paulo included the following: Adelheid Kock pointed out the two directions in which the feeling of omnipotence may develop as a defense mechanism, one destructive and the other constructive, the latter being bound up with sublimation. The clinical material appeared to show that an important factor of constructive omnipotence is the internalization of two good objects, one masculine and the other feminine, whose union within the subject favors the capacity of achieving sublimation in the professional or emotional field. Durval Marcondes sought to determine the basic factors of psychoanalytic cure connected with the analyst's attitudes in the counter-transference situation. He stressed the importance of the analyst's intuitive identification with the patient's infantile objects, relationships which are relived at every moment of the analysis. Through the action of counter-transference manifested in the interpretation, the analyst enables the patient to meet, in succession, his infantile objects, which, in the natural development of the individual, are represented by the parents in their behavior appropriate to each evolutionary stage.

In Rio de Janeiro the most outstanding event was the organization of the Rio de Janeiro Psychoanalytic Society, recognized by the International

Psychoanalytic Association and composed of several groups of psychoanalysts trained in England, Argentina and Brazil. Also an important fact was the recent organization of the Division on Psychoanalytic Research in the University of Rio de Janeiro under the direction of Prof. Decio Soares de Souza.

CHILE

Generally speaking, psychotherapy has definitely come to stay in Chile, even among the most recalcitrant "organicists." This may be partly the result of spontaneous evolution, but perhaps a good deal of it springs, directly or indirectly, from the influence of the titular Chair of Psychiatry at the Universidad de Chile, which is the most important university of the country. There exists a close union between the Chair and the Chilean Psychoanalytic Society, a recognized branch of the International Psychoanalytic Association; although both are independent from one another, almost all of the members of the first also belong to the second, with the result that their various activities exert an harmonious influence over the psychiatric environment.

The most salient developments during 1956 were 1. An increase of training activity at the Institute of Psychoanalysis. During the last 12 months 24 persons applied for training, of whom 8 were accepted. 2. Further developments in the teaching of psychiatry and elements of psychotherapy to the medical students. Group psychotherapy for all these students has been a regular part of the curriculum since 1953. In August, 1956, a summary of results was presented at the First Latin American Psychoanalytic Congress. 3. Short courses in various cities giving information to practitioners about psychopathologic problems in medical practice. 4. The official establishment of a complete training course for psychiatrists, with emphasis on psychotherapy. 5. The great development of group psychotherapy at the university outpatient department. Those who have especially worked at these developments in 1956 are Prof. Ignacio Matte-Blanco; Dr. Carlos Whiting, President of the Psychoanalytic Society; Dr. Fernando Allende Navarro, Honorary President; Dr. Ramon Ganzarain; Dr. Fernando Oyarzun, Dr. Hernan Davanzo and Dr. Carlos Nunez S., of the Catholic University of Santiago.

PERU

In Peru there still persists a clear antagonism between the "static" and "dynamic" factions in psychiatry. The former is embedded in genetic and phenomenologic concepts, leading to the intensive use of drugs and other biological treatments, with the application of, at most, some superficial psychotherapy of support. Dynamically oriented therapists, on the other hand, are intensifying their activities. The Peruvian Psychiatric Association, as their forum, is preparing the First Peruvian Psychiatric Congress. However, at present the only lecture course on psychotherapy is delivered at the Workmen's Hospital, where modern teaching techniques, including seminars, recorded interviews, etc., are regularly employed.

Uruguay

Until the creation of the Uruguayan Psychoanalytic Association, psychotherapy was principally that of support, along with the administration of medicaments, with some attempts at work-therapy, relaxation techniques and hypnotism. Recently, however, there have been two other developments: the application of group psychotherapy and the spread of psychoanalysis.

Group psychotherapy, following the methods of Bion, was started by Prof. Madeleine Baranger in 1955, and is exclusively performed by psychotherapists and observer-members of the Psychoanalytic Association. It was introduced into Velardebo Hospital, with psychotic and neurotic patients, on the initiative of Prof. Fortunato Ramirez, and in Maciel Hospital, and in Dr. Juan T. Fischer's Polyclinic of Endocrinology and Psychosomatic Medicine, with patients suffering from hyperthyroid disorders and hirsutism. In view of the interest with which group therapy has been greeted and the theoretic-clinical problems it poses, a seminar of group psychotherapists was organized as the nucleus of a future Association of Collective Therapy, which is to work alongside the Psychoanalytic Association.

Psychoanalysis is practiced in accordance with the views of the English School of Melanie Klein. Since 1956 the Association publishes its quarterly review, finding readers in medical, psychiatric and educational circles. Other types of psychotherapy have been offered for some years as follows: relaxation and work therapy at Velardebo (Psychiatric) Hospital; eclectic methods at the Medico-Psychological Clinic of the "Pedro Visca" Children's Hospital ("The Roosevelt School for Crippled Children"); the "Morey Otero" Psychopedagogic Laboratory for school children with personality and behavior problems; the Children's Council for waifs and strays and delinquent children and adolescents; and hypnotism at the "Pereira Rossell" Children's Hospital.

Psychotherapy in Cuba

JOSE ANGEL BUSTAMANTE

NEUROPSYCHIATRY IS PRACTISED IN CUBA by several groups whose concern, over the years, has been to raise both its level and that of the various branches or sub-specialties which came into being as a result of its upsurge. Conversely, as an increasing number of specialists were drawn into this field, these branches, which came about as a natural consequence of the neuro-psychiatric movement, provided the needed framework for the development of neuropsychiatry.

Early in the century the University of Havana created the Chair of Neurology and Psychiatry and this aspect of medical practice was included in the curriculum of the School of Medicine.

The Cuban Society of Neurology and Psychiatry, founded in 1925, was active for a number of years and later discontinued its activities until, in 1942, a group of psychiatrists undertook the task of reorganizing it and bringing it back to life. Dr. Oscar Sagredo, Dr. Rafael Larragoiti, Dr. Julio Reymondez and the author devoted themselves to such an undertaking and since then the Society has been fully active. By means of joint sessions with other scientific societies it also did much to introduce neuro-psychiatric concepts into other branches of medicine.

In due course its growth, the increased membership of those engaged in this specialty and the world-wide development and subdivision of neuro-pyschiatry was felt in Cuba, and specialized organizations branched off from the original Cuban Society of Neurology and Psychiatry: the Cuban Society of Psychotherapy and the Cuban Society of Psychoanalysis, the Group of Reflexologic Medicine, the League Against Epilepsy and the Cuban League for Mental Hygiene. Some years ago the latter once more resumed its activities.

The Cuban League for Mental Hygiene is a member of the World Federation for Mental Health. The Latin American Psychiatric Association was jointly founded by a group of psychiatrists, members of the Cuban Society of Neurology and Psychiatry, and other groups in Latin America. To enter the Cuban Society of Psychotherapy, founded in 1949, it is necessary to have had previous training and to pass the required tests and examinations. For that purpose, the candidate manages cases under the training supervision of a charter member until completing the specified number of hours and is then examined by three charter members of the Society appointed for that purpose.

The Cuban Society of Psychoanalysis, founded in 1951, requires the candidate to complete a training analysis and to pass the necessary seminars and tests. For over ten years the members of this group have been practicing psychotherapy for psychoanalytic orientation purposes. In 1949 Dr. Spartacco Scarizza, a member of the Italian Association of Psychoanalysis, came to live in Cuba; in 1950 he was authorized by the Cuban Medical Association to practise psychoanalysis in our country and began by analyzing the members of this group.

In 1951, due to the efforts of the author, who represented this group with Dr. Ernest Jones, Dr. Leo H. Bartemeier came to Havana. Dr. Bartemeier was interested by the activities of the group and was given full details concerning the status of Cuban psychiatry. Since 1951 and up to the present Dr. Bartemeier has been visiting Cuba twice a year and, by means of clinical lectures, has been teaching the psychoanalytic group techniques and the continuous followup of cases. In December, 1952, Dr. Phyllis Greenacre, of New York, came to Havana and conducted seminars for this group. Besides those already mentioned, other stimulating and enlightening visits were paid by Dr. Arnaldo Rascovsky, of Argentina, in 1950, Dr. Spurgeon English, of Philadelphia, in 1953, Dr. Rene Spitz, of New York, who participated in the National Congress of Psychiatry held in Cuba in 1954, and Dr. Frederick C. Redlich, of the Yale University Psychiatry Department, in 1955. Both Dr. Spitz and Dr. Redlich gave lectures to the group.

Dr. Frisso Potts and the author practice group psychotherapy.

There are thirty practising psychotherapists, members of the Society of Psychotherapy, in the city of Havana, and one or two in each of such cities as Santiago de Cuba, Camagüey, Holguin, Santa Clara and Cienfuegos. Ten have completed their training analysis and practise psychoanalysis.

As to the official centers, psychotherapy is practised in the Mazorra mental institution where a special department is concerned with the pictorial work of the patients. This department was created in 1954 by Dr. Armas Pacheco. It has also built a theater for the application of psychodrama.

Psychotherapy in Mexico

EMANUEL K. SCHWARTZ

THE HUMAN SITUATION

THE HISTORY AND PRESENT STATUS of psychotherapy in Mexico can be understood only in context of the life of the Mexican people. Some of the conditions impeding or facilitating the development of psychotherapy are briefly presented.

Mexico, a land of extreme geographic diversity, has a complex ethnic structure. Of its 25-30 million people, 15 per cent are white, 30 per cent are Indian, and 55 per cent are mixed. Language barriers arise. Many Indians do not speak Spanish or even the same Indian language. Illiteracy and a low general level of education exist. Although there has been a large-scale and concerted effort to eradicate illiteracy, for example, by producing reading materials in local Indian languages, the problem is still acute. Today, about 30 per cent of the total population ten years of age and over is analphabetic, as contrasted with nearly 75 per cent in 1900. In some rural areas with schools, not less than 20 per cent are absent because of economic reasons, and another 15-20 per cent because of illness. The relative number of physicians and other professionals is among the lowest in the Western hemisphere. Nevertheless, Mexico is ahead of the other Central American countries in the quality of medical training and care.

Difficulty in education as well as in psychotherapy is due also to ambivalence toward things foreign. There is almost fanatical retention of old customs and language, with much resistance to giving up what is their own, partly out of appreciation of its worth and partly as reaction to internal revolutions and foreign aggressions.

Mexico has a society with sharp group and class distinctions. People *de cultura* are different from the *campecinos;* 65 per cent of the Mexicans live in communities of less than 2500. The Indian, the *Mestizo,* the immigrant and the foreigner have subtle and reciprocal prejudices against each other. Male and female are hierarchically related in that order, and maleness is regarded by both as ideal.

Economic depletion has had dire effects. Only 48.8 per cent of the total number of children born alive survive to the thirtieth year; only about 25 per cent reach any age beyond thirty-five; in some communities, 50 per cent never reach the fifth year of life. But infant mortality is the second most frequent cause of death; the first is gastrointestinal infections related to poor hygienic conditions and low standard of living. Grave malnutrition is also a basic problem.

Superstition and unrest pervade the people. Witchcraft is a common experience. Although the majority religion is manifestly Catholic, it is super-imposed upon native religious practices and ideologies which interweave and foster confusion. An ethical foundation of the family is obedience, and brutality is sometimes used to assure it. Divorce is becoming more frequent. Problems of authority and aggression join to give Mexico the highest homicide rate in the world. The rate of suicide also is high, especially in adolescence, where the incidence for females is twice that of males. Juvenile delinquency and adult crime are common.

Violence, sorcery, alcoholism and the like are tolerated, removing individual and social pressure for change. Life is cheap. There is a widespread death cult. Pessimism is the prevailing mood.

THE PSYCHODYNAMIC SITUATION

Interest in cultural patterns and personality traits, in "Mexicanness," has been intense. More is known about small isolated groups than modern societal trends. In this connection, psychoanalytic practice may provide material not otherwise immediately available. Psychoanalysts and other social scientists have turned attention to contemporary family life and the quality of being Mexican. As in any culture, no one type of Mexican character obtains. At best, a few observations or generalizations having some concensual validation of some groups of Mexicans are offered here.

Machismo, that is, penility, or the idea of being a man, colors the relationship of father to mother and children. The male needs to prove himself, to be the tyrannical authority in the family; the woman is self-sacrificing, submissive without questioning; the children completely obedient to both. There is great hostility to the father and to paternity. Family difficulty is a prime motivation for seeking psychotherapy and being *macho* is resistance against it. To need help is not *macho.* If a husband finally seeks help and later the wife also enters treatment, the husband quits. It is always the woman's problem, even if he is impotent.

The mother, too, is resented. During the first year of life the child gets plenty of sucking; 95 per cent of the children are breast-fed. He is closely attached to the mother, wrapped in her *rebozo.* At the end of the first year he is separated from her, feels abandoned and left to his own devices, because of the next child. A large number of pregnancies influences the nature of mother-child relations and affects mental health. Many families are female-dominated because the father actually abandons the family or has a second family elsewhere. There is often a grandmother on the scene, part of the female-centered stabilizing force. As adults, men abandon women, but in song, art and literature it is the woman who abandons the man. He negates the reality and, in depression, reverts to abandonment feelings of early infancy.

There is vacillation between feelings of inferiority and superiority, between domination and submission, between old and new, between commiserating and being secretive about good fortune, between a paranoid orientation and a depressed one. The Mexican seeks to isolate himself from reality, to become invulnerable before his enemies or the impact of the external world. Even to the woman he loves he responds with reserve. He suffers with dignity, he dissimulates, is formalistic and ritualistic. If one is intimate there is no respect. In acts of aggression he maintains a manifestly middle tone; he does not express his violence loudly. Only fiestas, fireworks and the bullfight permit a break-through. He negates life and is indifferent to death. As the saying goes, life and death are never separated, and the sooner death the better. There is little present frustration for future gratification. Self-criticism is practically unknown behavior, and the idea of improving oneself is rare.

The Psychotherapeutic Situation

Six years ago Mexico had not a single psychotherapist. In view of the resistance already suggested, why are psychoanalysis and psychotherapy in general now more widely accepted? At least three reasons may be adduced.

First, much education of the lay and professional public has been done. The *Liga Mexicana de Salud Mental* conducts a program of publication and conferences, especially for the laity, and an information service. The World Federation for Mental Health (1951), with which the League is affiliated, the Interamerican Society of Psychology (1954), and the American Psychiatric Association (1954), for example, have held congresses in Mexico. Specialists from abroad have been invited to present their ideas, and foreign books are being translated into Spanish. Local and national professional societies and public health, education and social services also have contributed to an awareness of mental health.

Second, the number of trained professional personnel, although shockingly smaller than the need, has increased. Today there are about 25 psychoanalysts with training and a larger group of professional workers doing some kind of therapy. In the entire republic there are about 120 medical specialists in neurology and psychiatry, about 20 graduate clinical psychologists, only 5 graduate psychiatric nurses, and, at best, 2 psychiatric social workers. Almost all are located in Mexico City; a few are in other urban centers like Monterrey and Guadalajara. Many of these mental health workers engage in therapeutic and preventive activities.

Third, and probably most important, are the small beginnings of a middle class in a somewhat open society. A growing middle class seeks to convert and control the environment and rejects physical as well as behavioral disorder. The cinema, radio and television, and the presence on the market of such consumer goods as washing machines and deep-freezers, point to better standards of living. Change is not only desirable but possible. Psychotherapy can flourish only where there is the feeling that "one can do something about it."

Theoretical interest in psychotherapy began in the twenties and early thirties when dissertations scrutinizing psychoanalytic theory and technique were presented to the faculty of medicine and the graduate school. In 1937 the faculty of philosophy of the national university founded a three-year course in professional psychology. By 1950, under the leadership of the psychiatrist Ráu González Enríquez, courses in psychotherapy and character therapy were added to the curriculum. González Enríquez had also argued the importance of Freud in psychotherapy before the faculty of medicine (1949). He gathered around him a group of physicians who started to study Freud and the implications of psychoanalysis for psychotherapy. Articles on culture and personality with specific reference to Mexican family life had already been appearing.

Concern with reconstructive psychotherapy as a practical matter began in the 1940's when a group of young psychiatrists expressed openly their dissatisfaction with the kind of nondynamic psychiatry they had been taught and were practising. They left Mexico to get analytic training in the United States, Argentina, and France. The stay-at-homes were provoked into procuring, through González Enríquez, the services of Erich Fromm. The ethico-religious humanism of Fromm has a somewhat greater appeal to Mexicans than the Freudian approach; it has a less foreign feel. He accepted for training, about 1951, a group of ten psychiatrists. He also encouraged their study of the role of the mother in Mexican personality development.

The psychologist and psychiatrist Rogelio Diaz-Guerrero, who later wrote the first published paper on psychotherapy for Mexican psychiatry, gave leadership to the establishment in 1951 of a psychological service center at the Mexico City College. Counselling and psychotherapy for adults and play therapy for children were offered. The patient population consisted of native and foreign students at the college as well as Mexicans from outside. Testing for schools as well as other kinds of consultive services were provided. However, the center was closed under pressure one year later.

In 1954 Oswaldo Robles, the philosopher psychiatrist, who had been developing a kind of Thomistic-existential therapy (logoterapia), gave critical lectures on psychoanalysis which were later published under the title *Freud a la distancia.* The work aroused public debate and opposition by the psychoanalysts; if nothing else, it showed that growing forces for psychotherapy were developing.

The present state of affairs is that two groups of analysts and a few dynamically oriented nonpsychoanalytically trained psychotherapists are doing psychotherapy in Mexico. The first group consists of Fromm's ten trainees, among whom are some of the most politically influential psychiatrists, who hold the important teaching posts. They are joined in the *Sociedad Mexicana de Psicoanálisis.* One of the limitations of the Fromm school is that as a one-man-institution there is little opportunity for feedback, for checking and correcting individual distortions, since essentially analyst, teacher and supervisor are one person.

The psychiatrists who had gone abroad returned equipped to do analytic therapy. They founded the *Grupo Mexicano de Estudios Psicoanalíticos,* which is affiliated with the International Psychoanalytic Association. There are five full members and five candidates. They created also the *Fundación Psicoanalítica Mexicana,* which sponsors the *Clínica Mexicana de Psicoterapia.* The Foundation has twelve trainees, and the Clinic is the first low-cost, analytically oriented, out-patient treatment, training and research center in Mexico. The clinic, directed by Santiago Ramírez, who is also president of the Foundation, has an individual adult therapy department headed by Ramón Parres; a group therapy department headed by José Luis Gonzales; a child therapy department with Francisco Gonzales Piñeda and Estela Remus; a clinical psychology department headed by Luis Feder; and a social work department. José Remus is clinic administrator, Fernando Cesarman is in charge of admissions, and Nathaniel S. Wollf is head of the library. In addition, collaborating members of the Foundation, Carlos Corona and Rafael Barajas, are in Guadalajara and Monterrey, respectively.

At the Clinic, patients who cannot afford private fees are accepted for treatment. They are generally middle class professional and semi-professional people for whom the monthly charge averages 200 pesos ($16.00). A complete workup is done, with psychiatric interview, social work history, and psychological testing. From staff discussion, a treatment plan is evolved for those who are accepted in individual and/or group therapy.

In order to compare clinic patients with those seen in the private offices of psychoanalysts, I made a survey of about 100 patients. (I am grateful to the members of the Fundación for their cooperation.) These patients range in age between 20 and 54, with an average age of 33 years; 48 per cent are men and 52 per cent are women. So far as could be determined, no children are being treated privately at this time. About half (52%)

are Mexicans, and half are foreigners, including Americans, Canadians, Poles, Germans, Greeks, Bulgarians, and Spaniards. On the average, patients come for three individual analytic sessions each week, and the average fee per session is 60 pesos (approximately $5). There is at present no indication that anyone is doing group therapy in private practice, although attempts have been made.

In addition to psychoanalytic practice, some psychiatrists practicing psychotherapy cannot free themselves entirely of organic therapies; one hears of strange amalgams of psychological therapies and physical therapies. Others combine dianetics, psychoanalysis and conditioning; still others combine metaphysics, psychoanalysis and religion. There are some therapeutic activities which, at this time, cannot be reported in any detail. Much good individual counselling and group public educational programs are done by *Los Amigos de México* (Society of Friends). There is also a tiny group of Adlerians. Moreover, many educators and social workers do a kind of re-education or therapeutic-educational work with parents as well as with children. There are beginnings of music therapy.

One unusual development that needs to be reported more fully relates to the attempt to provide the medical student from his first year on with an opportunity to understand his own personal problems and the nature of interpersonal relations. Autobiographical material and dreams are brought to individual and group sessions. The student gets practical counselling for himself and, in turn, participates in personal tests and field studies, together with teachers and fellow-students. The aim is a new type of physician who has had personal counselling and practical experience in the areas of psychological orientation. The plan was created and implemented by Alfonso Millán, who is Chairman of the Department of Psychiatry of the university medical school, President of the Mexican League for Mental Health and a member of the Fromm group.

There is great and growing interest in various forms of group therapy. The earliest experience with group therapy began in 1948 at the *Hospital Infantil*. Twenty-six children of school age were treated in a group setting by the psychiatrist Ramón de la Fuente and the social worker Leonor Torres Cravioto. Two years later, at the same place, Luis Feder started two new groups of neurotic children (with some interviews with the mothers) and utilized an observer. Group therapy for psychotic adults was first initiated in 1954 at the neuropsychiatric clinic of Manuel G. Falcón, who was also the President of the Mexican Society of Neurology and Psychiatry. The idea of group therapy is attractive to the Mexican because it is much more economical and therefore more attainable than individual therapy. Group therapy sessions are being held for boys and girls at the domiciles of the Juvenile Court (*Centros de Observaciones* of the *Tribunal Para*

Menores). It has even been recommended that group therapy for pupils in the elementary and secondary schools be provided as part of the regular schedule.

Psychodrama is known in Mexico and has been utilized on and off in different settings. One of the most interesting adaptations of the psychodrama is a kind of short-term treatment in the *Centros de Observaciones* of the *Tribunal Para Menores*. The youngsters are given the opportunity to observe a dramatic presentation of improvised characters manifesting conflicts and problems of juveniles. Although the experience is somewhat removed and the discussion largely evaluative and educational, it has, nevertheless, some therapeutic effects. Play therapy, occupational therapy and something called "disciplinary therapy" are also part of the program of the *Centros*.

This discussion of children and psychotherapy cannot be concluded without mentioning the long history of efforts in Mexico with the physically and psychologically abnormal child. Robert Solís Quiroga instituted the therapeutic program of the *Tribunal para Menores* and fostered homogeneous grouping of mentally abnormal children, for whom he provided specialists in the particular area. Current estimates in Mexico suggest as many as 100,000 mentally retarded children. A large number may be trainable but have emotional complications. Locally developed norms for intelligence and other tests are lacking, although in recent years some work has been done to develop appropriate testing materials. At present, some of the psychological and psychodiagnostic tests in use are the Rorschach, the TAT (with and without modifications), the Bender-Gestalt, various forms of the Binet, and the Gesell scale.

BIBLIOGRAPHY

ARANDA LOPEZ, J.: Problemas psicológicos de los niños de las minorias. Criminalia 22:363-367, 1956.

BÁEZ, SANTOYO, R.: El trabajo social y la readaptación del menor infractor. Escuela de Trabajo Social, Universidad Nacional Autonoma de México, 1953.

BALLESTEROS USANO, A.: Suicides in adolescence. Proceedings of the Fourth International Congress of Mental Health. La Prensa Medica Mexicana, Mexico, D.F., 1952. Pp. 281-289.

CAMPOS, A.: El aprecio por la vida y los trabajadores. Psiquis 10-11:6-8, 1955.

CASTRO DE LA FUENTE, A.: Algunos problemas psicológicos presentan con la utilización de la lengua indígena en la enseñanza, entre los grupos Tarasco y Otomí del Valle de Mezquital. Criminalia 22:360-362, 1956.

DIAZ-GUERRERO, R.: Algunos aspectos operantes de la Psicoterapia. Arch. mex. Neurol. & Psiquiat. 2:17-22, 1953.

——: El criterio de profundidad en psicoterapia. Arch. mex. Neurol. & Psiquiat. 1:202-209, 1953.

———: Neurosis and the Mexican family structure. Am. J. Psychiat. *112*:411-417, 1955.

———: Teoría y resultados preliminares de un ensayo de determinación del grado de salud mental, personal y social del Mexicana de la ciudad. Psiquis *2*: 31, 1952.

ESCARCEGA PERAZA, H.: Ensayo sobre la Estructura Psicológica y Social de la Familia. Escuela de Trabajo Social, Universidad Autonoma de México, 1956.

FEDER, L.: Valoración Psicodinámica de los Cinco Principales Métodos de la Psicoterapia de Grupo. Universidad Nacional Autonoma de México, 1954.

LEWIS, O.: Life in a Mexican Village. Urbana, Univ. of Illinois Press, 1951.

MILLÁN, A.: La enseñanza de la medicina psicológica. Gaceta Medica de México *85*:329-340, 1955.

———: Some problems of Mexican student mental health. The department of medical psychology and mental health, school of medicine, University of Mexico. International Work Conference on Student Mental Health. Princeton, 1956.

NUÑEZ, R.: El psicodiagnóstico de Rorschach aplicado a niños. Departamento de Psicología, Universidad Nacional Autonoma de México, 1954.

PALERM, A.: Observations on the development of the middle class in Latin America. Working paper, 29th Study Session, International Institute of Differing Civilizations, London, 1955.

PASCUAL DEL RONCAL, F.: Teoría y practica del psicodiagnóstico de Rorschach. Sociedad Universitaria Mexicana, S.A., Mexico, D.F., 1949.

PAZ, O.: El Laberinto de la Soledad. Cuadernos Americanos, No. 16, Mexico, D.F., 1950.

Proceedings of the Fourth International Congress of Mental Health, Mexico City, December 11-19, 1951. La Prensa Medica Mexicana, Mexico, D.F., 1952.

Psychiatric Research Reports 2. American Psychiatric Association, Washington, D.C., 1956.

RAMIREZ, S.: Estructura psicológica del Mexicano. Sobretiro de Letras Potosinas *13*:115, San Luis Potosi, Mexico, 1955.

RAMOS, S.: El Perfil del Hombre y la Cultura en México. Pedro Robredo, Mexico, D.F., 1938.

RITZENTHALER, R. E. AND PETERSON, F. A.: The Mexican Kickapoo Indians. Milwaukee Public Museum, Publications in Anthropology No. 2, 1956.

SHORE, A.: Autoritarismo y agresión en una aldea Mexicana. Universidad Nacional Autonoma de México, 1954.

VELASCO ALZAGA, J. M.: Magnitud del Problema Mental en México. Departamento de Psiquiatría, Hospital Infantil, Mexico, D.F., 1954.

VIQUIERA, CARMEN Y PALERM, A.: Alcoholismo, brujería y homocidio en dos communidades rurales de México. América Indígena *14*:7-36, 1954.

WOYTINSKY, W. S. AND WOYTINSKY, E. S.: World Population and Production. New York, The Twentieth Century Fund, 1953.

Cross-Cultural Aspects of Socio-Cultural Therapy

JOHN GILLIN

THE IDEA THAT THE mental hospital may serve as a therapeutic community has moved toward the center of attention in psychiatric thinking during recent years. The concept involves not only a detailed technical knowledge of the social and cultural content and functioning of the hospital situation and the roles of staff and patients therein, but also the opportunity to experiment with various types of socio-cultural organization within the hospital.

The treatment of at least certain types of mental patients may be enhanced by measures that reintegrate them into something resembling normal group life and that give the patients experience in the practice of problem-solving activities approved of and expected by the followers of the general culture to which they are supposed to return. The therapeutic procedures based on this hypothesis we have called socio-cultural therapy.

The hypothesis has been tested without benefit of hospitals in a number of other cultures. I propose to describe certain aspects of folk psychotherapy that I had an opportunity to study intensively at intervals over a period of 12 years in a Guatemalan community called San Luis Jilotepeque. I shall not attempt definitive psychiatric diagnosis, but shall merely mention by way of orientation such diagnostic indicators as I have at hand.

San Luis is a rural community of about 10,000 population, 60 per cent of whom are Indians of the Pokomám linguistic Maya stock, the remainder Ladinos. The Indians are bilingual; the Ladinos speak only Spanish. The Indians follow a much acculturated but distinctive "native" culture; the Ladinos practice a rural version of the modern Latin American culture, which is a form of western civilization developed in Latin America over the last four-and-a-half centuries. Although at the time of the study most Ladinos participated to some extent in the system of folkloristic medicine and psychiatry, in order to simplify the presentation I shall here confine myself to certain aspects of "psychiatry," if we may call it that, in the Indian group.

The Indian culture, while stable, is restricted in scope and comparatively undiversified in content. Generally speaking, the only occupational roles open to men are those of farmer or farm laborer, cattle raiser, and part-time peddler. Women, most of whom make pottery in the home for sale, look forward only to being housewives. There are two Indians who operate barber shops and a few couples who tend small stores on a part-time basis. Although there are some more than usually expert craftsmen, there are no true craft or occupational groups. The Indians have several *cofradías,* or semi-religious fraternities, and there is a hierarchy of offices culminating in the six Principal Men of the community, a group that exercises religious, judicial, and some political functions. But participation in the offices is phrased as "assuming a burden" (*carga*) which one must take as an obligation rather than as a prize to be won in competition. Some Indians are richer than others, but there are no social classes based on wealth or any other criterion. Competition and overt aggression is socially taboo, although some of this sort of thing does occur under the influence of alcohol. In scope the Indian culture of San Luis is confined to the community and three neighboring communities. San Luis is one of only five places in the Guatemalan nation where the Pokomám tongue is still spoken. There are no pathways provided by the local Indian culture that lead to prominence of any kind outside the community. Socially, the Indians are in a caste position vis-a-vis the Ladinos, who consider themselves "better" and "higher" than the Indians and who withhold certain rewarding goals from them. So long as he follows his own culture and retains identity with his own social caste, however, the Indian is seldom punished.

Now I should like to mention briefly two psychiatric syndromes in this situation and say something about the folk socio-cultural therapy used with each. These are magical fright (or *espanto, susto*) and the personality types of curers themselves.

A generally recognized ailment in San Luis and many other parts of Latin America is a condition that in English can be called "magical fright." Many persons have suffered from this condition and consider that they have been successfully cured. In San Luis the pattern of onset in all cases is as follows. The history always shows that the attack has been preceded by a period of mental stress or physical illness or both. Sometime during this period of stress or shortly afterward the patient is suddenly frightened or startled, usually by an apparently trivial incident. He falls down in a fright, as they say, during which he at least momentarily loses consciousness. The fright causes the patient's mouth to fall open, at which time his soul escapes and is snatched and carried away by certain "devils" or renegade saints to a hiding place in the nearby mountains. Left unprotected by the soul, the body is invaded by evil winds (*aires*) that cause physical illness.

According to the native thinking, loss of the soul in this manner is extremely serious and must be cured as soon as possible, since a soulless body cannot live for long in this world, and a soul which has left its body before death cannot see heaven.

Returned to his dwelling, the patient exhibits a characteristic syndrome, the most prominent features of which are social withdrawal from family and friends, reluctance or failure to fulfill expected roles, and signs of depression combined with acute anxiety. The patient usually sits in a corner of the house in a sad, dejected manner, confining his verbalizing to whining complaints about his physical condition and worried, anxious ruminations of a general nature. Although this mumbling and moaning is often carried on in an apparently autistic manner, without being directed to anyone in particular, all the patients I have seen were capable of being reached by me. I have never seen manic behavior in such patients.

My impression is that within the culture of these people "magical fright" occupies somewhat the same position as the so-called "nervous breakdown" in certain circles of our own society. One patient may have an anxiety attack with depression, another a simple depression, still another may be suffering from hysteria, and so on. But the attack of magical fright is a culturally patterned and socially condoned escape hatch for individuals who, for one reason or another, are unable, at least temporarily, to stand the strains of life and who have suffered disorganization of the ego mechanisms.

Physical symptoms may vary, but they usually include a low fever (which does not respond to antibiotics or antimalarial treatment with quinine), "loose" bowels, headache, various other aches and pains, loss of appetite, lack of energy, and general listlessness. These are, as I have said, attributed to the evil winds that have entered the body at the time the soul escaped. In making the diagnosis a native curer regards a certain "jumpiness" of the pulses as the most important sign.

The cure involves many steps which, although rationalized in a different context, suggest at least a crude analogy with modern psychiatric practice. I will mention the successive stages of the cure, but I wish to underline the parallels with socio-cultural therapy. To start the recovery one of the six professional *curanderos* among the Indian population is engaged by an intermediary, usually a member of the family. Such a curer must be paid in cash and charges a fee which is high enough to be "felt." He supervises all phases of the "cure" which, without its aftermath, usually lasts from a few days to a week. The actual curing session itself can take place only on Friday night.

(1) The curer first conducts a diagnostic interview, including feeling of the pulses. The patient is induced to tell his recent preoccupations, activities and dreams. If the curer decides that the patient is suffering from magical fright rather than some other condition such as bewitchment, evil eye, or corpse sickness, the cure continues. The interview usually elicits a mildly cathartic "confession" from the patient. (2) Assurance is given the patient

and a certain "transference" established, that is, the patient is induced to have confidence in the curer. (3) The practitioner next endeavors to assuage the physical complaints, using pharmaceutical as well as folkloristic preparations. (4) The patient is drawn from his social isolation. (I shall return to this later). (5) A *Principal,* one of the six highest religious and civic authorities in the native community, is engaged to participate in the cure. (6) With the help of the Principal an elaborate ritual is carried out, explaining the situation to the images of the Christian saints. This is necessary to gear the cure into the Christian scheme of things because commerce must later be had with familiar spirits of the curer and renegade saints who have captured the soul. (7) An expedition is made in the middle of the night to the site of the alleged fright, where the occult captors of the soul are appealed to on a man-to-man basis by the curer and are provided an offering of worldly goods for their enjoyment. (8) The patient is massaged with eggs in the shell which are supposed to draw the illness out of him. The eggs are then broken in water and an augury is read in the shapes of the floating whites. Some curers use the eggs as part of the diagnosis; most practitioners employ them as a magical verification of the cure. (9) The curer takes the patient naked into the chill night air at 2 a.m. and, without warning, blows from his mouth numerous blasts of magic mixture over him. This is said to blow the evil winds out of the body, but also serves as a sort of "shock treatment." (10) The patient is given a cathartic drink. (11) He is thoroughly rubbed down, wrapped in blankets, and put to bed to sweat. (12) Before the patient goes to sleep a bowl of *copal* gum with hot coals is placed under his bed and is so manipulated by the curer that the *copal* bursts into flames and envelops the patient in a cloud of sweet-smelling smoke. (Copal was the sacred incense of the ancient Maya.) The flame is regarded as a sign that the soul has returned to the body. The patient usually sinks into a deep, relaxed sleep. Although he may have to get up during the night to empty his bowels, due to the cathartic administered during the curing session, he typically awakens the next day in a cheerful frame of mind and restored to his "normal" personality. Some patients catch cold during the curing session, but all cases I have seen had discarded their neurotic symptoms, at least for the time being. In many patients the "cure" lasts for life, with no further attacks of magical fright. On the other hand, one old woman in our series had been "cured" eight times up to the age of 63.

Whatever the therapeutic value of the other aspects of the treatment, the socio-cultural features are of great importance. All patients, as I have said, exhibit social withdrawal. And most of them in their diagnostic interview with the curer bring out certain material relating to interpersonal conflicts and feelings of social inadequacy. At the first session the curer makes it plain to the patient that the latter will be responsible for the staging and equipment of the curing sessions. Family and friends must be invited to participate and will help, and a "servant" is appointed or hired, but all such people are guests of the patient who is the responsible host and he is also expected and required to direct their activities. Thus the patient is made the center, in a well-defined and active role, of a group of people who show that they "care" about his recovery.

Diagnosis is always made several days before the Friday night curing session in order to allow time for proper preparations. Seldom less than 15 to 20 kinsmen and friends are engaged in the preparatory activities and as spectators at the all-night affair on Friday. Pharmaceutical products as well as herbs and simples must be secured in precise quantities, prescribed by the curer, and must be properly ground and mixed for remedies and magic potions. A Principal Man must be invited to take part in the cure. His very presence and participation symbolizes the interest of the whole Indian community in the patient. But since he is one of the most revered personages of the community, it is essential that he not be inconvenienced or annoyed by a managerial fiasco.

On the Friday night of the ceremony two sumptuous meals must be served to the company and suitable amounts of liquor must be provided. All ingredients of remedies and magic potions must be ready. The house must be properly decorated. Numerous candles of various sizes must be available for ceremonial as well as lighting purposes. Securing food, wood, and all the other essentials create many problems. All this is made to seem the responsibility of the patient with the aid of his helpers. Whatever the objective results (and the friends and relatives always see that a minimum level is reached), the patient is carefully praised by all present; he is assured that he is a social success.

Thus the patient is drawn back into social relations and nudged into playing a rewarded social role. This, I submit, is a form of socio-cultural therapy. Yet the costs of such an affair are so high in terms of bodily and mental pain, anxiety, and money that few persons in this community could afford to "take the cure just for the fun of it."

If we assume, for the sake of argument, that magical fright is a label for a type or types of neurotic condition, what about psychotics among the Indians of San Luis?

Let us turn to the curers or native psychiatrists themselves. At the time of the studies there were six practising members of this profession in the Indian portion of the community. (There were also two Ladino practitioners.) We obtained fairly full life stories and also Rorschach protocols on all of the Indian *curanderos*. The Rorschachs were mixed with a series from the general population and were read "blind" by Dr. Otto Billig, at that time a member of the psychiatric staff of Duke University, now at Vanderbilt. Dr. Billig picked out the six curers' protocols and set them aside with the notation that, although he had no idea what these individuals were in San Luis, if he were to see such records in the United States he would suspect that, if not schizophrenic, they were at least schizoid personalities. After going over the ethnologists' notes and life history material he felt that his first impressions, based upon the Rorschachs, were greatly strengthened.

This raises the question that is still being argued in the literature: whether there is a distinct process or syndrome that can be identified as schizophrenia cross-culturally among all groups or societies of the human species, regardless of the cultural details of its manifestations. For the present, let us assume that there is.

The curers do not learn their art from fellow professionals, but believe that they acquire it in dreams. These dreams have a common format, but each individual believes that a special patron saint appears to him and tells him it is his duty to take up curing, shows him various methods and recipes, and so on. Later, the spirits and saints who snatch away souls also appear in his dreams and he forms a friendly relationship with them. Some people resist such dream visitors and say that they are finally freed from them. All the established curers claim that they have resisted strongly but have finally given in. A successful curer is said to have the *resignación,* that is, he has yielded.

These men live what in North America would be regarded as an active fantasy life. They are frequently in verbal contact with their patron saints and their familiar spirits. They also "see" many things that other people do not. They spend a good deal of time alone. My co-workers and I have spent much time with them and have extensive notes of their conversations. There is no doubt in the curers' minds that their otherworldly contacts and experiences are to them "real."

But in San Luis these men are not regarded as "peculiar"; on the contrary, they are thought of as "gifted." There is a recognized and respected place for them in the local society. What in another setting might be seen as symptoms of mental illness are here read as signs of the strength of their spiritual contacts and knowledge gained therefrom. The curers all carry on farming and supposedly do their curing on the side. But in all cases the income they receive from their professional activities far exceeds the cash intake of other men. In 1948, when the average wage for a farm worker was still only about 35 cents a day, one of the curers was arrested by the Ladino civil authorities for the illegal practice of medicine. He produced a wad of $300 and paid his $30 fine immediately. Three hundred dollars in cash represented a prince's ransom in San Luis at that time. All of his clients with whom I talked resented the fact that he had been arrested and believed that he fully deserved his wealth because of the "good he did."

The curing institution in this community is also, I submit, a form of socio-cultural therapy. It happens that the socio-cultural situation, including the belief systems, is so organized in San Luis that schizophrenics and schizoid characters, instead of being locked up in institutions for the protection of society and their own treatment, are given a satisfying and, from the local point of view, a useful role to perform.

Of course, I am not suggesting that in our own society schizophrenics should be made into psychiatrists. But if one society can find useful social roles, according to its notions, for such personalities, it is worth considering whether useful roles cannot be found for them in our own system, according to our cultural beliefs.

Part VI: SUMMATION
Evolution vs. "Revolution" In Psychotherapy: A Biodynamic Integration

JULES H. MASSERMAN

IN A BRIEF FINAL CHAPTER no attempt can or need be made to sum up or review in detail the encyclopedic information in this and the previous volume of the Progress, including Zilboorg's and Moreno's concepts of successive "revolutions" in the field. Instead, I propose to formulate as clearly as possible certain broad generalizations that can be induced from these and other data on psychotherapy, as mustered into the three heuristic bases of all behavioral sciences: 1. the *historical;* 2. the controlled *experimental;* and 3. in the case of the biological sciences, the "bedside" or *clinical* (Gr. *klinikos,* "bed").

1. THE LESSONS OF HISTORY

A. ORGANISMIC INTEGRATION

Herbert Muller, in his "Uses of the Past," trenchantly remarked that "our age is notorious for its want of [any deeper] sense of history than the minutes of the last meeting." In psychiatry particularly we seem to prefer the trivial writings of yesterday to the deathless lessons of a half billion years of biologic evolution. Nor is a preceding cosmogeny tenfold as long irrelevant, since in modern metaphysics the distinction between "material" events and the "vital processes" which are their extension and apprehension can hardly be maintained. For example, in his masterly "Science and the Modern World," the mathematician-philosopher Alfred N. Whitehead expresses the thesis that there is an unbroken organismic line of past, present and future "events" and "locations," *from nuclear particles to human behavior:* "In being aware of the bodily experience, we must thereby be aware of aspects of the whole spatio-temporal world as mirrored within the bodily life. . . . In a certain sense, everything is everywhere at all times . . . every spatio-temporal standpoint mirrors the world. . . . The event is a necessary link in the pattern of transmission, by which the character of every event receives some modification from the character of every other event."

Or, as John Donne put it more poetically, "No man is an Island, intire of itselfe . . . never send to know for whom the bell tolls: it tolls for thee!"

This apprehension of universal interrelatedness was probably immanent in the first vital stirrings of the primal Algonkian slime; certainly, the most primitive living things still apply the Golden Rule in a way that gives a wry twist of meaning to the phrase "descent of man." For example, the cells of the lowly myxamoeba *Dictyostelium discorideum* ordinarily live a life of rugged individualism; however, should shortages of food or water develop, *a few individuals form the nucleus of a colony and then die to constitute a stalk upon which the others may sporulate and survive.* As J. T. Bonner points out in his "Cells and Societies," at only a slightly higher level of cellular aggregation—say that of the *Physalia pelagica*—no one can tell whether the creature we call a "Portuguese Man-of-War" is merely a group of independent cells, a loosely assembled colony of individuals, an "animal" in the biologic sense—or a fully organized and functioning society. George Simpson, in his "Meaning of Evolution," remarks, "I know that some students of the subject deny that any animals below man . . . are 'aware' or 'perceive' anything whatsoever; for the present purpose, this does not matter in the least; all animals *act* as if they had awareness and perception—even the ameba does. . . . The basic fact that all phyla of animals have survived since their origin bothered Sigmund Freud, who could not see why all ancient forms have not yielded to a death wish. . . . Nor, as Huxley remarked, does ascribing evolution to an *élan vital* [cf. libido, Thanatos] explain the history of life [any more] than . . . an *élan locomotif* explains the operation of a steam engine. Struggle is not necessarily or even usually of the essence. Precisely the opposite; selection in favor of harmonious or cooperative group association is certainly common."

Here, then, are the first entropic manifestations of the fundamental biodynamic principles of *interaction* and *aggregation*—names for the "forces" that assemble atoms into men and men into societies. In this sense even Mesmer was intuitively correct: human beings, like iron filings, are drawn to their kind by a sort of "animal magnetism;" further, as Saul has pointed out, *aggression* too literally means "to move toward."

B. ANTHROPOLOGIC INTEGRATION

Available records indicate that the earliest creatures that can be termed *homo sapiens* were already well advanced in respect to communion and collaboration, in that they lived not only in family groups but in cohesive clans organized for mutual welfare. That such organizations strove to preserve the most intimate of all biodynamic relationships—child to mother and man to woman—is indicated by the figurines of steatopygous females ("paleolithic Venuses") whose huge breasts, bellies and buttocks epitomized the acme of maternity and sexuality. Concurrently, there appeared man's projection of wishful imagery into the future, as represented in the cave paintings near Lascaux in France or Altamera in Spain. Gombrich, in his "Social History of Art," regards these scenographs and those of even earlier Acheuleian cultures as displaying nothing less than "formalized artistic perfection." However, it is not their esthetic striving that makes them uniquely human: crabs too, have decorated their shells since Cambrian times, bower birds and trade rats beautify their nests and many other creatures cheer themselves and the universe with color and song. But the Mousterian sketches of tribal hunts and customs depict not only *individual skills* and *aggregate actions,* but also a third principle fundamental to human behavior and therefore to psychotherapy: namely, that if a yearning hope is but eloquently and insistently enough expressed, some transcendently powerful Parental Surrogate will answer the plea and grant satisfaction to the supplicant. As H. L. Movius analyzes the evidence in "Archaeology and Earliest Art," their protoreligious function is the most likely explanation of why these paintings were placed in temple-like alcoves, covered over like palimpsests and surrounded by other objects of primitive worship. To quote Movius: "The stenciled or negative hands on the cave walls reflect possession or power . . . the darts or arrows piercing certain animals signify the casting of a spell on the game." To recapitulate, then, fifty or more thousand years ago man already derived essential comfort from three faiths utilized by all therapy today:

First, man's perennial trust in his capacity to control his milieu through various technologies, from chipped flints then to space satellites now.*

Second, a wishful reliance on the collaboration of his fellow-man.

Third, an indissoluble assumption of power to employ one or another form of Supreme Magic to serve his own purposes.

I have elsewhere explored the derivations and implications of these Ur-fantasies in considerable detail (cf. my "Practice of Dynamic Psychiatry"), and we shall again scrutinize their involvement in the history of psychotherapy in the last section of this paper. Here, however, let us examine what further generalizations we can derive from the contemporaneous behavior of man's fellow creatures.

2. EXPERIMENTAL APPROACHES TO INTEGRATIVE THERAPY

One of the corollaries of all of these Ur-defenses is that man tries desperately to retain as long as possible the conviction that he is unique as

---

*This is not uniquely human: wasps use pebbles to tamp their tunnels; finches use cactus spines to dig for insects: ant colonies raise food crops and tend aphids for their "milk"; and beavers engineer dams and build submarine cities. Moreover, like their intransigent human cousins, they continue to do so no matter how often their activities lead to frustration or catastrophe.

well as paramount in this universe. I refer not only to his doctrines of geocentricity, special creation, the immortality of the human soul, anthropomorphic gods robed and bearded like hired priests and prophets, or other such theologic narcissisms. What is of greater present import is the subtler drag of man's egotism on supposedly objective research and derived science. For example, long after Freidrich Wohler synthesized urea from ammonium acetate in 1828, many chemists refused to abandon Berzelius' "vitalist" distinctions between "inorganic" and organic compounds—a resistance recently rearoused by Stanley's demonstration that a crystallizable protein like the tobacco virus can also be a living thing. So also, nearly a century after the publication of Darwin's "Origin of Species" many presumably serious students of the field are loath to concede that man's anatomic and physiologic characteristics evolved in a continuous biologic line. It is therefore understandable that to defend a last bastion many men, including some psychiatrists, still contend that human behavior is, and presumably always has been, either completely unique, or else so much more complex than that of even the "closest" of man's fellow-creatures that a comparative-evolutionary approach is interestingly futile.

Admittedly, all analogies are in some sense misleading, but in this connection the following may be more helpful than trite: It is perfectly true that one cannot learn the labyrinthine anatomy of the human central nervous system solely by comparing it with the primitive neuraxis of say, an Amphioxus, since the human system, especially its telencephalic portions, is far more intricately evolved. And yet the dialectically opposite statement is equally true: one cannot understand the basic organization of the human system *without* studying that of the Amphioxus, since only then can the fundamental structure (or "plan") common to all vertebrates in the evolutionary sense be grasped. So also, one cannot analyze human conduct merely by studying mice in mazes, cats in cages or monkeys in ataractic hazes; nevertheless, such relatively objective and controllable studies can lead to the clarification of certain principles fundamental to all behavior. We may here restate four basic Principles of Biodynamics thus derived* as follows:

Motivation: All behavior is motivated by physiologic needs: survival, procreation and, possibly also, esthetic creativity—in various configurations of contingency and urgency.

Adaptation: Every organism reacts not to an absolute "reality," but to its own interpretations of its milieu in terms of its past experiences and uniquely developed capacities and patterns.

Displacement: Whenever object-directed activities are frustrated by ex-

---

*Cf. my "Behavior and Neurosis," 1943.

ternal obstacles, the organism tries either (a) different methods to reach the same goal, or (b) other partially or wholly substitutable objectives.

Conflict: However, when two or more urgent motivations are in sufficiently serious opposition so that the adaptive patterns attendant to each are mutually exclusive, the organism experiences a mounting internal tension ("anxiety"), while its somatic and motor behavior become persistently ambivalent, ineffectively substitutive and poorly adaptive (i.e., "neurotic") and/or progressively disorganized, regressive and bizarrely symbolic ("psychotic").

As another corollary to these principles it becomes evident that the milieu for optimum activity must be sufficiently challenging to maintain vitality and creativity, but not so frustrating as to cause excessively deviant conduct. However, if neurotic or psychotic behavior is induced by disruptive conflicts, it also follows that the objectives of therapy are to resolve these to the point of restoring the most favorable degrees of adaptation compatible with retained initiative. It is therefore of interest that hundreds of experiments by Pavlov, Gantt, Yerkes, Jacobson, Wikler, the author and their respective associates (cf. my "Principles of Dynamic Psychiatry," 1946), have demonstrated that the following procedures, analogous to those long empirically employed in human, are effective in relieving "experimentally induced" neuroses and psychoses in animals:

(1) A temporary or permanent change to a milieu less likely, either directly or by association, to induce frustration or conflict.

(2) The biologic satiation of one or more of the conflicting needs.

(3) Arbitrarily forcing the animal to surmount external obstacles or internal deterrents to necessary activities and thus to find new patterns of satisfaction.

(4) Placing the animal among others of its kind so that their "normal" behavior can furnish examples of favorable adaptation.

(5) Utilizing "sets" or "attitudes" derived from previous intra and interspecies experiences as a basis for effective "transference" relationships which may then be utilized to aid the animal to reexplore ("analyze") its past and current reactions to its milieu and thus resolve its conflicts.

(6) The measured use of various drugs that facilitate this process of reorientation by producing temporary amnesias for previously traumatic events and thus dulling derived associations and anxieties.

(7) The production when necessary for similar purposes of more persistent impairments of central nervous function either by metabolic paralysis (anoxia, insulin hypoglycemia) or by direct tissue diaschisis (electroshock or cerebral surgery).

The clinical significance of these therapeutic techniques has been developed elsewhere and need not be repeated here. However, it may be noted in this context that, like their clinical counterparts, each of these methods offers almost limitless variations and opportunities for influencing behavior, and each is hedged about by handicaps and contraindications. Nor, on deeper analysis, can they be as clearly separated from one another as would appear from the simplified listing above. For example, a monkey subjected to experimentally induced conflicts between hunger and an apparently innate "symbolic" fear of a toy rubber snake will develop serious "psychosomatic" dysfunctions and become progressively more inhibited, compulsive, phobic, pervasively suspicious (paranoid) and unrealistically stereotyped (delusional) in its behavior. "Method 5," say, can then be used in therapy, i.e., the animals' confidence in some mentor is rewon and it is then gently but progressively restrained to resolve its conflicts and once again to seek and secure food. However, this necessarily also implies (a) a psychologically changed "milieu"; (b) the concurrent alleviation of an impasse between hunger and supposed self-preservation; (c) an externally facilitated solution of the problem; and (d) a change in behavior pattern exemplified by the mentor—hence, all five "methods of psychotherapy" are involved simultaneously. But the therapeutic contingencies may be rendered even more complex by "constitutional" or other biodynamic factors: for example, Method 5 can be employed only in spider monkeys or in relatively young macaques, since only these will respond by becoming dependent on the experimenter's ministrations; in contrast, a neurotic vervet is comforted most effectively by the presence of a mate, whereas the group-oriented adult cebus is helped mainly by re-participation, perhaps necessarily in an altered role, in the life of the cebus colony. Nor are the therapeutic effects of drugs, electroshock or lobotomy to be regarded as specific, since their actions too vary not only with the particular drug or procedure and the physiologic status of the organism, but also with its concurrent motivations and adaptations, its life experiences before and after the therapy in question and, for that matter, the beliefs, attitudes and derived actions of the experimenter-observer. As stated in the beginning of this section, then, laboratory data may help to clarify biodynamic principles of behavior relevant to effective therapy, but at the same time their proper interpretation also reveals how intimately interrelated at all levels all treatment procedures are.

3. THE CLINICAL EVOLUTION OF INTEGRATIVE PSYCHOTHERAPY

It is a whimsical thought that although the word *experience* means "to pierce from outside," so little of the wisdom of seven millennia of empiric psychotherapy seems to have penetrated into clearly formulated consciousness. But this, too, is not as strange as it seems. Man fears to scrutinize too closely and disillusively that which he "loves," i.e., that upon which he hopes to rely; on the contrary, he prefers to clothe it in enhancing mystery. But whether or not our Idols of the Cave, though conceived in glory, are made of clay, they indeed have power over those that believe in them. Let us therefore here examine the Idols of Psychotherapy in a more enlightened Spencerian manner, provided we also avoid sacrilege by acknowledging their undoubted potency under whatever names, ancient or modern, their high priests worship and invoke them.

In the introductory section we saw how prehistoric man, in his struggles for survival, relied on a Triune Core of Faiths. We recall these as first, the extension of his own powers through personal inventiveness and skill; second, the development of wishful trust in and collaboration with his fellow-creatures (including domesticated plants, animals and humans); and third, the deification of omnipotent Beings who were then beseeched, bribed or bedevilled into serving man in larger matters of immortality and cosmic control.

It must be understood that the Ur-fantasies here enumerated were never made explicit any more than, in only a slightly different sense, were the guarded techniques of artisans, the shibboleths of select societies, or the magic names of Baal or Yahveh. Nevertheless, each of these primary faiths engendered so many interlocking traditions and customs that only the briefest indication of their nature is here possible.

Thus our great-grandfather 250± in Akkad, when troubled by frustrations and conflicts, was first required to attempt to solve his problems by his own skills and ingenuities. If these failed he could summon a group of his fellows in a designated Place of Succor for advice and assistance. If lay efforts were insufficient, a general physician or a specialist could be engaged at a standard fee, and with pre-set penalties for failure.* Should all human efforts prove inadequate, final recourse was had to the Temple, where accommodating female attendants were commissioned to comfort him in the name of Mother Ishtar, and where a priest commanded various supernatural minions to help the needful votary with both his earthly and heavenly affairs. In Eighteenth-Dynasty Egypt, thirteen centuries before Christ, temple therapy also included such regressively-cathected activities as prolonged ablutions, specially prepared foods, confessional prayers for forgiveness and a trance to induce dreams for interpretation by the priest. But even more than this was available: by following the magic ritual of the Book of the Dead, Seth, Osiris, and all lesser deities could be compelled by the knowledgeable Egyptian not only to remove his frustrations

---

*Such procedures and practices were later specified and regulated in the Code of Hammurabi (c. 1250 B. C.).

and slay his mundane enemies, but also to banish all obstacles to immortal suzerainty in the Land of Ra—especially if the magical formulae ended, as they do now, by an invocation of the supreme god Amen! We may well ask: could any system of therapy provide better escapes from harsh realities, more satisfying recourse to temporarily regressive physical satisfactions, greater alleviations of past and present anxieties, and more glowing promises of everlasting power and glory? By all accounts, the Egyptians of the middle millennia before Christ were indeed a happy people.

Nor was this empirically acquired wisdom of their forebears altogether lost on the iconoclastic Greeks. Their beautifully situated Asklepiad sanatoria (literally, "health resorts") were also made ancillary to Hellenic temples where, through the medium of esthetic Apollonian or ecstatic Dionysian ritual, priest and priestess offered religious as well as physical retreat and satisfaction to the devout and avid participant. But the Greek genius for development and detail now added to the essential Ur-processes the following maneuvers, each included in one way or another in their medico-religious therapy:

Faith in Self-help: On the physical side, calisthenics, athletics and other practices to develop the Body Beautiful and Triumphant. But physical strength was also to be multiplied manifold by Superior Knowledge, whether of the philosophical systems of the Ionic philosophers, the historical suppositions of a Thucydides, the cosmic harmonies of a Pythagoras, the encyclopedic "nature"-observations of an Aristotle, or the supposed certainties of Platonic absolutism. Nor, for that matter, did the Greeks fail to admire and utilize the technologic-scientific application of an Archimedes who, two centuries before Christ, could confidently proclaim "Give me but a place to stand, and with my levers I can move the world!" Greeks of the Athenian stripe were a confident breed, and they thoroughly exploited the reassuring maxims "Knowledge in Power" and "Knowledge sets men free!"

Faith in Fellow-men: This second Ur-fantasy was also utilized in a number of ways, divisible for purposes of discussion (though indivisible in dynamic essence) as follows:

Interpersonal: Depending on his conscious or unconscious needs, the patient could explore and satisfy *vis-a-vis* his physician-priest the following ("transference") expectations and attitudes:

(1) As a kindly and devoted parental or avuncular surrogate, who personally welcomed the troubled prodigal back to a haven of security and comfort. This was reinforced at the Sanatoria by intensive attention to bodily satisfactions through special diets (dietotherapy), baths (balneotherapy), massages (physiotherapy) and other services reminiscent of the attentions given a cherished infant (Gk. *therapos, "service"*).

(2) As a learned and experienced guide and leader, whose counsels and systems for more restrained and balanced, and therefore healthier and happier modes of life could be followed on rational and empirical grounds (e.g., as in the various Stoic schools).

(3) The patient could also regard his mentor as more personally interested in the supplicant's complaints ("present illness") and willing to explore their relationship through personal reminiscences to the patient's past experiences (history), derived meanings and values (semantics) and patterns of goal-directed action (operational analysis); the formulated "verbal" understandings so derived could then be applied to foster not only more satisfying, but more lasting and useful adaptations (operational "insight"). Socrates required his students to work through their own verbal perplexities; Plato understood the conative nature of dreams and symbols; Aristophanes, in his delightful comedy "The Clouds," pictured the distraught Strepsiades lying on a couch and trying to acquire understanding through fantasy and free-association; and Soranus records the cure of a case of "hysteria" by resolving an underlying sexual conflict by unequivocal action.

(4) Finally, the transference could also take the form of trusting submission to the healer as physician, with avid acceptance of the efficacy of his quasi-scientific, quasi-mystical remedies. And the armamentarium available to the Hellenic physician included not only the vast and mysterious pharmacopeoas of all the lands from Cathay to the Gates of Hercules, but also a vast variety of surgical and other manipulations (such as the Egyptian practice of trephining the skull and incising the cortex or, as described by Pliny the Elder, making electric eels discharge through the head) available for the treatment of the weak or ailing. We read of Hippocrates' condemnations of the ignorance and superstition inherent in many of these "false remedies" but this alone proves how widely practiced, then as now, they must have been.

Group Relationships: In this category of therapy too the Greeks anticipated us by nearly two and a half millennia. Moreover, they apparently were wise enough to recognize—where we sometimes forget—that although reversion to various forms of passive interpersonal dependence may be desirable in the first stages of therapy, excessive anaclisis may encourage paralyzing regression, and must therefore be followed as soon as practicable by measures designed to foster personal redevelopment and social rehabilitation. These may at first require a favorable and protected environment where special techniques and expert supervision are available, but the objective continually must be to re-deploy the patient's motivations, methods and skills for returning to creative interpersonal living. According to medical historians (cf. Garrison, Zilboorg, Fulton, Riese, et al.) the following would be only a partial list of the media for group communication and activity used in and out of sanatoria from Greek times to the present:

Music, giving opportunity for feelings of conjoint rhythm and harmony, esthetic expression, group belongingness and many other advantageous experiences (see my "Music as a Tool of Delightful Delusion" and other writings in this field).

Calisthenics and Dancing, with similar possibilities of group catharsis and communion.

Competitive Athletics, with opportunities not only for the joy of action but through nondestructive competition for public recognition and reward.

Dramatics: Here the poetic psychiatrist (and there can be no other) may again ask: What writings better explore or epitomize basic human relationship than the plays of Euripedes, Aeschylus or Aristophanes? And what productions can offer either the witness or participant more varied identifications, vivid experiences or vicariously tragic or comic solutions of his own interpersonal problems? The Greeks cherished and utilized these dramas for their deep human empathies and meanings; they endlessly varied their themes and were deeply involved as players, chorus or affectively moved audience. They thus explored in essence the basic individual-group interactions utilized in the psychodramas of Moreno and other forms of group therapy.

Institutional Service: This offered a transition between a passive dependence on the sanatorium to an eventual recognition of an obligation to return to a place in the community maintainable only through responsibility and service for the common good.

The Ur-defense of Transcendent Magic: As to this last belief, even the civilized Greeks demanded that Socrates pay the ultimate penalty for threatening the most cherished of all human defenses: a trust in the existence of celestial Beings who, though all-wise and all-powerful, were nevertheless gullible enough to serve man in exchange for flattery, cajolery or, at most, a little bribery. To capitalize on this ultimate faith the Asklepiad sanatoria, like many hospitals today, were ancillary to one or another religious cult which added the following powerful factors to therapy:

a. A "divinely revealed" doctrine in which all believers could feel an exclusively self-elevating bond of fellowship.

b. A reassuring ritual which, through its origin in human needs and through millennia of empiric refinement, included such exquisitely gratifying procedures as:

(1) The symbolic eating and drinking of the parent-god's body in the forms of mystically potentiating food and wine (as exemplied in the ancient worship of Melitta and Mithra).

(2) The temple hymns, sung and played in the simple, repetitive, rhythmic cadences of a mother's lullaby—and often resulting in the hypnotic trances of the "temple sleep." This could be varied with Dionysian orgies to be doubly enjoyed, since they also honored one's permissive and accommodating gods.

(3) The "anointing" or "laying on of hands" to cure an injured bodily part—a direct reminiscence of soothing parental care of an injured child. And, if necessary, the temple could make available occasional or even permanent cloistered retreats or "sanctuaries" from earthly stresses and problems.

(4) The corresponding emphasis on the *spiritual,* a concept as fundamental to life as is the neonate's first breath or *spiritus.* Every human is variously *inspired,* acquires an *esprit de corps,* becomes *dispirited,* and finally *expires* so that his immutable *spirit* can begin life anew. And here, too, the physician-priest functions in knowing the Spiritual World, or purveying professed contrition and remorse to the Spirits of our Fathers, and of requiring only a gratifying small penance with which to avoid the horrors of eternal punishment.

(5) And, finally, the priest mediates the supreme promise of all religious—or, for that matter, of all "scientific" systems: the conquest, through life eternal, of man's most grim and implacable enemy or humankind: death itself.

It is tempting to take dialectically opposite attitudes to the foregoing account of the evolution of the essentials of psychotherapy. One extreme would be to regard it as demonstrating that all was known and practiced to perfection in a Golden Age long past, and that we have simply deteriorated into greater confusion and awkwardness since then. Opposite views might be (a) to regard the descriptions above solely as pseudo-historical fantasies parallel to wishful screen-memories; (b) to accept them only as approximations of wisdoms that were not really possessed at the time, much as the atomic theory was only vaguely anticipated by Democritus, or evolution by Anaximander; or (c) to assert that until recently men knew only "intuitively" what they were doing and applied it only sporadically and incompletely. Actually, the last commentary would still be applicable to most of our psychotherapy, whereas the truth would lie somewhere closer to the first statement than to the strictures under (a) and (b). In fact, though admittedly there is no record that all of the practices mentioned were carried on to full potentiality at Ur, Memphis, Cos, or any other ancient citadel of healing, it is not altogether misleading to point out that no method of therapy in the intervening ages has utilized any *essentially* new principles or combination of techniques. Let us list a few of the seemingly diverse therapies that have remained effective through the ages because of this very fact:

Narcissistic Self-Assertions: Since men continue to equate bodily strength with personal, sexual and social dominance, purveyors of perennial physical panaceas, from the fakirs or yoga chimeras in ancient India to the fakers of yogurt cheese today, will always have a dedicated following. Closely related are the body-worship cults from Sparta to Bernarr Macfadden— cults so firmly entrenched under slogans such as "A strong mind in a strong body" that the most sedentary superintendent will still insist that his gymnasium is an essential part of his "mental hospital."

Also in the general category of narcissistic preoccupations, though less physically strenuous,* are the various Orders of Adulation of the Supreme Self. These range from the blandly narcissistic "Every day I am getting better and better" of the late Emil Coué, through the pseudo-social, pseudo-religious pap peddled by the Dale Carnegies or Norman Vincent Peales, to the existentialism of Heidegger, Jaspers, Sartre, and related prophets of be-mused or is-toxicated solipsism. And here, too, may be placed two other significant movements which have much in common, despite their contrasting techniques, i.e., one is justly condemned as an ignorant fad, whereas the other, because of its sincere aspirations toward objectivity, critical self-examinations and vectorial follow-up research as to the results of treatment, has been avidly accepted by equally sincere therapists in various universities and "counselling centers." I refer first to the "dianetics" of E. Ron Hubbard, which operated on the belief that any person, under the direction of an "operator" with only a minimum of knowledge and a few hours of training, can, in a session or two of recalling "engramms of association," not only "clear" his past, present and future of all obstacles and perplexities but emerge personally impregnable and capable of "operating" on others. The second system is the so-called "non-directive" and (sic) "client-centered therapy," which, with similar assumptions as to therapeutic time and training required, also postulates that the client's "Self," if merely given an opportunity to "grow" through "Self-expression" in the presence of a "counsellor" who acts only as a compliant observer, will spread its own "inner strengths" and likewise emerge transcendent and triumphant. Both of these understandably popular cults necessarily term themselves "permissive," "warm," "self-determinative," "research-minded" and "scientific," and both must deny communal fantasies and symbolic interpersonal relationships between patient and therapist. However, since narcissism here merges into a potent *folie a deux,* these and similar peren-

---

*Cf. also the kinesthetically detumescent "A relaxed mind in a relaxed body," *a la* E. Jacobsen.

nially recurrent movements may be placed in a transitional position between the solipsistic and the interpersonal-manipulative therapies.

Interpersonal Therapies: These are, of course, infinite in variety, but a few leading examples may be mentioned under related dynamic categories as follows:

Maternal: Everyone who has once been a cherished child will thereafter welcome contrectation in various forms with kindly or powerful parental surrogates, whether priest, king, masseur, physiotherapist or physician. Greatrakes "stroked diseases of the Flesh" out of supplicating thousands in post-Cromwellian times just as chiropractors do today, and troubled human beings will always like to lie a-couched and be tended to manually as well as verbally. And when even deeper regression is invited by soothingly reiterative inducements to "relax and sleep" under maternally protective control, some hypnotists exult in a supposedly mystic Power of the Word† and tend to forget Bernheim's maxim: "It is a wise hypnotist who knows who is hypnotizing whom."

Medico-magic: Here the psychiatrist can employ not only the physician's armamentarium against bodily pain and diseases, but also specially developed methods for altering cerebral function either temporarily or lastingly by metabolic changes (CO_2, insulin), pharmacologic influences (barbiturates, "ataraxics"*), physical diachisis (EST) or surgical incisions (lobotomy, thalamotomy). However, all of these inevitably carry or acquire a rich overlay of wishful belief, and when such fantasies of omniscience or of power over life and health (*sanatos*) are too intimately joined by the psychiatrist, the quasi-delusional interchanges thus constituted may produce highly charged favorable or unfavorable results.

"Psychoanalysis": Despite the rigidity of theory, teaching and technique professed by some proponents who forget its dynamic evolution,

---

†Cf. also other systems of guidance that expand (and sometimes pervert) that branch of logic and philology known as General Semantics into a rationale of therapy in which the specific use of the "precisely referential" word or phrase is *in itself* supposed to be therapeutically thaumaturgic.

*The predictably insistent demand for "miracle drugs" to assuage psychosomatic sorrows was met successively by ancient extracts of precious stones, dragon's teeth, unicorn horn, or Galen's Samian Clay; medievally by powdered martyr's blood or the secret nostrums of university Professors of Physic; and more recently by glorified antibiotics, hormones and "tranquillizers." As may also be expected, each new panacea is proclaimed and for a time defended by its devotees with a fervor formerly reserved for the manifestations of divine healing. In contrast, neurotic animals in our laboratory not directly or indirectly affected by such publicized enthusiasms respond much more favorably to the demonstrable pharmacologic actions of the barbiturates, alcohol, morphine and bromides than to nearly all of the supposedly miraculous ataractics being foisted upon and accepted by an avid public.

psycho-analysis, if truly regarded as a deeply searching and individualized method of studying, formulating and altering human behavior, can constitute the most inclusive and effective combination of narcissistic-supportive, interpersonal-transactive, and even religio-philosophic approaches to therapy. In effect, it develops all the categories outlined above as follows: From the personal standpoint, it affords a more detailed and dynamic re-examination and re-evalution of determinative life experiences, symbol formations and derived patterns of defense or goal-achievement. In parameters of interpersonal re-exploration, it presents rich opportunities for controlled "transference"* and "counter-transference" interactions with the analyst as confessor, rival, expiator, erotic object, judge, pedagogue, protector, and many other roles leading optimally to that of a maturely accepted friend. Finally, group-reorientative analytic experiences may become generalized and meaningful far beyond the analyst's office, and thus lead to more

---

*"Transference" is another term that any writer who respects clarity and specificity of meaning must now hesitate to use. Freud employed it originally to connote the experientially derived attitudes which "from the beginning" color the patient's evaluation of the analyst, and which he "works through" in the therapeutic process. However, other writers (e.g., Sterba, Strachey, Glover, Klein, Alexander, Zetzel, et al.) have used the term variously and variably to mean interpersonal projections developed either *in* or *out* of the analysis proper, either *confined* to the analyst or *generalized* to others, either *influenced* or relatively *independent* of the therapist's methods or "counter-transference" and, most redundantly involved of all, either "narcissistic," "ego-syntonic" or "Super-ego-cathected," in shifting *normal, "normally neurotic"* or *"analytically-neurotic transference"* contexts. Moreover, a currently popular cult (e.g. Brill, Reider, Gitelson, et al.) contends that what peculiarly distinguishes psychoanalysis from (sic) psychotherapy is the formation of an emotionally disruptive "transference neurosis" as the most necessary part of the treatment. Freud himself (cf. his "Autobiography" and "Analysis Terminable and Interminable") strongly implied that the development of excessively regressive, aggressive, erotized or other neurotic transference relationships was an "artifact" of poor therapeutic technique; but then Freud, like other leaders before him, lost his status as a teacher and examplar long before he was canonized. Parenthetically, the peculiar doctrine that neurotic patients can be helped by analytic therapy only if the analyst makes them temporarily or even permanently more neurotic is whimsically reminiscent of Garrison's quotation of Teodorico Borgogni, who wrote six centuries ago:

"For it is not necessary . . . as many disciples teach and as modern surgeons profess, that [laudable] pus be [deliberately] generated in wounds. No error can be greater than this. Such a practice is indeed to hinder nature, to prolong the disease, and to prevent the conglutination and consolidation of the wound."

Needless to say, Teodorico was bitterly attacked for differing with the wisdom of current authorities and for his consequent ignorance of the best surgical technique of the day. For that matter, the desirability of "laudable pus" as a medium of healing was vigorously maintained long after Pasteur, Koch and Lister in their time also condemned it as an "artifact of poor technique."

adaptive, stable and creative familial, occupational and other social read-justments. True, psychoanalysis can also be prostituted into an escapist, sterile cult for both patient and analyst, but this is unfortunately true of all methods.

Group Methods: I have discussed the principal theories and techniques of the group therapies elsewhere (cf. my "Practice") and have noted their historic role in total therapy above. Whether formally so designated or not, they can foster and guide an essential final series of steps in which the patient extends whatever insights and skills he has acquired to optimal familial, marital, occupational and other social and cultural transactions. Without such consistent operational results all therapy, whatever theoretical claims made for it, is only delusive or ephemeral.

Magico-Transcendent: In an article published in the International Journal of Psychoanalysis a decade ago, I ventured the predictions, based on an exploratory analysis of the Triune Faiths of Man, that during the postwar period of atomic fears and political, social and moral disorganization there would arise various world-wide movements, among which the following would be most prominent:

Cults of the Glorified Self—in philosophy, ethics, art and psychology; *Formation of Cohesive Defensive-Aggressive Groups by supposedly strong mutual interests* (such as occupation, age, nationality, language, etc.) with the corresponding adultation of glorified leaders by each such group. And, less overtly but perhaps most deeply significant of all,

The increased influence of organized mysticisms, especially expressed in the renewed appeal and power of various anti-rationalistic and religious institutions.

It is the relationship of this last phenomenon to psychotherapy with which we are here finally concerned. As but one example, the Christian Science Church, despite the supposed "materialism" of the past decade, has grown tremendously in appeal and power precisely because it combines in astonishing number of the potent therapeutic techniques already discussed under each of the Ur-fantasies dealt with above. In brief, each Christian Scientist is aggrandized by assumed knowledge not only of the one true religion (Christianity) but of all relevant Science; each member is personally vouchsafed the canonized presence of a most energetic and provident Church mother—Mary Baker Eddy; the faith of each is daily renewed by her sacrosanct book, the "Science and Health," as exclusively and inter-minably quoted by "readers" in the church services; each member is offered warm acceptance and intimate communion with a remarkably cohesive group of fellow-believers; and each is granted influence over other mortals through a Power of Healing not only by direct contact but by the quasi-

divine magic of "absent treatment." Such appeals are multiple and universal, and their potency is reflected in the fact that, however much we deplore
its tragic consequences in individual cases, it is nevertheless true that
Christian Science, with over 3000 highly active and proselytizing branches
and societies in 46 countries, every year gives some measure of refuge and
comfort to many more millions of people than will be directly helped
by all psychiatrists in the next half century. Concurrently, "pastoral counselling" in other denominations has become increasingly important, will
continue to grow in general acceptance and influence, and may also tend
to become more narrowly cultist, dogmatic and mystic as man's vaunted
sciences threaten to suffocate rather than succor him. Without belaboring
the point, it becomes evident that the sophisticated therapist truly devoted
to his calling will not only accept man's mystic yearnings as an essential
determinant of human behavior, but will utilize them as among his most
effective media of therapy.*

OPERATIONAL INTEGRATION

Clinically speaking, then, the essentials of psychotherapy are the following:

1. The maintenance of the scientific prestige, ethical integrity and social
influence of the psychiatric and allied professions and of the individual
therapist. Differences of honest opinion, as in any mystico-scientific field,
are acceptable; extreme claims, public polemics and transparent exhibition-
isms diminish our status and thereby our capacity to help.

2. The warm, unashamedly personal acceptance of each patient, not as
another "interesting case" in support of some preconceived theory, or as
an object of "objective diagnosis," or even as grist for another therapeutic

---

*In this connection it is significant to note the rapid growth in membership and
influence of the National Academy of Religion and Mental Health, headed by two
psychoanalysts, K. Appel and L. Bartemeier. In a single year the Academy has found
acceptance as advisor to various departments of pastoral psychiatry at Loyola, Yeshiva
and other universities granted nearly a half million dollars for the purpose by the
National Institute of Mental Health.

In the meantime an apparently irresistible gratification of all of the Ur-defenses
(technologic, social and theophilic) is being offered in the "Dial-a-Prayer" service
by which, for the price of a telephone call, any supplicant can hear a 30-second prayer
recorded on a magnetic drum by a minister of his selection. A sample from Man-
hattan's Fifth Avenue Church is this: "My grace is sufficient for you, for my
strength is perfected. When we . . . call upon God for help, His divine power flows
into our lines and turns defeat into victory." The Y.M.C.A. in Los Angeles already
answers 10,000 calls for its "Dial-for-Inspiration" daily, and the Catholic Order
of Our Lady of the Bell is endeavoring to make its own offerings nation-wide. (Time,
Dec. 10, 1956)

mill, but as a hurt, frightened and troubled human being seeking relief and guidance. These should be accorded him in the following way:

a. The skillful utilization of every medical means available to relieve bodily pain and dysfunction, or to suspend undesirable activities (at a minimum risk of permanent addiction or defect) until more favorable ones can be established.

b. The tactful and sympathetic exploration of the nature of the patient's motivations, the origins of his conscious and unconscious symbolic representations and value-systems and the objectives of his characteristic patterns of behavior in relation to their interlocking advantages and disadvantages in the present and probable future. This exploration may be formal, minute and detailed (including "free-associations," screen memories, dream material, and so on), or it may be confined to a careful and perceptive analysis of interview, psychological test or other clinical data. In either case, the first objective will be *to help the patient recognize that his previous patterns of behavior were neither as necessary nor as advantageous as he had implicity assumed them to be.* But to leave the patient here would be to place him in a new quandary: his former ways are no longer even delusionally effective, but he has not as yet learned new and better ones to take their place. It is therefore equally necessary *to utilize optimal transference situations and other therapeutic opportunities to impart the second essential portion of the dual dicta of insight, namely, that new patterns of conduct are really preferable*—not alone because they are legal, moral or "mature," but because in the long run they will result in greater over-all satisfactions for all concerned. Such reorientations, which must be achieved without letting the patient become too regressive and dependent in the "anaclitic" phases of transference, may be rendered more effective by combinations of the following techniques: Re-education of the patient by the therapist, through reason, demonstration and, implicitly or explicitly, personal example; utilization of every available system of progressive social participation through enlightened self-interest, whether in supervised "milieu" or group therapy" or as indirectly arranged with the patient's family, friends, employer, or social group. Here, too, the deep influences of the patient's religious, political or other loyalties, instead of being attacked, may be used to their best advantage. Indeed, it is the eventual efficacy of all of these re-adjustments that determines whether or not the patient will be re-accepted as a happy and useful member of his society—and this in turn will spell the success or failure of the therapist.

No one but an osteologist can be truly entranced by a human skeleton, whereas, a physician can accurately imagine that skeleton clothed in the flesh and blood of a man and can then picture that man exquisitely alive and creative. It is with this reliance on the supplemental imagery, knowledge and experience of the readers of this volume that I have offered the skeletal outline of psychotherapy above—with the added recognition that both the structure of skeletons and our knowledge of them also change over the ages. Nevertheless, to reiterate the theme of this paper: such changes occur not by violent revolutions and counter-revolutions, but by an orderly *evolution* along pre-set and significant patterns.

BIBLIOGRAPHY

ACKERMAN, N. W.: Group therapy from the viewpoint of a psychiatrist. Am. J. Psychiat. *6*:78, 1953.
——: The family group and family therapy. Int. J. Sociometry *1*:52, 1956.
ALEXANDER, F.: Psychoanalysis and psychotherapy. J. Am. Psychoan. A. *2*:722, 1954.
——: Psychoanalysis in western culture. Am. J. Psychiat. *112*:692, 1956.
——: Two forms of regression and their therapeutic implications. Psychoanalyt. Quart. *25*:178, 1956.
—— AND ROSS, H.: Dynamic Psychiatry. Univ. of Chicago Press, 1952.
ALLEE, W. C.: Cooperation Among Animals. New York, Henry Schuman, 1951.
ALLPORT, F. H.: Theories of Perception and the Concept of Structure. New York, Wiley, 1955.
ALLPORT, G.: Becoming: Basic Considerations for a Psychology of Personality. New Haven, Yale Univ. Press, 1955.
APPEL, K. E.: Psychoanalysis: reflections on varying concepts. Am. J. Psychiat. *112*:711, 1956.
ASCH, S. E.: Opinions and social pressure. Scient. Am. *193*:31, 1955.
ASHBY, W. R.: Design for a Brain. New York, Wiley, 1952.
BAILEY, P.: The great psychiatric revolution. Am. J. Psychiat. *113*:387, 1956.
——: JANET AND FREUD. Arch. Neurol & Psychiat. *76*:1859, 1956.
BASOWITZ, H., PERSKY, H., HORCHIN, S. J. AND GRINKER, R. R.: Anxiety and Stress. New York, McGraw-Hill, 1955.
BENNETT, A. E., HARGROVE, E. A. AND ENGLE, BERNICE: The Practice of Psychiatry in General Hospitals. Berkeley, Univ. of Calif. Press, 1956.
BERNAL, J. D.: Science in History. London, Watts, 1954.
BION, W. R.: Group dynamics; a review. Internat. J. Psychoanal. *33*:235, 1953.
BONNER, J. T.: Cells and Societies. Princeton, Princeton Univ. Press, 1955.
BRENNER, C.: An Elementary Textbook of Psychoanalysis. New York, Int. Univ. Press, 1955.
BRIDGEMAN, P. W.: Probability, logic and ESP. Science *123*:15, 1956.
CAMERON, D. E.: General Psychotherapy. New York, Grune & Stratton, 1950.
——: Psychic driving. Am. J. Psychiat. *122*:502-509, 1956.
CAMPBELL, D. T.: Adaptive behavior from random response. Behav. Sci. *1*:105, 1956.
CARROLL, J. B.: The Study of Language. Cambridge, Harvard Univ. Press, 1953.
    (Rev. by Smith, H. Lee. Language *31*:59, 1955)
CARTWRIGHT, D. AND ZANDER, A.: Group Dynamics. Evanston, Dow, Peterson, 1953.
CHILDE, V. G.: Man Makes Himself. New York, Mentor, 1951.

CLECKLEY, H. M. AND THIGPEN, C. H.: The dynamics of illusion. Am. J. Psychiat. 112:334, 1955.

COHEN, I. B.: Isaac Newton. Scient. Am. 193:73, 1955.

COLBY, K. M.: Energy and Structure in Psychoanalysis. New York, Ronald Press, 1955.

CURRAN, F. J.: Convergent and divergent views in the problem of religious confession. Bull. Isaac Ray Library 2:135, 1954.

DIETHELM, O.: Treatment in Psychiatry, 3rd Ed. Springfield, Thomas, 1955.

DINGLE, H.: The Scientific Adventure. London, Pitman, 1952.

DIRECTORS OF ROBBINS INSTITUTE: An integrated psychotherapeutic program. Psychother. 1:89, 1956.

DOWNS, R. B.: Books that Changed the World. New York, Mentor, 1956.

DUCASSE, C. J.: A Philosophical Scrutiny of Religion. New York, Ronald Press, 1952.

EINSTEIN, A. AND INFELD, L.: The Evolution of Physics. New York, Simon & Schuster, 1938.

ELLIS, A.: Psychotherapy techniques for use with psychotics. Am. J. Psychother. 9:452, 1955.

FARRELL, B. A.: Psychological theory and the belief in God. Internat. J. Psychoanal. 36:187, 1954.

FIEDLER, F. A.: A comparison of therapeutic relationships in psychoanalytic, nondirective and Adlerian therapy. J. Consult. Psychol. 14:436, 1950.

FLETCHER, J.: Morals and Medicine. Princeton, Princeton Univ. Press, 1954.

FORD, J. C. (S. J.): May Catholics be psychoanalyzed? Liancre Quarterly 5:25, 1954.

FREUD, S.: Analysis terminable and interminable. Internat. J. Psychoanal. 18:312, 1937.

———: Outline of Psychoanalysis. New York, Norton, 1949.

———: An Auto-Biographical Study. London, Hogarth, 1950.

———: The Origins of Psycho-analysis; Letters to Wilhelm Fliess, 1887-1902. New York, Basic Books, 1954.

FROMM, E.: Psychoanalysis and Religion. New Haven, Yale Univ. Press, 1950.

FROMM-REICHMANN, FRIEDA: Psychoanalytic and general dynamic conceptions of theory and of therapy. J. Am. Psychoanal. A. 2:711, 1955.

——— AND MORENO, J. (Eds.): Progress in Psychotherapy. New York, Grune & Stratton, 1956.

FULLER, J. L.: Nature and Nurture: a Modern Synthesis. New York, Doubleday, 1954.

FULTON, J. F.: Medicine, warfare and history. J.A.M.A. 153:482, 1953.

GALDSTON, I.: Dynamics of the cure in psychiatry. Arch. Neurol. & Psychiat. 70: 287, 1953.

GANTT, W. H.: The Origin and Development of Behavior Disorders in Dogs. New York, Psychosomatic Monogr., 1942.

GARRISON, F. H.: History of Medicine, 4th Ed. Philadelphia, Saunders, 1929.

GERARD, R. W., KLUCKHOHN, C. AND RAPAPORT, A.: Biological and cultural evolution. Behav. Sci. 1:6, 1956.

GILLIN, J.: Cross-cultural aspects of socio-cultural therapy. Estudios Anthropologicos, Mexico D. F., Manuel Ganico, 1956.

GOMBRICH, E. H.: The Story of Art. New York, Phaedon, 1951.

GORDON, H. L.: Psychiatric concepts in Bible, Talmud and Zobar. In: Jews in the arts & sciences, J. Acad. Arts & Sciences, 1955.

GOTTSCHALK, L.: Understanding History. New York, Knopf, 1950.

GROTJAHN, M.: Problems and techniques of supervision. Psychiat. *18*:9, 1955.

HARMS, E.: Simon-Andred Tissat (1728-1797), the Freudian before Freud. Am. J. Psychiat. *112*:744, 1956.

HARROWER, M.: Projective counseling—a psychotherapeutic technique. Am. J. Psychother. *10*:74-86 (January), 1956.

HAUSER, A.: The Social History of Art. Vol. I. New York, Knopf, 1951.

HOCH, P. H.: Failures in Psychiatric Treatment. New York, Grune & Stratton, 1948.

——: Progress in psychiatric therapies. Am. J. Psychiat. *112*:241, 1955.

HOEBEL, E. A.: The Law of Primitive Man. Cambridge, Harvard Univ. Press, 1954.

HOMBERGER, F.: The Medical Care of the Aged and Chronically Ill. New York, Little, Brown, 1955.

IRWINE, W.: Apes, Angels and Victorians. New York, McGraw-Hill, 1955.

JONES, E.: The God Complex. Essays in Applied Psychoanalysis. London, Hogarth Press, 1951.

——: The Life and Work of Sigmund Freud. Vols. I & II. New York, Basic Books, 1955.

KARDINER, A.: Sex and Morality. New York, Bobbs-Merrill, 1955.

KNIGHT, R. P.: Borderline states. Bull. Menninger Clin. *17*:1, 1953.

——: How should the non-psychiatrist handle the psychiatric problems in his patients? J. Phil. Psych. Hosp. *1*:8, 1956.

KUBIE, L. S.: Practical and Theoretical of Psychoanalysis. New York, Int. Univ. Press, 1950.

——: The fundamental nature of the distinction between normality and neurosis. Psychoanalyt. Quart. *23*:2, 1954.

LaBARRE, W.: The Human Animal. Chicago, Univ. of Chicago Press, 1954.

LEIGHTON, D. AND KLUCKHOHN, G.: Children of the People. Cambridge, Harvard U. Press, 1947.

LINN, L.: The renaissance of "neuropsychiatry." Psychiat. Quart. July, 1955.

——: A Handbook of Hospital Psychiatry. New York, Int. Univ. Press, 1955.

LIPMAN, M. AND PIZZURO, S.: Charismatic participation as a sociopathic process. Psychiatry *19*:11, 1956.

McALLISTER, D. T.: Is there an accepted scientific jargon? Science *121*:530, 1955.

MACKINNON, H. L. AND ALLEN, A.: Special techniques in brief psychotherapy. Dis. Nerv. System *16*:271, 1955.

MASSERMAN, J. H.: Psychobiologic dynamisms in behavior. Psychiatry *5*:341, 1942.

——: Behavior and Neurosis. Chicago, Univ. of Chicago Press, 1943.

——: Civilian morale and the professional worker. J. Am. Diet. A. *19*:91, 1943.

——: The psychodynamisms of propaganda and morale. Dis. Nerv. System *5*:101, 1943.

——: Wartime industrial psychiatry. Ment. Health Bull. *21*:1, 1943.

——: The contribution of psychoanalysis to the civilian defense program. Psychoanalyt. Rev. *31*:34, 1944.

——: Dynamic psychology and war-time communication and morale. Dis. Nerv. System *5*:101, 1944.

——: Language, behavior and dynamic psychiatry. Internat. J. Psychoanal. *25*:1, 1944.

——: Report of the committee on animal experimentation 1943-44. Psychosom. Med. *7*:46, 1945.

——: Psychiatry, mental hygiene and daily living. Ment. Hyg. 29:650, 1945.

——: Principles of Dynamic Psychiatry. Philadelphia, Saunders, 1946.

——: Una contribucion experimental al problems de la Neurosis. Rev. argent. de neurol. y psiquiat. 11:3, 1946.

——: A note on the dynamics of suicide. Dis. Nerv. System 8:324, 1947.

——: Tension in modern living. N. U. Rev. Stand 9:6, 1947.

——: How to relax. N. U. Rev. Stand 10:22, 1948.

——: Mental hygiene in a world crisis. Dis. Nerv. System 9:210, 1948.

——: Psychological medicine and world affairs. In: Harris, G. (Ed.): Modern Trends in Psychological Medicine. New York, Hoeber, 1948.

——: A biodynamic psychoanalytic approach to the problems of feeling and emotion. In: Reymert, M. L. (Ed.): Feelings and Emotions. International Symposium, 2nd, Mooseheart, Ill., 1948. 1st Ed. New York, McGraw-Hill, 1950.

——: Mental hygiene; half-century mark, part 2. Today's Health 28:40, 1950.

——: New experimental approaches to psychiatric problems. Scient. Am. March, 1950.

——: Some current concepts of sexual behavior. Psychiatry 14:67-72 (February), 1951.

——: Experimental approaches to psychoanalytic concepts. Samiksa 6:4, 1952.

——: Music and the child in society. Music Therapy, pp. 183-187, 1952; also in Am. J. Psychother. 8:63-67 (January), 1954.

——: Music as a tool of delightful delusion. Music Therapy, pp. 3-14, 1953.

——: Psycho-analysis and biodynamics—an integration. Internat. J. Psychoanal. 34: 3-29, 1953.

——: An integration of group therapeutic techniques. Dept. of Med. & Surg. Inf. Bull., Psychiat. & Neurol. Serv., VA (February), 1954.

——: The conceptual dynamics of person, religion and self. Psychoanalyt. Rev. 41:303, 1954.

——: Proceedings. Music Therapy, pp. 5-7, 1954.

——: Moreno's "Transference, counter-transference and tele." Group Psychother. 7:309, 1954.

——: Moreno's "Interpersonal therapy." Group Psychother. 8:62, 1955.

——: Emotional reactions to death and suicide. In: Liebman, S.: Stress Situations. New York, Lippincott, 1955.

——: Practice of Dynamic Psychiatry. Philadelphia, Saunders, 1955.

——: Sociologic and psychologic correlates of music therapy. Music Therapy, 1955.

——: Fundamentals of psychotherapy, with special reference to respiratory diseases. In: Sparer, P. (Ed.): Personality, Stress and Tuberculosis, New York. Int. U. Press, 1956.

——: Psychiatry in Latin America, part I. Northwestern Univ. Quart. Bull. 30(3): 270, 1956.

—— AND BALKEN, EVA R.: The clinical application of phantasy studies. J. Psychol. 8:81, 1938.

—— ——: The psychoanalytic and psychiatric significance of phantasy. Psychoanalyt. Rev. 26:343, 1939. Ibid: 26:535, 1939.

—— ——: The language of phantasy, J. Psychol. 10:75, 1940.

—— AND CARMICHAEL, H. T.: Diagnosis and prognosis in psychiatry. J. Ment. Sc. 84:893, 1938.

—— HECKER, A. O., PESSIN, J. AND BOOTH, B. E.: Philosophy and methodology in the training of 500 psychiatric residents. Am. J. Psychiat. *106*:362, 1949.

—— AND JACQUES, M. G.: Do lie detectors lie? The Nation *174*:368-9 (April), 1952.

—— AND PECHTEL, C.: An experimental investigation of factors influencing drug action. Psychiatric Research Reports 4. Am. Psychiat. A. (April), 1956.

—— ——: Symposium: the role of drug therapies in current and future psychiatric practice. Psychiatric Research Reports 4. Am. Psychiat. A. (April), 1956.

—— —— AND CAIN, J.: Création de névroses experimentales chez le chat par un traumatisme psychologique. Soc. de Biol. *118*:2041, 1954.

—— —— AND GROSS, Z.: Abnormalities of behavior. Ann. Rev. Psychol. *5*:263-280, 1954.

MEAD, M.: New Lives for Old. New York, Morrow, 1956.

MICHEL, A.: Bibliography of psychoanalysis of music and musicians. Samiksa *8*:3, 1954.

MOLLEGEN (Rev.) A. T.: Utilization of religious attitudes in clinical psychiatry. Bull. Isaac Ray Library *2*:116, 1954.

MOLONEY, J. C.: Mother, God and superego. J. Am. Psychoanal. A. *2*, 59:4, 1954.

——: Understanding the Japanese Mind. New York, Philosophical Library, 1954.

MONTAGU, M. F. A.: Man—and human nature. Am. J. Psychiat. *112*:401, 1955.

MORENO, J. L.: Who Shall Survive? 2nd Ed. New York, Beacon House, 1953.

——: Interpersonal therapy, group psychotherapy and the function of the unconscious. Group Psychother. *7*:191, 1954.

——: Transference, counter-transference and tele. Group Psychother. *7*:(3&4):309, 1954.

——: The dilemma of existentialism. Internat. J. Sociometry *1*:55, 1956.

MOVIUS, H. L.: Archaeology and earliest art. Scient. Am. *109*:39, 1953.

ODIER, C.: Anxiety and Magic Thinking. New York, Int. Univ. Press, 1955.

ORR, D. W.: Tranference and countertransference. J. Am. Psychoanal. A. *2*:31, 1954.

PETERS, H. N. AND JENKINS, R. L.: Improvement of chronic schizophrenic patients with guided problem-solving, motivated by hunger. Psych. Quart. Suppl., Pt. 1, 1954.

RAINES, G. N. AND ROHRER, J. H.: The operational matrix of psychiatric practice. Am. J. Psychiat. *111*:721, 1955.

RIESE, WALTHER: An outline of history ideas in psychotherapy. Bull. Hist. Med. *25*:5, 1954.

ROBBINS, B. S.: The myth of latent emotion. J. Robbins Inst. *1*:3, 1955.

——: Insight activity and change. J. Robbins Inst. *1*:304, 1956.

ROGERS, C. R.: Some directions and end points in therapy. *In:* Mowrer, O. H.: Psychotherapy: Theory and Research. New York, Ronald Press, 1953.

ROSE, A. M. (Ed.): Mental Health and Mental Disorder; a Sociological Approach. New York, Norton, 1955.

ROSEN, J.: Direct analyses. Proc. An. Inst. N. J., p. 39, 1953.

RUBENSTEIN, R. AND NEWMAN, R.: The living out of "future" experiences under hypnosis. Science *119*:473, 1954.

RUESCH, J.: Transference reformulated. Acta. Psychother. (Schweiz) Suppl. *3*:596, 1955.

——: Communication difficulties among psychiatrists. Am. J. Psychother. *10*:432, 1956.

RUSH, B.: Medical Inquiries and Observations upon the Diseases of the Mind. Philadelphia, Kimber & Richardson, 1812.

RUSSEL, B.: Power, a New Social Analysis. New York, Norton, 1938.

SAUL, L. J.: The Hostile Mind. New York, Random House, 1956.

SCHIVING, GERTRUD: A Way to the Soul of the Mentally Ill. New York, Int. Univ. Press, 1954.

SCHMIDHOFER, E.: Mechanical group therapy. Science 115:120, 1952.

SCHUETZ, ALFRED: Multiple realities. Phil. & Phenom. Res. 5:533, 1945.

SECHEHAYE, MARGUERITE: A New Psychotherapy in Schizophrenia. New York, Grune & Stratton, 1956.

SELIGMANN, K.: The History of Magic. New York, Pantheon, 1948.

SIMPSON, G.: The Meaning of Evolution. New York, Mentor, 1949.

SINGER, C., HOLMGARD, E. J. AND HALL, A. R. (Eds.): A History of Technology. New York, Oxford Univ. Press, 1954.

SMITH, JACKSON A.: Occupational stress and emotional illness. J.A.M.A. 161:1038, 1956.

SONNEMAN, U.: Existence and Therapy. An Introduction to Phenomenological Psychology and Existential Analysis. New York, Grune & Stratton, 1954.

SPARER, P. J. (Ed.): Personality, Stress and Tuberculosis. New York, Int. Univ. Press, 1956.

STELSEL, W.: Conditions of Nervous Anxiety and Their Treatment. New York, Liveright, 1950.

STERN, A.: Science and the philosopher. Am. Sc. 44:281, 1956.

SULLIVAN, H. S.: The Psychiatric Interview. New York, Norton, 1954.

SZASZ, T. S.: On the experiences of the analyst in the psychoanalytic situation. J. Am. Psychoanal. 4:197, 1956.

THURBER, J.: The psychosemanticist will see you now, Mr. Thurber. Science 123:705, 1956.

TYLER, R. W.: Study center for behavioral scientists. Science 123:405, 1956.

VITELES, M. S.: The new Utopia. Science 122:1167, 1955.

WALLERSTEIN, R. S., et al: The Psychotherapy research project of the Menninger Foundation. Bull. Menninger Clin. 20:221, 1956.

WARNER, W. J.: Common denominators in theory for psychotherapy. Group Psychother. 8:82, 1955.

WEINSTEIN, J. J. (Rabbi): Religion looks at psychiatry. CCAR Journal (January), 1953. p. 3.

WHEELER, J. A.: A septet of sibyls: aids in the search for truth. Am. Sc. 44:360, 1956.

WHEELIS, H.: The vocational hazards of psychoanalysis. Internat. J. Psychoanal. 37:171, 1956.

WHITEHORN, J. C.: Understanding psychotherapy. Am. J. Psychiat. 112:328, 1955.

——: Stress and emotional health. Am. J. Psychiat. 112:773, 1956.

WHITEWELL, J. R.: Historical Notes on Psychiatry. London, Lewis, 1936.

WOLBERG, L. R.: The Technique of Psychotherapy. New York, Grune & Stratton, 1954.

WOOD-JONES, R.: Trends of Life. London, E. Arnold, 1953.

YERKES, R. M.: Chimpanzees, a Laboratory Colony. New Haven, Yale Univ. Press, 1943.

ZILBOORG, G.: A History of Medical Psychology. New York, Norton, 1941.

254